The Spirit Of The Coalition

DATE DUE

BRODART, CO.

Cat. No. 23-221-003

Bill Berkowitz, PhD
Associate Professor
Department of Psyc
University of Massa
Lowell, MA 01854
(978) 934-3655
(781) 646-6319

Tom Wolff, PhD
Community Development
HEC/Community Partners
ssachusetts Medical School
24 South Prospect Street
Amherst, MA 01002
(413) 253-4283

Copyright 2000 by the American Public Health Association

American Public Health Association
800 I Street, NW
Washington, DC 20001

Mohammad N. Akhter, MD, MPH
Executive Director

Printed and bound in the United States of America

Cover Design: Kathy Keler Graphics, Washington, DC.

Typesetting: Ruth Burke for Magnificent Publications, Inc.

Set in: Berkeley

Printing and Binding: United Book Press

ISBN: 0-87553-244-6

1.5M 5/00

Library of Congress card catalog number 99-0735690.

NOTE: Any discussion of medical or legal issues in this publication is being provided for informational purposes only. Nothing in this publication is intended to constitute medical or legal advice, and it should not be construed as such. This book is not intended to be and should not be used as a substitute for specific medical or legal advice, since medical and legal opinions may only be given in response to inquiries regarding specific factual situations. If medical or legal advice is desired by the reader of this book, a medical doctor or attorney should be consulted.

Table Of Contents

A Note To The Reader

This is a book about community coalitions, as a way to create change in local community life. What these coalitions do is join people from different parts of the community to deal with community problems. It's no more complicated than that.

But such coalitions are very effective structures for getting things done. They cost relatively little, the time commitments can be modest, no special expertise is required; yet they can accomplish a lot. Why do they work? Largely because coalitions bring together diverse community members who do not normally meet face-to-face. They provide a neutral community gathering place, a forum, a lively market for information and ideas that had been absent before. When people meet and talk with each other as equals in the coalition arena, good outcomes are likely to happen. And they do.

We have been involved in creating, leading, and consulting to community coalitions statewide and nationally for more than 15 years. We have seen them succeed beyond expectation, on both public health and other issues, and sometimes yield results that are little short of stunning. So we are partisans as well as participants, not unbiased observers.

Of course, coalitions are not the only way to create community change. They don't always succeed (though one can learn to make them more successful). They don't always solve the problem or heal the wounds. They are not magical cures for what may ail a community—for most cures take work, not magic at all. But they are structures that can be used to good effect in almost every community, in one variation or another. We think they can be used in your own.

In this book, we want to share our enthusiasm, and our learnings, with you. Our practical goal is to guide you in starting and operating a community coalition most effectively. If you have never been part of a community coalition, we hope we can provide the spark to get you involved. And if you are experienced in coalition work, we hope we might deepen your understanding and broaden your impact.

To achieve our goal, we'll limit our lectures. Instead, the lessons we want to convey can best be expressed by the stories of people who have led distinctive coalitions and have led them for years. Their stories, their first-person accounts, are at the heart of this book, woven together with some explanatory text and summarizing lessons. Some actual documents used by these coalition leaders in practice round out the picture.

What emerges from these stories is not only a repository of community-building and public health wisdom, but also a certain spirit entwined with the work. What are some synonyms? Conviction, engagement, wholeheartedness, passion. All of these have to do with the inner qualities of the actor. Organizational skills are indispensable, and we describe them in some detail; but skills and techniques alone make less difference unless they are joined with inner strengths.

"Spirit" best describes what we mean by these strengths. Our primary lesson is that community builders must have spirit, to complement their skill. It may not be directly teachable, but it can certainly be transmitted; we hope it will be transmitted here.

That is why we call this book "The Spirit of the Coalition." Our wish is that you will nourish that spirit and blend it with skill in your community work—for your own greater effectiveness, and for your community's welfare.

Acknowledgments

Sometimes acknowledgments are ritual acts of politeness. But not this time.

A grant awarded to us by the W. K. Kellogg Foundation enabled us not only to begin this book, but also to extend our ability to initiate and assist local community coalitions in Massachusetts over a five-year period. Kellogg Foundation support has been instrumental to our work; we are deeply grateful for it.

But the merits of this book rest squarely on the coalition leaders whose stories are told here. Without their expertise, their insights, and their full cooperation in speaking with us, this text could not have come into being. So it is a pleasure to acknowledge the leaders who made it possible: Brian Angus, Al Bashevkin, Barbara Corey, Heather Danton, Geraldine David, BL Hathaway, Ramon Hernandez, Wendy Krom, Monica Escobar Lowell, Mary Lou Pettit, Eugene Rivers, Phil Salzman, Christine Sicinski, Carlos Vega, Dave Weed, and Beverly Wing. We learned from each one of you. We are thankful to have collaborated with you.

Several others also helped bring the manuscript to fruition. First among them was Nancy Barrett at AHEC/Community Partners, who took the lead in manuscript production with abiding grace and spirit of her own. A special thanks goes to Linda Sharkey of AHEC/Community Partners for proofreading the final text, as well as to Amy Bowman of Magnificent Publications for her expert copyediting and production skills and Ruth Burke for designing the body of this book. We acknowledge, too, the special competence of Arlington Typing and Mailing in transcribing the interview tapes.

Finally, we profited greatly from the careful reading of a draft manuscript performed by Dr. Connie Evashwick of California State University at Long Beach, Anne Caputo-Pearl of Long Beach's Community Health Councils, and Ron Arias, Director of Health and Human Services for the City of Long Beach—each with plentiful coalition experiences of their own, in different settings and on a different coast. Ron also served as liaison to the American Public Health Association's Publications Board for this book. Ron, Judy Castagna, Production Manager at APHA, and Ellen Meyer, APHA's Director of Publications, provided us with kind and sensitive guidance throughout. We greatly appreciate their support, and especially Ellen's encouragement from the beginning of this process. Many thanks to all of you.

Chapter 1

Introduction:
Strengthening Community Life

We are concerned about community life in America today. Perhaps you share some of our concerns. Perhaps, by thinking together, we can find ways to address them. And perhaps we can then take some actions to make community life richer and happier, more responsive and supportive, more involving and rewarding for all of us.

These goals are ambitious, but they can be achieved. And you who are reading this book can achieve them.

Our concerns about American community life are numerous, but they come down to these:

■ Participation in local organizations and community activities is low; according to some experts, such participation has been declining for a generation.[1]

■ Social connections among residents are weak; many people simply do not know more than a few others in their own communities, not even their own long-term neighbors—nor do they place particular value on those connections.

■ Levels of social alienation, as measured nationally by an annual Alienation Index, are near all-time highs; while trust of other people may be at an all-time low.[2]

■ The familiar social problems—poverty, violence, abuse, and others—remain very much with us; as measured by another index, many of these problem levels also ranked higher throughout the 1990s than in the 1970s or 1980s.[3]

■ Both public and private dollars to address and resolve local social problems continue to be scarce at best, with no short-term turnaround in sight.

We don't want to overgeneralize. Some communities may not fit this description fully, or even at all. There will always be cross-currents and counter-trends. A few communities may have high levels of public participation and interconnectedness, with few glaring social problems and plenty of resources. But we think these are exceptions; by and large the patterns we describe are far too prevalent.

What will it take to address this situation and do something about it? One type of solution is financial. Of course, it would help if we could generate more public funding to solve local problems; solutions often cost money. An activated citizenry could help generate such funding (although such activation rests on prior participation and connectedness). We support these efforts, while realizing that in the present social and political climate, success will not come easily. Sometimes it is hard enough to hold the line.

An alternative is to find other kinds of resources. One thesis of this book is that many such resources do exist, close to home, in our backyards or even closer. We can view every community resident as a community resource, as someone with something to give. The words of activist and writer John McKnight have left a deep impression on us:

> *Every living person has some gift or capacity of value*
> *to others. A strong community is a place that recognizes*
> *those gifts and ensures that they are given.*[4]

We find these words profoundly true.

If they are indeed true, the task would be to identify and publicize these varied community resources, to coalesce them, to point them in the right direction. That won't happen all by itself. **The structures for organizing and mobilizing community resources are generally not in place.** Many citizens—up to 63 percent in one poll we've seen—believe that people would be willing to pitch in and fix what's wrong with their communities, if only they knew how.[5] But frequently they don't know how. The mechanisms for involvement too often don't exist. So in many cases, these mechanisms will need to be created.

In other words, we are looking for new local community structures that will bring together the diverse citizen resources of a community to respond to and solve local social problems. We know of one such structure that can help do the job. We have been working with it for the past 15 years. It is the local community coalition.

The Community Coalition

"Coalition" is a popular term nowadays. Coalitions themselves are popular, too. In our home state of Massachusetts, at least 500 active coalitions have recently been identified, while a recent national count has turned up 3,500 substance abuse prevention coalitions alone. But many writers use the term differently, with different shades of meaning. Some working definition is therefore in order. Here is ours: **By a coalition, we mean a group involving multiple sectors of the community, coming together to address community needs and solve community problems.**

The emphasis here is on multiple sectors and multiple issues. And the focus in this book will be on coalitions operating in a specific community (often a town, sometimes a neighborhood or city). There are other types of coalitions, too, based less on geography, and it's important to acknowledge them: regional and national coalitions; electoral coalitions; coalitions working on a narrowly focused single issue; and ad hoc or temporary coalitions, designed to end when the dust dies down. All of these have value, and deserve praise; many of the principles we will describe later apply to them as well.

Yet we have been especially impressed with community coalitions as a unifying community structure, because when handled right they can:

- reduce the fragmentation among local services;
- reduce duplication among those services;
- provide for better coordination of existing services;
- monitor the quality of those services;
- evaluate that quality;
- assess the need for new services in the community;
- raise public awareness about new service needs;
- advocate for those new services; and
- generate the fiscal and personnel resources to bring those services to life.

And in addition to generating service improvements, strong coalitions can also:

- provide a common forum for diverse members of the community to come together for problem solving;
- foster the development of trust among those diverse members and groups;
- supply a new nonpartisan structure for the identification and achievement of community goals;
- give opportunities for previously inactive members of the community to become engaged in community life;
- develop leadership skills among participants;
- offer a pleasant place to meet and enjoy the company of others;
- promote the development of additional, independent community activities stemming from informal contact; and
- raise community competence, self-sufficiency, and spirit.

This is a long list. And even if only some coalitions did some of these things some of the time, it would still be worth our while to explore them as community-building mechanisms. But actually, we are understating the case. For it is probably truer to say that a lot of community coalitions do a lot of these things a lot of the time, and do them very effectively.

But anyone can make a general claim. Let's back it up with actual examples of coalition accomplishments. Some from our own experience are listed in the box on the following page. In each case, in a small way, the quality of community life improved. More generally, we have seen community coalitions become visible and

Some Examples of Coalition Accomplishments

Coalitions we have worked with have created or generated:

1. a regional community development corporation;

2. a television show on local community issues;

3. a curriculum on child sexual abuse delivered in all local elementary schools;

4. a series of convenience-store "stings," leading to reduced tobacco sales to youth;

5. a full-day conference to lower cultural barriers;

6. a "Book of Dreams"—children's hopes for the future, published with public-private sponsorship;

7. those same dreams, posted on highway billboards;

8. a computerized information and referral network, based at the public library;

9. a new neighborhood organization in the poorest part of town;

10. a "Valuing Our Children" parent education program, later spread to other communities;

11. a child care center—and a parent center;

12. an interfaith coalition for the homeless, spun off from the original coalition;

13. a homeless shelter;

14. an oral history project based on the community's fishing heritage;

15. a special legislative appropriation for domestic violence services;

16. a directory of preventive services (10,000 copies distributed);

17. a float in a parade;

18. an eight-page anti-racism supplement, printed in 12,000 copies of a local newspaper;

19. a toll-free telephone number for citizens in need to learn about Medicaid; and

20. grant awards, over time, in the millions of dollars.

respected forces in their home communities, bringing about major community changes sometimes verging on the transformative.

Our examples are only illustrative. Not every coalition yields the same results. Some stumble and fall; others are probably even more successful than suggested here. But the fact that even a few coalitions do as much suggests that others could, too, with more external push from their communities, and with more internal skill and will. We cannot provide the community push on these printed pages, but we can teach some skill and maybe rouse some will as well. That is why this book is in front of you.

Now that you have come this far, we want to confirm that the purpose of this book is to guide you in building and operating a coalition in your own community. Our explicit aims are to show you how you might start a community coalition—or, if you already are involved, how to make your coalition work most effectively. And whether you are rookie or veteran, we'd like to suggest how you can deal with the key issues that just about all coalitions face, at one time or another:

recruiting   **structuring**   **meeting**   **leading**

publicizing   **funding**   **advocating**   **sustaining**

These are the fundamentals, as we see them.

When you close this book at the end, we hope you will be able to (and will, in fact) apply your learning back home, to take up and help solve the problems of your own community. Application—use in practice—is our ultimate goal. Perhaps it will also be yours.

The Plan of This Book

Now, how can we best convey the true spirit of the coalition? What's the best approach? We considered, and then rejected, the idea of writing a textbook or manual. These can certainly be helpful; but too often they tend to be on the dry side, removed from everyday experience, without the feeling of what it's like to do the work day-to-day. And besides, several good manuals have been written already (see the reading list at the back of this book, which includes a manual of our own).

We are making a different choice instead, which is to bring you closer to the people who have done exemplary coalition-building work, and to let their personal stories, reflections, and lessons be your teachers. What is it truly like, for example, to hunt for new members, or run a difficult meeting, or deal with opposition, or launch a new program, or keep moving forward when you're running on empty? What does it actually take to lead a coalition from moment to moment? What are the most useful tips, the little secrets of success? And what is the larger learning—the deeper wisdom gained from the effort? These are lessons no text can teach.

For us, the first-person form has more immediacy, more flavor, more correspondence with day-to-day reality. We believe first-person accounts can move and inspire as textbook prose cannot. In other words, we think stories well-chosen and well-interpreted will generate more reader interest, and more accurately convey the spirit of coalition work. That is our intent here.

So in preparing this book, we set out to interview community coalition leaders of distinctive skill, experience, and accomplishment. We looked for leaders of different types of coalitions, of different cultural and ethnic backgrounds, facing different primary issues, with different starting points, and operating in communities of different sizes and characters. We found 16 such leaders, and met with them for about two hours each.

Our interview method was straightforward. We prepared our leaders in advance. We came with some starting questions, and we guided the interviews, but basically we were interested listeners. We tape-recorded and transcribed the interviews, then selected key stories for inclusion. The stories here are edited down for space, and occasionally for clarity and syntax, but otherwise they are presented verbatim. Occasionally, we added stories of our own, based on our own direct experience in building and consulting to coalitions since the mid-1980s.

The heart of this book, then, is its stories, with some interpolated text to weave them together. But within each chapter, we have also included two other key features. One is "Lessons From The Field," which highlights in short form the most important principles we and our leaders have learned about that topic. The other is sample coalition documents in each topic area, actually used in practice. These include, just for example, recruitment letters, publicity flyers, descriptions of special events, fund-raising appeals, and evaluation forms. We present them here as helpful models from which you and your coalition can borrow and adapt.

The chapters ahead follow a typical pattern of coalition evolution. We begin at the beginning, with a chapter on how coalitions get started, noting some favorable conditions and principles of success (Chapter 2). Membership comes next: How do we attract members, especially from the diverse groups we seek, and keep them active in the coalition? (Chapter 3) And once members are recruited, how should they be organized? What kind of coalition structure is best? (Chapter 4)

Coalition meetings can be decisive events, and deserve a chapter of their own (Chapter 5). So do the key functions of coalition leadership (Chapter 6), coalition promotion (Chapter 7), and coalition funding (Chapter 8). Most coalitions also engage in advocacy some of the time, and some advocacy approaches work better than others; we look at these in Chapter 9. We move next to a chapter on maintaining the coalition (Chapter 10), because we have learned that once a coalition is working well, it requires regular maintenance just to keep it that way. And should the coalition grow, or stay the same (if that were possible)? These are important questions for any group to consider.

Toward the end, in Chapter 11, we review some common pitfalls and challenges in coalition work (there are plenty), and how best to deal with them. We summarize many of our findings in Chapter 12, together with some conclusions about coalition work and where the coalition movement is heading. Contributor credits and a short reference list conclude the book.

There is one last point to emphasize before getting under way. We believe the stories and lessons that follow lead to useful and effective principles that will strengthen your own coalition work. We'll say it more directly: There is a technology of coalition building that can be learned and applied, and much of it may be found in these pages. It is not a finished technology, because humans, possibly as part of their own evolution, are still learning how to operate effectively within larger social structures. We are still learning ourselves; but we think we have learned enough by now to share our knowledge with you.

Of course, the technology means little if it is divorced from spirit. The mechanics alone can only take you so far. The spirit propelling the work counts for as much or more. Ultimately, coalitions operate with and for multi-dimensional human beings; a coalition must be a place where their full human-ness can find a home. And a coalition, its leaders—and the whole community—must be sparked by the same kind of spirit that sparks your own life when you are at your best.

To find the right mix of knowledge and spirit in one person, or even in one group, is not always easy. But whatever your situation right now, however you came to this book, you can deepen both parts of yourself and weave them together. When your reading here is done, perhaps you will have moved in that direction.

Enough of introductory words. Let's get going.

NOTES

[1] Putnam RD. The strange disappearance of civic America. *Am Prospect*. Winter 1996;24:34-48. See also Taylor H. *The Harris Poll*. July 1997;31, and Guterbock TM, Fries JC. *Maintaining America's Social Fabric: The AARP Survey of Civic Involvement*. Washington, DC: AARP; 1997.

[2] On high levels of alienation, see Taylor H. *The Harris Poll*. December 1998;71. On lower levels of trust, see Paxton P. Is social capital declining in the United States? A multiple indicator assessment. *Am J Sociology*. 1999;105:88-127. See also The Washington Post/Kaiser Family Foundation/Harvard University Survey Project. Why don't Americans trust the government? Menlo Park, Calif: Henry J. Kaiser Family Foundation; 1996; trend data on trust are reported in the *Washington Post*. January 28, 1996:A1, A6.

[3] Miringoff, ML. 1998 index of social health: Monitoring the social well-being of the nation. Tarrytown, NY: Fordham Graduate Center, Fordham University Institute for Innovation in Social Policy; 1998. See also trend data indicating recent low levels of civic health, reported in The National Commission on Civic Renewal. *A Nation of Spectators: How Civic Disengagement Weakens America and What We Can Do about It*. College Park, MD: The National Commission on Civic Renewal; 1998.

[4] Kretzmann JP, McKnight JL. *Building Communities from the Inside Out: A Path toward Finding and Mobilizing a Community's Assets*. Chicago, Ill: ACTA Publications; 1994:27.

[5] DYG, Inc. What creates health?: Individuals and communities respond. San Francisco, Calif: The Healthcare Forum; 1994:(pt 1)7.

(A)	(B)
PROBLEMS IN COMMUNITY SERVICE SYSTEMS	CHARACTERISTICS OF COMPETENT COMMUNITY SERVICE SYSTEMS
DUPLICATION OF EFFORT	COORDINATION
FRAGMENTATION	HOLISTIC APPROACH
LACK OF PLANNING	INTEGRATED MULTISECTOR PLANNING
COMPETITION	COOPERATION / COLLABORATION
LACK OF / LIMITED INFORMATION	ACCESSIBLE INFORMATION FOR CLIENTS, PROVIDERS, AND CAREGIVERS
SENSE OF POWERLESSNESS	EMPOWERED / ADVOCACY
PASSIVE / REACTIVE	PROACTIVE
CRISIS ORIENTATION	PREVENTIVE
OVERPROFESSIONALISM	USE OF PROFESSIONALS PLUS EXISTING INFORMAL SUPPORTS
CAN'T DEAL WITH NEW EMERGENT PROBLEMS	CAN PROBLEM-SOLVE NEW ISSUES
DISCONNECTED FROM CLIENTS AND COMMUNITY	LINKS TO CLIENTS AND COMMUNITY: PROGRAMS DEVELOPED BASED ON STATED NEEDS
COMPETITIVE SCRAMBLE FOR LIMITED RESOURCES	MAXIMIZATION OF RESOURCES: JOINT DEVELOPMENT OF NEW RESOURCES

Two types of community service systems. Which comes closer to your own? Coalitions can help bridge the distance between (A) and (B).

Chapter 2

How Coalitions Get Started

> What are some reasons coalitions start?
>
> What are the community conditions leading to success?
>
> What personal factors are involved?
>
> How can you tell if the time is right?

O ur first task is to learn more about how and why coalitions get started. We hope to answer the questions in the box above—about reasons, about timing, about indicators for success—and we want especially to focus on the initial steps you should take if you are interested in starting a coalition of your own.

These are very big questions. Rather than try to answer them all at once, let's take a look at one actual coalition's start-up story. We'll tell it without interruption, in the left-hand column below, and make some interpretive comments along the way, on the right:

One Start-Up Story

Our coalition really grew out of response to gangs and gang violence. Back then we clearly had an emerging gang problem. We had gang organizers in here from Lowell, from Worcester, from Boston, from New Jersey. You couldn't walk down the streets without seeing young kid wannabes wearing bandanas.

This coalition started with an issue—in this case (as with most others) a visible and undesirable situation in the community. Here, it was gangs. A few other common coalition issues: crime, drugs, housing, jobs, schools, spend-

9

ing, taxation, or traffic. Community issues are typically seen as threats to local quality of life; very often people will come together to reduce or remove that threat, frequently with no added stimulus at all.

Do you need a live community issue to start a coalition? No; but a coalition does need some purpose, some reason for being. A live issue is such a reason. It makes start-up easier, and it contributes to success.

So the mayor called together the typical group—the superintendent of schools, the police chief, four or five social service agencies, some others, and said, "Let's see what we can do about this gang problem." They met for about eight or nine months and came to a consensus that you really couldn't isolate gangs as an issue. You couldn't say, "Okay, this is the issue, we're going to do something about gangs," without doing something about drugs, without doing something about the racism, without doing something about all of the other things that contributed to gang existence.

Right from the start there was leadership, from a powerful figure in the community—the mayor. By virtue of position, the mayor can call people together, and this mayor did. Strong leadership, from the very beginning, was a key to getting this coalition under way. Of course, you don't need to be the mayor to start a coalition; you can be almost anyone. But someone needs to lead, with desire and conviction, and having some authority behind you (or within you) does help.

When they came to that conclusion, that's when they started asking, "Well, what's wrong with society, what's going on here that needs to be addressed?" And that's when they said, "Let's form a coalition that includes neighborhood people and has a focus on organizing neighborhoods, and that doesn't just deal with one kind of issue." So our mission statement lays out family stability, health, racism, a whole lineage of things. And we said, "Let's not limit ourselves. Let's address them all."

Many coalitions are centered around agency staff and local officials; that is, the professional providers and caregivers in the community. This coalition was different, since it involved neighborhood residents from the outset and focused on neighborhood issues. Such a mixed group of residents and providers is less common in coalition formation—partly because professionals and residents are often uncomfortable with each other, and partly because professionals often hesitate to give up control. But when this broader type of coalition does come about, its breadth is usually a strength; you are serving the people you aim to serve, and they are telling you what they want.

And early on I remember some conversations with the prevention center people and some others that told us we were wrong, just flat-out wrong: "You've got to pick an issue. . . ." The old-style organizing: You pick an issue, you win a little fight, and that builds confidence, and you move on to the bigger fight. But we were not about fighting anymore; we were about building consensus.

Though it started with gangs, this coalition branched out into multiple issues. Was that for the best? This is a strategic choice for the membership to decide early on. Single-issue coalitions are surely simpler to manage. But issues (and problems) are often interconnected, and multiple-issue coalitions can become a broader force for community change—if the organizational structure is strong enough and dedicated enough to sustain the work. Fortunately, this choice is not either/or. You can also start with a single issue, branching out as your roots grow stronger.

We were trying to build consensus, and so from there the first thing we did was send out a letter to everybody in the city, every name we could get. We invited people to a meeting and said, "This is what we're going to try and start. If you want to be in our first meeting, come and talk." . . .

This coalition was inclusive, and deliberately so. Participation was open to all. Would discussions have progressed more easily had the group been uniform? Very likely, but diversity of membership is a long-term asset, for three important reasons: 1) Diversity draws upon more community resources; 2) diversity broadens the base of community support; and 3) diversity spreads the impact to a wider group of people.

We had 60 or 65 people show up, which was a good start. From that, we would call that group together about three times a year. It wasn't a steering committee. It was "the coalition," which was everybody in the world that was invited; but in between we had all these issues that we were going to deal with. We set up a committee for each one of those issues, and that was slow going. That was something I'm not sure I'd recommend. I mean, it's hard not to recommend it because it ended up working, but boy, those first few meetings. . . .

Sixty to 65 people indicate real community interest; though, as you might guess, that's much too large for a working group. Breaking up into committees, one issue per committee, was actually a good way to go. But just having a committee is no guarantee of accomplishment (*see Chapter 4*). Most committees swim; but some committees sink.

It had to be six, eight, nine months, maybe a year, meeting every month and seemingly not accomplishing much. Finally, the coalition sat back and said, "Well, if we're supposed to know what is needed in the city, what do we think really it is?" And the vice president of the hospital said, "We need a community health center." And everybody else at the table said, "That's right. That's what's needed. Let's do a study and find out what it's going to take to bring a community health center to the city." And the process from that point on just took off because that's clearly what everybody was into.

The organizers could have pushed the process, leaned on people gently or not so gently, to get some action. They chose not to—probably wisely, as it turned out. As one consequence, though, this coalition took a long time to get going before something actually happened. The organizers and leaders had to have patience, no small virtue. And they had to believe their patience would be rewarded. They needed faith.

Now, there's a lot of people that would say, "Well, it would have been a lot easier if the hospital had simply gone out and built a community health center," because they had the money to do that. But I don't think you'd have as good a center. People would have been skeptical, and certainly the neighborhoods wouldn't have felt any tie to it. Also, the process built a lot of relationships that would not normally have been built. For example, the union and the hospital were going at it tooth-and-nail every day, but the unknown, behind-the-scenes story is that these same two groups came to our coalition every month, because they both came to see their self-interest was in the development of a community health center.

And in a way, it really might have been easier if the hospital had built the community health center. Yet it's also true that such a center would probably not have been as successful. A health center (and most any other program) needs the active support of its participants; they need to believe in and buy into the idea. And the best way for them to believe it, then buy it, is if they have a chance to discuss it and convince themselves that this is an idea that belongs to them, that is theirs, that they own.

So all the time that went into those early coalition discussions—hundreds, even thousands of hours of meeting time—one could argue, in the long run, was time well spent. This does not count the value of the personal relationships developed along the way, among people who otherwise might never have met. Those new relationships may build the foundation for later community action, in unpredictable yet lasting and remarkable ways.

Some Other Reasons for Starting

You've read one start-up story. And while every story is unique, the story above is reasonably typical. Yet having a live issue is only one of several reasons why a coalition may start. What are some of the others?

- One of them is new money on the table:

Before we started, there had been two efforts to get human service people together in the city. Both of those efforts were fairly brief. People came together, and many people had some great ideas, but there was nothing to sustain them. The third time, the state economy was booming, and the school department was getting enormous dollars. Looking back on it, I'm recalling that there were money and budgets to do things, and plenty of people to go around to get things done. That certainly helped. We had a big boost in that regard.

■ Or a coalition may start because it is mandated from above. (Watch out for problems when this happens.)

I belonged to a coalition which was started by a health office in the state. Their idea was to divide the whole state up into 27 geographic areas and have a coalition in each area come together to figure out its health needs. Nobody I know asked for this; the directive just showed up in the mail. But people also felt that if they didn't play the game, their area or their agency could get hurt. They might have been right. Anyway, they played.

My coalition had representatives from six neighboring towns. Many of them had never met each other before—and you could see that many of them didn't want to be there. Their agency probably made them go. They were listless; they seemed half-asleep, which they probably were. They sat at the back of the room, they never said anything, and when the meetings were over they went straight for the door.

The coalition kept meeting only because the state pushed it. And yeah, some members figured, "Well, as long as we're here, let's do something." They elected an "ad hoc coordinator," since nobody wanted to be "chair." She tried to make it work, to give her credit. Eventually, our coalition organized some kind of day for the community on HIV and substance abuse, I think, and a few people showed up. It wasn't totally bad. But nobody's heart was really into it. Maybe things will keep going as long as there's pressure from above. But I'll tell you, if the state decides to pull out, this coalition will be history.

The key point here was made earlier in the chapter; it surfaces again. Successful coalitions—and successful community actions—are best built from the ground up. The participants must buy in. When the impetus comes from the top, members may go through the motions, but they are less likely to be moved.

■ Another reason why a coalition starts is simply because people with similar interests want to learn more about what their colleagues are doing:

Coalitions are highly social. They introduce people to each other. The first thing people want to know is who else is on the block, what are they doing, what are they like? And out of that comes "What can we do together?"

13

So that makes a big difference at the beginning. Bringing together people when they all have a need to know, or at least have a curiosity, about who is out there and what the heck are they up to—and is there anything they're doing that I need to know about? That kind of stuff brings people to the table a lot.

■ A coalition can also start from a community crisis—something stronger than an "issue," rather a dramatic, high-intensity event shaking the community to its core. Crisis and opportunity, Chinese wisdom suggests, are closely intertwined. Here's how one crisis led to the opportunity to bring church leaders together as never before, and to a coalition that's now a city-wide force. (Note also the frank description of recruitment techniques used to bring members into the coalition, which we'll cover in more detail in Chapter 3.)

Morningstar Baptist Church was attacked by some gang members in the middle of a funeral service. And there was a hue and cry, and there was the fairly standard ritualized press conference to decry the crime. Three hundred clergy showed up. We started a coalition because of a recognition that otherwise you wouldn't get anything done that was real. I mean, you could get press coverage for your heroic efforts, but you'd never produce anything else.

So, when we worked up the first draft of our Ten Point Plan, we got some ministers to be signatories. That was the first part of the process. And they were credited with being co-authors, when, in point of fact, a number of them had absolutely nothing to do with it. We gave them credit anyways. Because as the press visibility increased, it was clear that we could get some stakeholder involvement. So we worked very, very hard to promote a slate of names as co-authors and co-founders. And worked on identifying some personalities that would be politically digestible for other clergy, and that's where Ray Hammond surfaced, and Reverend Brown, because they were pastors of mainstream churches that had name recognition and credibility.

So next, we started reaching out to the other ministers. Call them up on the phone, take them out to breakfast, and ask them what kinds of needs they have in their respective ministries. We'd say to them, "We've been working on a plan to mobilize churches. We'd like to get your feedback on what needs to be done to help churches more effectively engage young people in crisis." Some of them were in denial. In the immediate aftermath of Morningstar, they didn't know quite what to do. But many were receptive; they were very receptive, because, I mean, kids coming into a church and shooting it up was over the line. This thing had completely blown them away.

And then I'm trying to think of how many different ways can I pitch this to make these guys feel important. Because that's very essential. Oh, yeah.

Absolutely. Listen, the average preacher has major ego needs that have to be satisfied. So if you don't factor that into your equation, you're not going to be very successful.

So you give them some strokes. Big time. Lavish them. Major part of what you do. You tell them how crucial they are to the project. Their leadership is needed. They can make a unique contribution. All of which is true, actually. But you're emphasizing it if you want to get these guys' involvement. It's not heavy-handed. But you do it in such a way that you're affirming their importance and centrality to the initiative. And you do that times 20 or 30. That's what you do.

And then you're networking downtown trying to sell the business community and the political leadership on the importance of the church as a driving force in getting stuff done around the violence of the kids. If you really wanted to make a difference, you had to have strategic alliances across the board. So, the coalition involved reaching out to business, the private sector, the political sector, the law enforcement sector. That becomes a major deal. . . .

If gang members had not disrupted the funeral service, that coalition might never have started, at least not in its present form. Not every cloud has a silver lining, but the organizers here really did convert crisis into opportunity and action. Of course, that momentum, that action needs to be sustained.

So these are some reasons why coalitions start. A compelling issue. Money on the table. A requirement from above. The need to know what's going on. A community crisis. But while these are among the most common reasons, our list is not yet complete. Coalitions are also more likely to begin when:

■ New resources come into the community, going beyond money. Those resources could be **people**. (A new school service program has started; how best to use all the new student help?) Or they could be **property**. (The warehouse down the block is closing; could we get together and share it as office space?)

■ Resources leave the community, the direct opposite of the situation above. There might be plant closures, funding cuts, staff cuts, or all these reductions combined. To keep services going, community members now have an added incentive to collaborate, to come together to preserve existing services and programs.

■ An opportunity appears from the outside. A major company considers locating nearby, or a grant announcement is released. To get the grant, or land the plant, there is an added incentive to join together, even if people have not joined together before. In practice, grant-making agencies—foundations and governments—often encourage collaboration in their grant applications; some go further and require it.

In each of these cases, a significant community event occurs—it needn't be a five-alarm-fire crisis, but it is typically some notable change, often coming from the outside. And here is a law of community life: An event that affects the community will generate a proportional community response. In other words, any community change, positive or negative, can be a stimulus for coalition building. The change generates community energy, and that energy can be harnessed within a coalition to create community improvements.

The presence of any of these community factors will increase the likelihood of a coalition being started, and will also raise the likelihood of coalition success. But having said this much, these are not the only conditions when a coalition can start and be successful. A coalition-builder can do more than react to a community event; he or she can also seize the initiative, be proactive, and create the coalition from square one.

But how?

Principles of Success: Group Factors

In presenting the stories in this book, we are interested in identifying common principles of success—because any action, reactive or proactive, will yield better results if those principles are followed. And those principles do exist, over and above specific conditions in the community; people wanting to start a coalition will be helped by knowing what they are.

Let's summarize some basic group principles we have identified before, from our opening story:

- Strong leadership
- Emphasis on citizen concerns
- Inclusiveness
- Member support and ownership

These alone will carry you a long way. Yet there are other important principles that come into play right at the beginning. One that must be emphasized here is building trust and teamwork among potential or actual coalition members, once they have assembled. This is especially important if the members did not know each other before. If coalition members don't know, like, and trust each other, if they do not feel tightly connected to the group, they can't act effectively as a group.

On the other hand, if everyone knows everyone, if they have worked together successfully in the past on other projects, and if personal connections, respect, and trust have been established, then the coalition is off to an auspicious start:

> *I've been living here since I've been two years old. So I recruited 13 other people to join me. One of them was my sister. Then I just went to a couple of the seniors that were like second mothers, and their daughters that I grew up with, best friends, and said, "Hey, we've got to do something here."*

More often than not, though, people won't know each other well—that shared background doesn't exist. Many, or even most members may be strangers to each other. Then a team feeling must be built, by setting aside some time to build it. When a team sense is lacking, you are heading for trouble. Here's an example:

I've been on an initiative where they brought three neighborhoods, the city, and the state together to look at the issue of mental health. I was on that about three and a half years, and it's still going on, but it's what I consider my least successful collaborative. We were never really successful, in my eyes, in building the foundation as a group.

We never did the team building, we never did the trust building. It was always reacting to something that someone else wanted. Even though we went on retreats, by the time you got to the retreat it was always other agendas, private agendas, things we would sit around and fight over. We never learned how to come to consensus, or to set standards for processing as a group.

And we had professionals, together with parents, and there was a big lack of respect. I mean, I've never seen such disrespect in my life. Calling people "stupid"—I remember one time a woman said to a parent, "I can't help it if you're so stupid you can't read." And I'm thinking, "Wait a minute. . . ."

By contrast, here is the same speaker, reporting a very different experience in a different coalition:

Now in our Healthy Boston coalition, we've been solid since it started. It's a small coalition, so everybody's had burnout, but we've been able to maintain and build, because we've taken the time to know each other. We trust each other.

Number one, when we started, everybody had the opportunity to share where we were from and what we were doing. We would come together for a meeting, usually at 6:00 at night. So we sit down around a table, and we have something to eat. And then we work together on what we were going to do. So, the opportunity to know each other, where each other was coming from, even though some of our agendas were different. . .

I think we've been able to lay the foundation so there is mutual respect, so that when I share something, people don't think, "Well, I'm just going to steal it, and take it," or "I don't want to be bothered," or "I think it's stupid." You have to have laid the foundation so that you can trust one another, and so you feel you can throw something out where, I don't care how dumb it is, no one is going to criticize you.

How do you build trust, and a team feeling? At the beginning, it starts from the simple act of setting aside time for people to meet each other, and talk to each other, without a formal agenda. This is the general rule: When people meet and talk, on equal footing, in a relaxed setting, a trust-building process is set in motion. This point was suggested in the start-up story at the beginning of this chapter. It's simple, it's profound, and it's too often neglected. Another coalition leader makes the point again:

To me, what needs to happen is that people need to get together and start talking and getting to know each other. That was my thing with this partnership. We have providers, we have residents, we have police and city that don't really talk to each other. Let's get together and start talking. Then you get to know each other, and then hopefully through that process you begin to work together effectively.

Principles of Success: Personal Factors

Trust-building and teamwork are examples of group or "external" principles, which are properties of and are visible in the coalition. Many other principles are similar in this respect. But some additional principles that make for coalition success are more personal or "internal" in nature. They are less visible, and if they reside anywhere, it is inside the person. But they are no less important. If you want to bring a bunch of strangers together for a common purpose, you need to have some strong personal qualities, on the inside, and bring them to outer manifestation. Coalition building does not happen simply by applying external technique. More is required.

One such internal principle, or quality, is persistence. Let's admit that it's not always easy to organize a coalition—you are creating something in the community that may never have been there before. And it's not so much that you will face active opposition (though that can happen) or total apathy (though that can happen, too)—but, more frequently, something closer to inertia.

People have limited time and well-established habits, which, even though imperfect, get them through the day. You are asking them to adopt a new community habit—being an active member of a coalition—and to make room for it in their schedules. And you are asking many different people to do so, all at the same time. It takes some push to make that happen. The pusher needs to keep on pushing, and pushing again, and maybe again after that. It can be hard work. But you can't quit.

This is especially true when previous coalition attempts have failed; for there is now skepticism to overcome:

I had been involved in other organizations that had tried to organize a bilingual professional network. And just the title of "professional" excluded some people, who had worked for years in the community, who may not have had degrees, but had a lot of experience. The term "professional" cut them out. And in the end those problems caused the network to fold.

So the buzz around was that there had been a couple of attempts to organize Latinos, and things had just not worked out. And now here was another attempt. I had learned a lot about the causes of the failure, and I was hoping that this wouldn't have the same pitfalls as the other groups. But people were very skeptical. They were saying, "Oh, no, here we go again. And what is it that's gonna make a difference here so that we don't get stuck?" I just think people were on their guard. And the fact that there was a negative history before, and that those other coalitions did not fly, has had a long-lasting effect on the way we operate.

I think what basically made a difference here was that we said let's just interview people and see if they are willing to give a coalition one more chance. And if they are, let's get together. Let's not get hung up on the structure, because if we do, we're doomed. But let's work toward some goal or goals that are going to put us in an outcome mode, and then we can start having some success. People were willing to try. So that's what did it.

This coalition leader persisted. She had to. Starting a coalition—starting anything, really—often takes persistence, tenacity, true grit. All those qualities lie within.

And there's a related quality that applies, though the term is not used frequently in community development work. It is faith. Here it means the belief that the coalition will take hold, that hard work and good work will be rewarded, that things will turn out okay. Faith dictates action, in community work as elsewhere. You might not choose the term "faith"; then pick something similar. But the coalition worker has to believe in the coalition. It's a core principle of life, worth restating: You've got to believe in what you are doing.

If you're doing the work, you have to believe in it, or else you're not going to get anywhere. People will sense whether you believe in what you're doing or you don't. You can say, "I'm a coalition worker. I'm trying to get parents together." But, I mean, if there's no firm belief in your voice about what the work is, people are going to respond accordingly. People just have an innate sense about that.

And people may say, "Well, you're the 50th person who's tried this in the neighborhood in the last 20 years." Then you might say, "I know this project was tried, and I know that was tried. But this is what I'm doing, and this is what I'm working on, and this is what I believe in."

And there are people who will not believe you and will not come along. You know, they will think, "Well, I'll sit on the sidelines for a while and see what happens." And then, maybe later, "Okay, well, he's been doing it for six months, and he's still there. So, let me go to a meeting or let me call and find more information or whatever."

So this is really a lot of responsibility—this is where it becomes exhausting work for the organizer. Because if you stop believing in it, emotionally as well as cognitively, the people you're working with are not going to be as committed as they were.

I think that's a very critical piece. You don't take a coalition-building job because it's a job. You have to have a certain belief in the purpose of the job and the mission of the job, or else you're setting it up for failure. . . .

Lessons From The Field

For the succeeding chapters in this book (except the last), we want to conclude with "Lessons From The Field," a short summary of what we've learned about each topic from the coalition leaders we have spoken to, and from our own experience. In future chapters, we'll cite these lessons mostly in shorter bulleted sentences. But this first time around, we'll put our summary lessons in more conventional prose:

If you want to start a coalition, the first steps are internal. You take these steps inside yourself, before acting in the outside world. Community accomplishments (any accomplishments) begin with mental acts, internal acts, and the best accomplishments are preceded by plentiful inner work. This work is less visible, but no less crucial. The inner foundation must be laid before the outer structure can be built.

The internal work of coalition building begins with taking a look around your community. What is going on? Specifically, are the community conditions favorable for starting a coalition? Which means to ask:

- Is there an issue?
- Are there people to lead, and to share in the work?
- Are there changes in the resources available to the community?
- Is there an incentive—a dramatic event, a funding opportunity—
  to motivate people to come together?
- Is there a past history of working together successfully?
- Is there general good feeling about working together, regardless of history?

These are some of the conditions that will increase the likelihood of a coalition being successful. The wise coalition-builder will have a good sense of what's happening in the community, and be able to judge how favorable the conditions are. Is the community ready for a coalition? If it is, you may not need to do much more than supply a spark. If readiness is marginal, then maybe you can light a fire. But if the community is not ready at all, the effort involved in organizing a full-scale coalition may not be worth the price, even if you could succeed. Maybe there is something smaller you could do at the start, to pave the way for larger-scale coalition building later on.

Taking an honest look at the community is one part of the internal work that needs to be done. That part is cognitive. The other part calls more on feelings, on positive affect.

You've got to want to start a coalition. You've got to feel some inner urge, some inner drive, the same drive that (on good days) propels you out of bed in the morning and energizes each waking hour. It's got to be important to you, ideally as important or more important than just about anything else going on in your life right now.

And you've got to believe you can do it, too—that if you put the right effort into it, the coalition will actually happen. Real belief radiates and permeates. Affect leads to effect. This is much of what we mean by the spirit of the coalition.

The internal qualities are necessary, but not sufficient. Belief, drive, and spirit will take you far, but not the whole distance. There are other things you are will need as a coalition-builder: plans, goals, and then, very soon, members, and a structure, and publicity, and possibly money—all the usual attributes of successful organizations. But let's not get too far ahead of ourselves. Let's take one step at a time.

Suppose, for now, that the outside conditions are right. The community will really be better off with a coalition. It could make a major community impact. And the inside conditions are right too. You want to do it. You believe you will succeed.

What comes next?

The Boston Globe

Violence erupts at drive-by victim's rites

By Victoria Benning
GLOBE STAFF

A funeral service for a 20-year-old Dorchester man shot to death at a party Saturday night ended abruptly in pandemonium last night when a group of youths entered the church and chased down one of the mourners, stabbing him nine times.

A panic ensued inside Morning Star Baptist Church as more than 300 people who had gathered for the service ran for cover. Shots reportedly were fired both inside and outside the church.

"It was like a herd of cattle coming through," said a shaken Debora Miller, a member of the church choir. "I saw a crowd coming from the back of the church and I jumped under a bench and prayed. I prayed the bench would hold and I prayed God would protect me."

Hundreds of friends and relatives had gathered at the church at 1257 Blue Hill Ave., Mattapan, last night to say goodbye to Robert Odom. Odom was shot in the head Saturday as he danced at a party in a second-floor apartment on Westville Terrace, Dorchester. Witnesses at the party said Odom was the victim of a drive-by shooting by youths angry about not being allowed into the party.

About 8 p.m. last night, during the service for Odom, witnesses said a group of 12 to 14 youths wearing black hoods entered the sanctuary and took seats in chairs that had been placed in the middle aisle to handle the overflow crowd.

For a while, nothing happened.

Later into the service, someone from the group yelled, "That's him," pointing to a young man seated in a front pew. The man took off running and the group followed him, witnesses said.

The group chased the mourner
SERVICE, Page 31

Coalitions sometimes start from crisis events. The crisis event here was a shooting at a funeral service inside a church.

10

Point Plan
to
Mobilize
the
Churches

We seek to generate serious discussion regarding the specific ways in which the Christian community can bring the peace of God to the violent world of our youth. We therefore call upon churches, church agencies, and the academic theological community throughout the nation to consider, discuss, debate and implement, singly or in collaboration, any one or more of the following proposals:

1. To establish 4-5 church cluster-collaborations which sponsor "Adopt-a-Gang" programs to organize and evangelize youth in gangs. Inner-city churches would serve as drop-in centers providing sanctuary for troubled youth.

2. To commission missionaries to serve as advocates and ombudsmen for Black and Latino juveniles in the courts. Such missionaries would work closely with probation officers, law enforcement officials, and youth streetworkers to assist at-risk youth and their families. They would also convene summit meetings between school superintendents, principals of public middle and high schools, and Black and Latino pastors to develop partnerships that will focus on the youth most at-risk. We propose to do pastoral work with the most violet and troubled young people and their families. In our judgment this is a rational alternative to ill-conceived proposals to substitute incarceration for education.

3. To commission youth evangelist to do street-level one-on-one evangelism with youth involved in drug trafficking. These evangelist would also work to prepare these youth for participation in the economic life of the nation. Such work might include preparation for college, the development of legal revenue-generating enterprises, and acquisition of trade skills and union membership.

4. To establish accountable, community-based economic development projects that go beyond "market and state" visions of revenue generation. Such economic development initiatives will include community land trusts, micro-enterprise projects, worker cooperatives, and democratically run community development corporations.

5. To establish links between suburban and downtown churches and front-line ministries to provide spiritual, human resource, and material support.

6. To initiate and support neighborhood crime-watch programs with local church neighborhoods. If, for example, 200 churches covered the four corners surrounding these sites 800 blocks would be safer.

7. To establish working relationships between local churches and community-based health centers to provide pastoral counseling for families during times of crisis. We also propose the initiation of drug abuse prevention programs and abstinence-oriented educational programs focusing on the prevention of AIDS and sexually transmitted diseases.

8. To convene a working summit meeting for Christian Black and Latino men and woman in order to discuss the development of Christian brotherhoods and sisterhood that would provide rational alternatives to violent gang life. Such groups would also be charged with fostering responsibility to family and protecting houses of worship.

9. To establish rape crisis drop-in centers and services for battered women in churches. Counseling programs must be established for abusive men, particularly teenagers and young adults.

10. To develop an aggressive Black and Latino history curriculum, with an additional focus on the struggles of women and poor people. Such a curriculum could be taught in churches as a means of helping our youth understand that the God of history has been and remains active in the lives of all peoples.

The Reverends Jeffrey L. Brown, Ray A. Hammond, Eugene F. Rivers III, and Samuel C. Wood (members of the Executive Committee of the Ten Point Coalition)

Out of the shooting at the funeral service, the Ten Point Coalition arose, led by local African-American clergy. This coalition's work has had national impact.

HEALTHY BOSTON

> ***Healthy Boston*** is a community development initiative to improve the health of the city, its neighborhoods, and its people. It mobilizes residents and links them with organizations, agencies and funders to implement the solutions to the problems they have identified.

Healthy Boston joins initiatives from other cities around the U.S. and the world in forging a new way of approaching urban issues. The features of the ***Healthy Boston*** model include:

- Defining health broadly to include education, economic development, public safety, housing and human services

- Utilizing coalitions of residents and agencies as the means of empowering communities

- Improving coordination within city government and among all funders

- Emphasizing multi-cultural outreach and inclusion

- Creating partnerships between and within communities and government

- Leveraging outside resources to support and recognize community coalition-building, problem solving and collaborative action, and to foster the self-sustainability of coalition activities.

- Assessing community resources and assets, not just needs and problems

- Funding both planning and new service collaborations

- Linking coalitions citywide in a learning environment through training and collaborative problem-solving

> Healthy people and healthy communities require more than medical care. They require jobs that can support a family with dignity, decent housing, and enough food to eat. They require quality education that opens the door to opportunity. They require safe, thriving neighborhoods where people help each other.

This coalition was launched with federal money. Because its founders worked hard to build in local community control, 21 smaller neighborhood coalitions were generated.

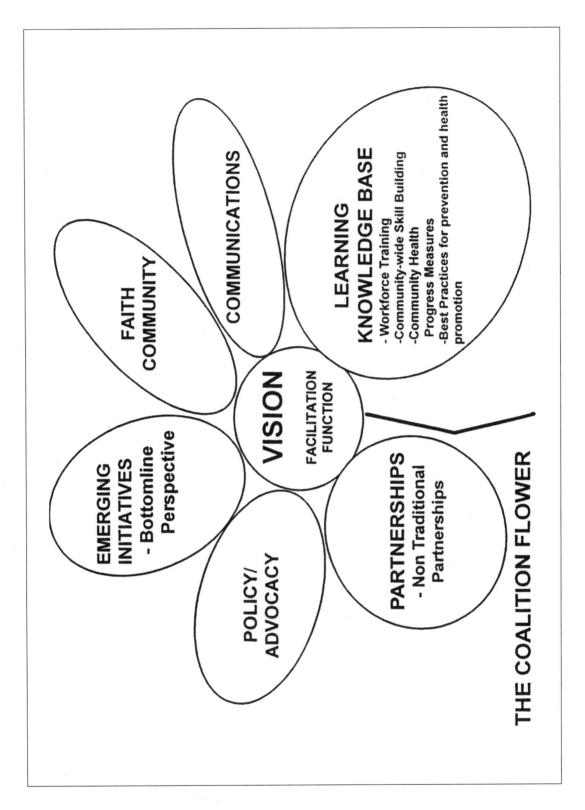

THE COALITION FLOWER

However a coalition begins, a key start-up ingredient is a coalition vision. It's right by the stem of this coalition flower.

HOLYOKE COMMUNITY PARTNERSHIP - COMMUNITY NEEDS ASSESSMENT

Neighborhood
Barrio _____
Organizer
Organisador(a) _____

Address
Direccion _____
Apt. #
Apartamento _____

Problems - Problemas

Causes - Causas

Solutions/Ideas - Soluciones/Ideas

Where do people go when they have a problem?
¿A donde va la gente cuando tienen un problema?

Would you be willing to:
¿Estaria usted dispuesto(a) a:

☐ *go to a meeting with other neighbors who have similar concerns?*
  ir a una reunion para hablar de sus preocupaciones con otros vecinos?

☐ *put your name on our mailing list to receive more information?*
  poner su nombre en nuestra lista de correspondencia para recibir mas informacion?

Name
Nombre _____

Telephone
Telefono _____

When is the best time for you to go to a meeting?
¿Cual es la major hora para usted para ir a una reunion? _____

L _____
AA _____
W _____
O _____
_____

Once the vision is formed, an assessment of community needs often follows. In this bilingual example, street workers went door-to-door to talk to residents. A similar assessment done today might also include questions on community resources and assets, as well as needs.

WORCESTER LATINO COALITION

WORCESTER LATINO COALITION

THE WORCESTER LATINO COALITION IS A RESOURCE AND ADVOCACY ORGANIZATION. OUR MISSION IS TO IMPROVE THE QUALITY OF LIFE OF LATINOS LIVING IN WORCESTER. OUR GOALS ARE:

SHORT-TERM GOALS

- TO INCREASE ACCESSIBILITY OF QUALITY HEALTH CARE

- TO INCREASE THE SENSITIVITY OF AREA HEALTH ORGANIZATIONS TO THE NEEDS OF THE WORCESTER LATINO POPULATION

LONG-TERM GOALS

- TO DEVELOP AN ADVOCACY CAPACITY, TO LOBBY FOR APPROPRIATE SERVICES FOR THE LATINO POPULATION OF WORCESTER.

- TO ENSURE THAT INSTITUTIONS IN WORCESTER PLAN FOR AND PROVIDE QUALITY SERVICES THAT ARE RELEVANT AND ACCESSIBLE TO LATINOS.

- TO DEVELOP A PLANNING BODY THAT CAN PROMOTE GREATER COOPERATION AMONG ALL THOSE DELIVERING SERVICES TO LATINOS IN WORCESTER.

- TO COLLABORATIVELY SOLVE PROBLEMS REGARDING THE MAJOR ISSUES IN HEALTH, HUMAN SERVICES, EDUCATION, HOUSING AND QUALITY OF LIFE FOR LATINOS IN WORCESTER.

- TO PROVIDE INFORMATION TO COMMUNITY PROVIDERS AND RESIDENTS TO INCREASE ACCESSIBILITY AND VISIBILITY OF SERVICES.

- TO MONITOR SUCCESSFUL IMPLEMENTATION OF PLANS DEVELOPED BY THE COALITION.

MEMBERSHIP

THE COALITION WAS FORMED BY A GROUP OF LATINO PROFESSIONALS WHO WORK IN SCHOOLS, HIGHER EDUCATION, AND HEALTH AND HUMAN SERVICE AGENCIES THROUGHOUT THE CITY OF WORCESTER. MEMBERSHIP IS OPEN TO ANY INDIVIDUAL OR ORGANIZATION INTERESTED IN FURTHERING THE MISSION OF THE COALITION.

CURRENT FOCUS

LOOKING AT THE SUITABILITY, AVAILABILITY AND OVERALL QUALITY OF INTERPRETER OF SERVICES AVAILABLE TO LATINO PATIENTS THROUGHOUT THE CITY OF WORCESTER.

From the vision, and from the assessment, often emerges a coalition plan. Here is a simple example, focusing on broader goals. A more complex plan might include detailed objectives, action steps, and timelines.

Chapter 3

Coalition Membership

How do you find coalition members?

How can your coalition represent the whole community?

Should members pay dues?

How can you keep the members you have?

"I think membership is one of those things that's not very sexy. I mean, we've struggled continuously with our Member Services Committee, to get people to be on it. Yet membership is at the core of it all. We really do need to keep bringing in new people, or else we're dead. Membership is the glue that keeps it all together and moving toward the other goals. . . ."

Imagine a coalition with 30, 40, 50 members, or even more. And they are *active* members; they come to meetings every time and on time; everyone has some specific task to do, and they do it. The meetings themselves are fast-paced and productive; many different segments of the community are included; everyone there seems glad to be there; spirits and energy run high.

And in this coalition, everyone supports and respects the strengths of the other members. Everyone is willing to go out and recruit new members as the need arises. Everyone is an excellent spokesperson for the coalition, and, through their enthusiasm and competence, they promote and extend the work of the coalition throughout the community.

This is an ideal coalition, and an ideal that can be approached. In your coalition, you can come that much closer by paying full attention to coalition membership.

Our goals in this chapter are to explore some key membership issues most coalitions face: 1) finding new members (and bringing them into the coalition), 2) member diversity and inclusiveness, 3) membership dues, and 4) membership retention—keeping the members you've got. You will learn how successful coalitions have dealt with these issues, and we will identify the key principles behind their success.

But first, a one-minute review of why members are important to any coalition. You may know some good reasons already; let's make them explicit:

■ Members increase the productivity of the coalition. Putting it very simply, if you have more (active) members, you can usually get more things done. There really is strength in numbers.

■ Members increase the visibility of (and support for) the coalition. Each member has his or her own network in the community, and by virtue of being a member, that network is likely to be activated. The coalition's accomplishments reach more people; more new members get drawn in; more accomplishments are then possible.

■ Members can become empowered as a result of their membership. Your members can learn new skills in their coalition roles (often from other members), skills that will help them outside of their coalition work. The members help the coalition, and the coalition helps its members. Everyone gains.

A strong and involved membership is a win-win proposition. But now let's get to the specifics: How do you find the members you want? How do you include members from different parts of the community? What about membership dues? And once you've found your members, how do you keep them active and happy?

Bringing New Members into the Coalition

The best way to bring new members into a coalition is often the old-fashioned way—eye-to-eye, and face-to-face:

> *A part of my job that is really important is to pick up the phone and call people. The most recent example was a person who's been hired to take on the development of a local community TV channel. She was only on the job a few days, but I just didn't want any time to go by. It seemed important to meet with her and give her a call, which I did. . . . I introduced myself and told her that we have this community coalition that's now in its 11th year, and doing good things, and it might be helpful to her to get a flavor of community people as well as issues by coming to a meeting.*
>
> *So we met, and I brought a copy of our newsletter, and she was very excited, actually. I feel real lucky to have her; she sounds like someone who is going to make a difference; and I think the coalition can benefit, for heav-*

en's sake, from this kind of connection. And I really believe that for her pur-poses, she can get up to speed better.

Sometimes, it can help to use indirect approaches, such as a survey, to get poten-tial members interested:

> *I happened to know a lot of people. When we started, I went around to them. I developed a questionnaire, "What are our greatest needs?" questions like that. It was like a needs assessment, though I hate that word. Then I called people up and said, "Could I talk to you?" I met them, person-to-per-son, with this list of questions.*
>
> *A number of people were skeptical, because two previous attempts to do this had failed. But people knew me. I worked for an organization that was perceived as a neutral party. I didn't have any baggage. At the end of the survey, I asked, "Would you be interested in a coalition? Can we get it going?" Out of 20 people I saw, about 8 or 9 showed up at the first meeting.*

Or alternatively, you can create a useful product, then distribute it, and gain pub-licity (and members) that way:

> *So we started out to make ourselves visible, and put together and pub-lished a guide to community services. Now that doesn't sound like a mem-bership tool, and people questioned it: You put a hell of a lot of effort into them, and they become outdated fairly soon. But we got contributions to get it printed, about 10,000 copies, and we saturated the Lower Cape with that guide—no one had ever done one like that before. I mean we were in doc-tors' offices, we were in the libraries, we were in the banks, it fit into the phone book. It became a bible, and it got our name out there in very strong fashion. I would rate it as a healthy tool, both to attract attention and to get people to think, "Maybe I ought to join this group."*

The techniques in the above three examples—building (then using) a personal relationship; stimulating interest; responding to need; showing a benefit; securing a mild implicit commitment; increasing exposure; and offering a free sample—are basic and powerful community development principles, here used openly and aboveboard. When that's the case, "technique" is to be welcomed. We advocate it; it's good to learn more of it.

But most of the time, technique alone will not do the job. Most of the time, bring-ing people into any community organization, including a coalition, requires a person behind the technique—a person willing to put in persistent and ongoing work, with not-always-successful results. That may be a sober reality of community life:

I think the big challenge with membership is that it's extremely time-consuming. We're beating the bushes; we're not really sure how to do it, other than by getting the word out that we exist. Beating the bushes is basically me—whenever I meet somebody who does anything at all that's related to the coalition, I say, "Look, we're doing this through the coalition, did you know that we existed?" And every once in a while I'll have a membership form available to give to them, and the brochure that explains about what we are.

But beating the bushes doesn't always result in people coming to meetings. It might result in their doing something for us, but it doesn't result in coming to a meeting, necessarily. People have enough meetings to go to. . . . But that's what happens when you beat the bushes—maybe they come, and maybe they don't. And if they come once, that doesn't mean they're going to come again. But I'm not giving up—I might be able to hook them into something that interests them.

I think in a way we have to lay the groundwork for people to want to join. My not-so-hidden agenda for the parents we're working with now is for them to become more trusting of each other, and then we could kind of get them to trust us, because we'd be working with them in that context. The building of trust is the key to making the coalition work. And of course to getting new members. And that takes time.

Building trust is central, and trust does take time. Here's one concluding example of what can happen when your coalition has earned that trust, and the community stature that comes with it. Membership then happens naturally, because members themselves see a need. "Technique," and even effort, become less essential. Your coalition role instead becomes one of giving sanction and support to naturally existing forces in the community, then getting out of the way:

One good example is the Young Men's Coalition. This was created by predominantly Sicilian men in their 20s for boys who were growing up without significant men in their lives. These men came to us. And they said we want to do something for these kids.

[Q: They had heard of you?] Well, we all know each other. It's a small town, so once you do a few major community events, people know. And one of the staff members was cousins with one of these young men, so the connection was very clear. . . . So basically, they came in and said we want to do something with these boys, it's not happening for them; we think we can help—we're not sure how or what—but we would like to get involved. And so they started to develop a coalition.

Their coalition is very informal, in comparison to others. But in terms of passion, and direct work, it's very productive. They meet once a month with about 35 boys who are elementary or middle-school age. And they do activ-

ities, predominantly for fun. Last month they did a sleepover at the Museum of Science. Next week they're having their annual pizza bowling party. But what's happened over the past three years is that these 11 men have maintained a consistent relationship with these boys over time.

These young men are informal, but that doesn't mean they are less efficient. They don't have formal membership forms, or by-laws to the coalition; they don't have Robert's Rules of Order at the meetings. When they do a big meal, they don't have a subcommittee to plan it, because they know that Joey Parmesano is going to go to the wharf and get fish, and that Ronnie Goulart is going to get bread from Virgilio's, salad from Lenny's, and so on, because that's what they know how to do, and that's what they will do.

Try to get them into a committee, and it's gone. They might make 15 calls to each other over a two-day period of time; but if you ask them who is going to call who, it wouldn't happen.

So what we've done with them is say, "You know how to do this." We support them. We have resources: We have the capacity to publish, print, mail—you know, some of those very basic functions. And we've given them some guidance, done some trainings on how to conduct a meeting, things like that. There are times when I, as a professional, wish it were more formalized, but it's not. And that's a big part of how this community works. Some of the most valuable people in the community in terms of getting real community change going are people who don't want to be identified in a formal way. . . .

Diversity and Inclusiveness

One limitation of many coalitions, even those with active members, is that they are composed of the same kinds of people. More often than not, those people are representatives of local service agencies—which makes sense, in that 1) service is their paying job, and 2) going to meetings is part of that job.

Good things can be done in a coalition that is all of one kind. But a diverse coalition will reach a broader spectrum of people who live in your community: your own neighbors and townspeople. Such inclusiveness helps, not just because it seems politically or morally wise, but because it's pragmatically effective. With diversity of membership, you are broadening your available range of community skills, interests, connections, and motivations.

Yet reaching out to include different segments of the community isn't always easy. We may feel uncomfortable. People with economic power, for example—why should they join us? Here's how one coalition did it:

The strength of this coalition has been its ability to see the interrelationships between health and human services and housing and job opportunities. You couldn't just deal with the service needs if you didn't also deal with the basic causes, and those included lack of housing for people and some of the highest unemployment in the state in the wintertime. These are issues that are close to bankers—I mean, if the economy isn't moving, they can relate to this.

And by the time we went in to talk to the bank vice president and other business people, we had a couple of years of experience, plus a lot of good press. We had proved we were a group that was going to stay around, that they could depend on. And we weren't talking to them as if they were the enemies of the poor; we saw them as people who could shape better conditions.

This coalition went further, by creating social "mixers" of bankers with other kinds of people:

At our meeting to talk about a community development corporation, we had representatives from various banks, and also fishermen, and single moms. People mingled before the discussion started—we did this on a Saturday morning; we provided child care, on site—and some of our committee members made sure that certain people got introduced to others.

Then citizens would get up and in their own way talk about what they were experiencing about housing costs, and how they couldn't find a rental, and also their job problems: "Look, I'm trying to get a job, and I can't find one." "My car won't work in the morning when I want to get out." Later on I could hear people representing the banks and business groups talking to these citizens, sometimes for the first time, about their mutual needs. And some minds were really being turned around a bit.

This doesn't mean that "power brokers" have to attend every coalition meeting. They can send representatives, or otherwise be kept informed:

I find myself calling on powerful people for specific reasons. They don't come on a regular basis, but if we're going to have a meeting on domestic violence then certainly I'm on the phone to the police chiefs in a couple of the bigger towns. And if it's a transportation thing, then certainly I'm going to give a call to the head of the Chamber of Commerce, and ask him to make recommendations for whom he should bring.

* * *

Here it's a little bit of a defeatist attitude. It's like "Well, these are the big guys; we won't expect them to participate, we'll just keep them informed." We've invited them to meetings, and they've been guest speakers—the state senator, the mayor, that sort of thing. But in terms of getting a big-rolling business person, or banker, or church person, we have not been real successful, except around very specific issues.

> *But I don't know if it would be a good idea if they came regularly. A lot of these meetings would be a waste of their time. As long as we can easily get access to them around issues we know are relevant to them—at that point, they would want to participate. And, for example, the president of the hospital has a vice president on the coalition, which is okay. I'll take that, that's pretty powerful.*

But "diversity" and "inclusion" of course mean more than including people of formal power. They also mean, very typically, bringing in people of different cultural, racial, ethnic, educational, vocational, class, and economic backgrounds—the citizen activist, the new immigrant, the talented loner, the agency client—diversity in its full array. Inclusion on this level has its own challenges, hard to overcome for many coalitions:

> *We've worked with some parents, mostly bilingual, bicultural, and they know what the coalition is—but we can't get them to come to meetings. I mean, it's just out of the question, and it has nothing to do with the meeting time.*
>
> *They just wouldn't come. . . . You'd talk to them about coming, and if you went and picked them up and took them to the meeting, they would sit there, and they would kind of squirm and feel really uncomfortable. I have, in fact, driven people to meetings. It's time-consuming on my part, but if they say they will come and if that's the only way I can get them there, I'm happy to do it. We've also had the regional transportation authority send out a bus and make a lot of stops and take people for free.*
>
> *In the end, they would feel okay about being there, but it wasn't really something that they wanted to do regularly. One Portuguese woman said after the meeting, "This is really interesting, but I'm not really sure that I fit in. And I'm happy to do whatever you want me to do, but, you know, why don't you just call me if you need me. . . ." She just didn't feel comfortable in that group situation.*
>
> *It's a mixture of cultural and economic reasons, a lot of different things. The whole idea around "the meeting," the kind of meeting that we hold, is not something that's very familiar to a lot of people. And I can tell you that a large coalition group really can't come across as being very welcoming. The meetings themselves are just chock full of information and communications, and we have an hour and a half every month to do it, and for somebody new coming in, a lot of it is just going to be noise.*
>
> *And that's part of the recruitment challenge, if we're really serious about recruiting community folks. I hate to say that we're just giving lip service to it, because I think people really are trying. . . .*

So, two basic lessons: To get inclusion, you have to touch a person's interests, and also make them feel comfortable. Neither one is easy for citizens in what's often called a "human service coalition." (*See Chapter 11 on this topic.*) One alternative is to work toward generating coalitions made up primarily of citizens, based on citizen-defined needs. What do you think of the following approach?

> *Our model is to identify the systems of daily life. We spent about a year and a half identifying those systems. Then our mission was to coalesce the people who identified themselves as having primary interests in a particular system, to build a coalition around that function.*
>
> *So we have 11 coalitions, all made up of citizens of the community. Probably the one with the largest capacity is sports and recreation. That's a coalition. In this community of 28,000 people, we have approximately 5,000 kids playing community sports every year. So it's the second largest system where youth-adult partnership takes place. There never was a community-based coalition around it. But it's a huge function.*
>
> *So we had a community organizer who's very, very knowledgeable and wise about that system, and we spent a year convening all the formal and informal participants in sports and recreation in the city, which includes eight neighborhood organizations, Little League, the YMCA, girls and boys clubs, the school system, others, and invited them to city-wide meetings, put it in the paper, a totally open process.*
>
> *People came for different reasons. Initially, I think they came to check it out. But the bottom line is that 98 percent of those folks, regardless of what their agenda is, genuinely care about youth. And experientially, sports and recreation had been meaningful in their lives. And that's why they get involved, for no pay. They do it because something in their own experience was meaningful to them.*
>
> *And the same thing is true of parenting, the same thing is true of the workplace, the same thing is true of public safety. These are all coalitions here. Regardless of the community function, most people who choose to stay in that function for a long period of time have a very personal reason for doing that. And part of the coalescing process is establishing common ground, and giving people an opportunity to discover what they have in common with others. . . .*

This organization, part of a community prevention network, is presently developing a household membership program, 5,000 household packets for every household in the community. Every household can become a member. Everyone will be able to identify what they would like to get, and what they can give.

Membership Dues

What about dues? Should the coalition ask its members for dues? And if so, how much, and how do you go about it?

One view is that dues are desirable, both to increase member commitment to the coalition, and also to provide some cash on hand:

> *I really believe that members should take ownership, and paying dues sometimes helps to create that feeling. Sometimes when things are absolutely dollar-free, people maybe don't value it as much.*
>
> *Our dues are $10 for an individual, $25 for an organization that has a budget of under $100,000, and $75 if the budget is over $100,000. Nobody's ever said they wouldn't pay. There have been years when some just haven't been able to, but that's rare. People honor that budget definition.*
>
> *I think dues are really important for start-up. And they are important over the long term, too, because they definitely give us a nice sum of money for doing small things. We don't make a lot of money overall—maybe a couple of thousand during the year that we can depend on—but it's great if we want to do a special event. Like at our meeting last week, someone said we should do a holiday thing, and somebody said, "Who's going to buy the cider?" — and we can use our dues for that; we can do little stuff. You can also leverage other money, too, like in grant applications. It's useful that way.*

This viewpoint may be correct. But it's also possible to run an effective coalition without dues, especially when members represent themselves rather than larger organizations, and when coalition goals do not involve starting new programs:

> *We don't have any dues. I don't know about dues—what do other coalitions do? If you have dues, that's almost segregating people. It gets rid of the openness, even though people could afford it. We're not agency-based. Whoever is there wants to be there for themselves. They are not representing organizations. If we started to collect dues, that would lower our inclusiveness.*

This particular coalition has been operating successfully for five years, without dues or outside funding. So if you have dues, you should be clear on why.

But suppose dues are decided upon: The more diverse the coalition, the more a sliding dues structure makes sense, as in the first story in this section. Another coalition we know has a sliding structure, with both individual ($10) and corporate memberships, which seems to be working.

And how should you go about collecting? An explicit, personal approach usually works best, with gentle follow-up as needed:

> *So I put a notice in the newsletter on a regular basis. Then, as the year is drawing to a close, I sit down and write a letter to the people I know who would want to pay. Sometimes I ask the members of the Steering Committee to divvy up that task, and that works well. A lot of times people aren't pay-*

ing because they haven't been reminded. I mean, if they see it in the newsletter, it's just too automatic.

But if they get a personal letter. . . You tell them that we depend upon you to pay the costs of the newsletter, the rent, that kind of thing. It's individually typed. It's not a form letter; it's adjusted for each one.

But sometimes, when advance notice is given, you may not even need to make the actual contact. The "threat" of being called is enough:

We have a committee, and we're supposed to split up the calls. We actually did that in the past, a year and a half ago, because we were having major problems with dues. As a result of that, it's interesting, this year we sent out the dues notice, and we got 30 replies right back. Everybody paid their dues right away. They didn't want to get the phone call—maybe it's a little embarrassing or something. . . .

There's one more advantage to dues, less commonly realized, and that advantage is evaluative. Dues payments can tell you how members feel about the coalition. Checks in the mail are at least a partial endorsement, while no checks are a warning sign:

There's one agency that for some reason just hasn't come up with the money. They just have not. They haven't come to us and said we can't afford it, but they haven't sent it in either, and this is after repeated phone calls.

[Q: What do you do?].... Nothing. We really don't do anything. We feel like if we have to struggle that hard to get money from them, then we're doing something wrong. We need to step back, we need to figure out how to do something more relevant to what people want to happen. Because if it's really relevant to people's wants or needs, they're going to invest the $10, or whatever it is we're looking for.

Keeping the Members You Have

The last main topic to cover about membership is retention—keeping members once you've got them. Experience tells us that many people will come to a meeting once, or maybe twice, out of curiosity or good will; but to keep them coming, they (and you) need other motivations. What are they, and how do you provide them?

Once again, personal contact and a welcoming coalition climate are the keys:

For people who come on a regular basis, I think the networking function of the coalition is critical. In human services, there are program changes, there is turnover. So I think it helps enormously for people to catch up and keep track of what's going on. It's not enough to read that there's a new outreach worker—they need to make that connection, they need to meet that person in the flesh, instead of just being a voice at the end of a phone.

And I think the coalition is a very safe place. "Safe," meaning people feel they can say what they want to say. It's not competitive. It's a very neutral environment. It's friendly, it's hospitable, it's warm. It's non-threatening; it's absolutely non-threatening. I think it's a critical feature for people to feel comfortable. I know myself when I go someplace, I don't want to feel uneasy, or feel I'm going to be trapped.

What do I do? I make sure I know who everybody is. I look them in the eye, and I shake their hand and let them know I'm glad they're there. And I feel as if actually they're coming into my home. After all these years, I guess it does seem . . . well, it's a personal thing . . . it's like my second home. I'm like the first person at the door, and that's the first impression that they have of the group, so that part is important for me—and I think it makes a difference. You don't want people to just sort of slip in and slip out; you want them to feel acknowledged.

An additional possibility is to set up a structure, not only to assist in retention, but also to provide worthwhile membership benefits:

We came up with a Member Services Committee—if the coalition was actually doing things for its members, and responding to ideas or questions or needs, that would also help as a retention strategy. So if a member had an idea for a story, and wanted to get in touch with the newspaper, they could come to the committee, and we would help. And people were saying, "Can we use the coalition to bring in outside speakers, or to spend some time after the meeting to discuss a broader issue?" So we started this whole roundtable discussion series—it's been fairly successful.

But almost always, however you go about it, keeping your members active and happy and engaged takes time. And if you want to keep particular members, you may need to give them particular attention:

To keep people coming, you almost have to take them individual by individual. Figure out what their hot buttons are, really. It's like being a salesman. I mean, some people are just going to come because they know they should do it. But with people on the edge, you have to follow up.

We have one guy that heads up an employee assistance program in our area. He was a very regular member, and came to every single meeting. But over the last six months, I haven't seen him once. And I don't know why. But it's going to take follow-up. I mean, somebody needs to get on the phone, and call him up, and say, "Hey, Keith, you know, what's going on with your life? Have you just decided that you don't have time, have you lost employees, are we just not doing something that interests you?" Somebody's got to call.

We say "almost always," rather than "always," because we have found coalitions where membership retention is not perceived as a major issue. Special attention is not necessarily given. People come, or don't come, and the work goes on, and no one worries too much about it:

> *It's not something on my to-do list. We don't have a membership committee. We have change and movement; it's very elastic. If we take attendance, and all that, then it's a job.*
>
> *Every once in a while, I think, "Gee, maybe there are not as many people showing up." It does cross my mind a little. Then someone calls me, and says, "I saw something in the newsletter three months ago, Monica, and I've been away, but I'm going to try to come." And I say, "Great. We miss you. We'd love to see you." Then at the next meeting there will be twice the number as last time. It takes care of itself.*

But that is an exception, most commonly found in tight-knit, long-established coalitions with strong underlying cultural or ethnic bonds, or with personal bonds outside the coalition. Even then, attention to retention might improve coalition effectiveness. Which involves time, as we've noted before, and also the personal touch. A key conclusion from our experience is that there's no easy substitute for either:

> *The personal touch. Absolutely. I can't stress it enough. I can't stress it too much. Because I definitely do not think it happens with form letters. I use three-by-five cards a lot, postcards, just maybe to drop a line and say it was good to see them at a meeting.*
>
> *This happened three-four weeks ago, with a new person coming for the first time: She had some comments to make, she spoke out, and I dropped her a line and said it was really good to have her, and I felt it, and it was important. I sent her a postcard, a standard U.S. postcard. I buy them in blocks of 50; it's true.*
>
> *And a lot of my job is talking directly to people—if not in person, then certainly on the phone. You've got to call. And I've gone way beyond the feeling of "My God, why is it that I have to do this?" because the fact is—you do. So why not just accept it? It isn't some kind of fantasyland we're living in. It's the real world, which says you've got to do that. And I've come to know that, and I understand it, and I accept it. And I don't think it's a big deal either; it's easy enough to do. It's not a chore. . . .*

Lessons From The Field

Finding New Members

- To bring new members into the coalition, personal contact counts most. Face-to-face personal contact works best.

- In making personal contact, it helps to learn the *interests* of your potential member, and to show how joining the coalition can fulfill those interests.

- Potential members also need to see *benefits* from joining. What will they get in return? The benefits should exceed the costs. The moral: Find the benefits for this particular prospective member, and point them out.

Including Diverse Members

- Diversity is a plus: The more diverse and inclusive your coalition membership, the broader your base of community support, and the more community resources you can tap into.

- To include everyday citizens in your coalition—especially poorer people, and often those from different cultural and economic backgrounds—the previous principles apply; make personal contact, find their interests, show the benefits. But doing so may take more work on your part.

- Some community members with great talents to offer may have difficulty coming to meetings for a variety of practical reasons (transportation, child care, meeting times, work) or psychological ones (unfamiliarity, discomfort). Setting convenient meeting times and places can help address the former; friendly personal contact, repeated over time, can help overcome the latter.

- Members can also participate without necessarily coming to formal coalition meetings. They can do coalition work at their workplaces and homes, in small groups, or by themselves. The boundaries of "membership" can then expand.

Membership Dues

- The advantages of dues: They can give you cash for small operating expenses; they can strengthen members' commitment to your coalition; and potential funders are often impressed when members care enough about the coalition to pay to belong.

- Some disadvantages: Dues may be unaffordable; dues can exclude people you'd like to join; dues can run counter to the spirit of your group—where the work, and the people doing the work, come first.

- One resolution: Let everyone who wants to join the coalition be a member. But ask everyone who can do so to support the coalition by making an added contribution. Contributions should be affordable, perhaps on a sliding scale.

■ If you ask for dues support, make sure that a) everyone receives a friendly dues notice, b) everyone knows what they are being asked to give, c) the dues-return instructions are clear (e.g., "Please mail by October 1").

Retaining Members

■ To keep members active and engaged, they need to feel comfortable with other members of the coalition. A warm and welcoming atmosphere is a definite attraction.

■ But most coalition members also join because they want to do something, however small. Every member should be given specific opportunities for accomplishment that meet both personal and coalition goals. Principle: The more personal accomplishment, the more member involvement.

■ Finding good members, and keeping members involved, both take time. Membership development is labor-intensive. All members, new or old, need care and feeding. When you start taking members for granted, that's when you start to lose them.

■ Membership development time should therefore be budgeted. A coalition membership committee, or rotating task force, often makes sense. And each member can carry some share of the membership responsibility.

Sampler of Membership Criteria

Anyone who works or lives in the Northern Berkshire area and is interested in the work of the Northern Berkshire Health and Human Services coalition is considered a member of the Coalition.
(From the Northern Berkshire Health and Human Services Coalition)

Leaders and line staff from health and human services, business and industry, community leaders, political leaders, representatives from town government, schools, clergy and citizens. Membership shall be open to persons, organizations, or corporations interested in furthering and supporting the purpose of the Coalition.
(From the Athol/Orange Health and Human Services Coalition)

Membership is open to all persons, organization, or businesses interested in furthering and supporting the Coalition's mission of improving the quality of life as it relates to health and human service issues on the Lower/Outer Cape. Members include individuals from: health and human services, clergy, businesses, local schools, higher education, local and state government, chambers of commerce, local citizens, and consumers.

Sponsors make an annual donation to the Lower/Outer Cape Health and Human Services Coalition as an indication of support. Recommended donations are $10 for individuals and $25-$50 for organizations depending on their size.
(From the Lower/Outer Cape Health and Human Services Coalition)

Membership is open to residents of the Holyoke Latino community, staff members of agencies working with the Latino Community and any individual committed to the HLCC mission statement. An individual or agency becomes a member by paying the designated fee at the time of application. (Refer to ARTICLE XI for annual fee waivers.) Members receive mailings of the organization's activities. Meetings are open to the community at-large.
(From the Holyoke Latino Community Coalition)

Membership in the Council with the right to speak and vote at corporate meetings shall be open to any person or organization willing to promote the purpose of the Council upon approval of the Executive Committee.

To be a member in good standing an individual or organization must pay the annual dues and serve on one standing committee. Membership will automatically terminate within 90 days of non-renewal of membership dues.

Dues structure for the following fiscal year shall be proposed to the membership at the annual meeting and approved by 2/3 of the voting members present.
(From the Gloucester Human Services Council)

Who is a member? Here are some sample definitions which coalitions have used.

WHAT WE DO

The Greater Taunton Health and Human Services Coalition meets monthly to:

○ Share Information
○ Network
○ Learn about funding opportunities
○ Provide a forum for discussing important issues with local leaders, residents, organizations and business people

Much of the Coalition's work takes place in task forces and committees which meet monthly and are open to all.

JOIN A COMMITTEE AND HELP US TO MAKE GREATER TAUNTON A BETTER PLACE TO LIVE AND WORK!

○ Substance Abuse Committee
○ Member Services Committee
○ Health Issues Committee
○ Multicultural Committee
○ Council for Children

A FEW ACCOMPLISHMENTS

○ Convened legislative forums
  - local, regional, state-wide

○ Sponsored Medicaid Managed Care Conference
  - to answer questions of area doctors and other medical providers about changes in the Medicaid system

○ Prioritized Social Service Needs in Coordination with the City of Taunton

○ Collaborated with Other Community Groups, including:
  - Drug Free Schools and Community Advisory Committee
  - Taunton Cares: A Violence Prevention Task Force
  - Adolescent Health Council

○ Initiated an area-wide Health and Human Services Needs Assessment

○ Developed Strategies Addressing the Many Needs and Issues Within Our Culturally Diverse Community

PLEASE JOIN US!

MEMBERSHIP is open to everyone in the community interested in supporting the mission and work of the Coalition.

Simply complete this form and mail it with a check made payable to the Greater Taunton Health and Human Service Coalition.

☐ $10 INDIVIDUAL

ORGANIZATIONAL BUDGET
☐ $25   under $100,000
☐ $40   under $500,000
☐ $60   over $500,000
☐ $80   over $1,000,000

Name_____

Address_____

Phone_____

Organization (if applicable)_____

Mail to: Treasurer, GTHHSC
          P.O. Box 2894
          Taunton, MA 02780

To gain members, personal contact is fundamental. But membership brochures such as this one (reproduced in part) can definitely support the outreach work. Note also the sliding membership dues scale.

Be A Coalition Sponsor

Can You Even Remember What Life Was Like **BEFORE** the LOWER/OUTER CAPE COALITION?

Instrumental In Establishing:
- Interfaith Council for the Homeless of Lower Cape Cod
- "Project Home Share"
- Lower Cape Community Development Corp. (State Grant Awarded)
- Barnstable County Human Services Advisory Council

Coordinated Efforts For:
- 7 Town Small Cities Grant for Transportation and Child Care ($434,000 State Grant Awarded)
- Town Funding of Human Services
- Human Service Advocacy Support at State, County and Local Levels

Increased Lower Cape Human Service Awareness:
- Monthly Newsletter and Community Meetings
- Media Focus on Coalition Issues
- Community-wide Involvement on Human Service Issues

Sign Me Up!
Sponsorship is important. The Lower/Outer Cape Coalition does not exists without its sponsors. Right now we have an increased need for funds. Our financial base is shrinking and our office costs are increasing.
 We count heavily upon our sponsors to provide necessary resources. You can help further the goals of the coalition. Please sign on again for 1992 sponsorship, or join us as a new sponsor for 1992...

Sponsorship Form

Name_____

Organization_____

Address_____

Phone No._____ List as member? Y N

Special Interest_____

☐	$10.00 Individual
☐	$25.00 Organizations with budgets under $100,000
☐	$50.00 Organizations with budgets over $100,000
☐	$100.00 Organizations with budgets over $250,000

Please make checks payable to and return this form to::
Lower/Outer Cape Health and Human Service Coalition
P.O. Box 797
Eastham, MA 02642

As a variation, anyone can be a coalition member without dues or other costs. But financial contributors are also solicited and may be called "sponsors."

How can I get involved?

Steering Committee Nominations

The Berkshire Partnership is an alliance of citizens working together to prevent alcohol, tobacco and other drug abuse by building healthier communities. The Steering Committee helps to guide Partnership activities.

The Partnership's Steering Committee currently has two openings. We are seeking nominations to fill these openings. Your recommendations are welcome.

We strive to have a representative Committee, by geography, ethnicity and role in community. At this time, we are particularly looking for representation from southern Berkshire County, clergy, elected officials, elderly or women.

Being a Steering Committee member will require just a few hours per month for a one year "term of office." We will try to meet by telephone as often as possible to limit travel time. Members will be offered special training opportunities. They will develop and implement a county-wide Strategic Plan for Prevention and shape the Partnership for the future.

If you know someone who would be interested in and willing to serve on the Steering Committee, please list names and phone numbers (if you know the number) below.

Self nominations are encouraged!

Name_____

   Tel. Number_____

Name_____

   Tel. Number_____

Please complete other side.

Other ways I could help!

I could help with the newsletter, *Partnership News*
____Collecting articles from my part of the county

____Writing articles for publication

____ Suggesting ideas for Feature Articles

____ Working on the computer (typing or formatting)

____ Folding and Bulk mailing

I could help with Gatherings
____ Planning, with the committee

____ Finding location

____ Getting the word out to media, etc.

I could help with Public Awareness
____ Writing press releases

____ Making contacts with local media

____ Clipping articles from my local newspaper

____ Working on a Partnership Scrapbook

Other Ways I could help:

Yes, I would like to get involved! Please call me.

Name _____

Address _____

City, Town, Zip _____

Telephone _____
          Home   Work

Once members join, they need to become involved. This simple form prompts new members to take on tasks, right from the get-go.

Human Service Coalition Checklist

Directions: Please indicate which items you think are a "GOOD IDEA" and which items you might wish to "GET INVOLVED" in this year.

	Good Idea	Get Involved
1. Breakfast forums like this one.	✓	
2. A combined health and human service resource directory.		✓
3. A slide-tape or video presentation of Local health & human service resources.		✓
4. Joint orientation programs for new staff.	✓	
5. Joint training programs for current staff.		
6. Recruitment and training of bilingual staff.		
7. Conferences on particular themes (which?: homelessness, AIDS, etc.?)	✓	
8. Training programs for neighborhood leaders and groups.	✓	✓
9. Further development of hotline or information-line programs.		
10. Centralized information on funding resources and opportunities	✓	
11. Centralized information on needs assessment and demographic data.		
12. Centralized information on legislative action in human services.	✓	
13. Fund-raising for human services activities.	✓	
14. Sponsorship of local cultural events.		
15. Social events for ourselves (picnic, softball games, etc.)		
16. Long-range planning for human services in Fall River.	✓	
17. Developing joint position papers on key community issues.		
18. Expanding outreach through the media.	✓	
19. A human services fair (planning underway).	✓	✓
20. A human services newsletter (planned for May).	✓	✓
21. Coming to meetings of the Human Services Coalition	✓	✓
22. Becoming a member of a Coalition task force (any particular topic?)	✓	✓

This simple flyer did double duty—first as a needs assessment tool (in the left column), and then as a membership involvement device (on the right). In practice, this form was placed at each table setting at a coalition breakfast. A red star was affixed to one form per table. The person picking up the form with the red star was asked to collect the forms of all others at the table. Using this simple technique, the return rate approached 100%.

You're Invited...

Fall River Health And Human Services Coalition

cordially

invites you to attend

COALITION AFTER HOURS

Tuesday, May 22

5:00 P.M. to 7:00 P.M.

PARROT'S DEN

Cash Bar - Free Hors d"oevres

EVERYONE   WELCOME

Enjoy a chance to get better aquainted with fellow coalition members.
If you are not already a member this is the perfect opportunity for you to find out about the Coalition.

R.S.V.P. Debbie or Donna at the YMCA 675-7841

FREE RAFFLE....PLEASE BRING YOUR BUSINESS CARDS

Coalition membership should not be all work and no play. Why not invite your hard-working members to a social event to meet their colleagues and kick back a little when the business part of the day is done?

Chapter 4

Coalition Structure

> *How much structure is really necessary?*
>
> *What structure is best for my coalition?*
>
> *What about voting?*
>
> *How can the coalition's work best be distributed among its members?*

When the coalition has first formed, when members are lined up, when things are beginning to move, when you start to smell success, then—and no later—it's time to think seriously about coalition structure.

"Structure? Do you mean organizational charts, and rules, and (perish the thought) committees? Why should we be thinking about that stuff? We're starting to make something happen in the community. We're on a roll. And there's just too much to take care of right now. Thanks anyway. Later, maybe."

It's great that you're on a roll. But the reason to think about structure so early on is that you probably won't be on a roll forever, at least not rolling at the same rate. The pace of accomplishment is uneven, a poignant truth of both human and organizational life. Coalition life, in particular, has its peaks and troughs. Structure prevents the troughs from becoming too deep.

By structure, we mean the framework around which the coalition is organized. Or pick other construction metaphors: the underpinnings, the wiring, the girders that keep the coalition erect. The structure defines the procedures of the coalition. It's the operating manual, explicit or implicit, that tells members how the coalition is put together and how it works. More specifically, structure relates to how members are accepted, how leadership is chosen, how differences get mediated, and how decisions get made. And it does so without apology.

For at some point, the bloom will come off the rose. Coalition members will be less excited than they used to be. They may stop always agreeing with each other, and start to think about other things they could do with their days. At those times, which is much of the time in most organizations, structure is desirable and necessary.

It is desirable and necessary for at least four reasons. First, because structure gives members clear guidelines on how to proceed. Soon enough, uncertainty will arise, and so will disagreement. And when there is too much uncertainty or disagreement in a coalition, or any organization—in particular when channels for resolving disagreement are absent—that's when people imagine how nice it would be to be someplace else, and disinvest, or flat-out leave. A clearly established structure gives the coalition a means to cut through the uncertainty, resolve the disagreements, and sustain the investment.

Second, because structure gives meaning and identity to the people who join the coalition, as well as to the coalition itself. It satisfies the basic human needs for form, regularity, and order, which are no less important in our organizational than in our personal lives.

Third, because structure helps ensure that the coalition will keep going regardless of the participation of a few particular members. Leaders may quit, lose their steam, move away, occasionally get overthrown. A structure will reduce coalition dependence on any such persons, no matter how talented (or untalented) they happen to be.

And fourth, because some degree of structure in any lasting organization is inevitable—an organization, by definition, implies a structure. Your coalition is going to have some structure whether it chooses to or not; so it might as well be the structure that best matches up with what kind of coalition you have, what kind of people are in it, and what you see yourself doing.

That's why it's wise to be dealing with structure early in the coalition's history. It's best to do so in a way that doesn't impede coalition development, but enhances it. How? Structural development can occur *in proportion to* the other work of the coalition, so that it neither crowds out that work nor hogs too much space. And it can occur *parallel to* your coalition's growing accomplishments, so that they take place side by side.

While the need for structure is clear, the best structure for a particular coalition is harder to determine. That is because coalition structure should be custom-tailored. Some structures are tight, others are loose. Some are simple; others glitter. Some are worn casually; others are all business; others still are trotted out only for formal occasions. The best structure for any coalition, including your own, will depend on its size and shape—and specifically on whom its members are, what the setting is, and how far the coalition has come in its organizational evolution.

What's more, that best structure can change. And it *will* change, according to different stages in a coalition's life. The task for any coalition is to find that structure best suited to its own character, members, time, and place.

So we can't give definite answers for a particular coalition, but we can describe some structures that different coalitions have adopted so that you can hold them up for inspection and understand more clearly which one might be right for you. Our game plan in this chapter is to do just that. We'll cover three primary structural topics: governance, voting, and committees. As the chapter unfolds, some general principles of structure and its applications should become clearer. Our objective is to help you choose or refine a structure that best supports you and your work. For ultimately, the structure is there to serve the coalition and its members, not vice versa.

Governance

Governance is first on our list. Once your coalition grows past a certain size, not everybody is likely to take part in every coalition decision or coalition action. Even if they could, it wouldn't be efficient, nor would it be smart. It will be too hard for everyone to come together all the time, and not all of them will be interested in—nor well-informed about—every coalition issue. So you form a governing structure, as this coalition did, in a fairly typical manner:

> *Our average coalition meeting would be 45 or 50, a small one would be 35, and for a large meeting we could be over 100. You can't make decisions with that many people, based on the number of things we want to cover.*
>
> *So it's our Steering Committee that really does that. The Steering Committee meets monthly for an hour and a half the Tuesday following the full coalition meeting. There are 17 people who get notices. And basically, we set the agendas for the monthly meetings and for the coalition. The coalition has empowered us to make decisions based upon how people feel about an issue. But we really try to ask the coalition membership how it feels about the issues that are there.*

When do you get "past a certain size"? There's no absolute figure, but 10-15 is a ballpark estimate. Beyond that point, it makes sense to have a smaller group take primary responsibility for some coalition decisions and actions. That group will provide much of the governance of the coalition—the decision making—which is a central part of coalition structure.

When we talk about structure in general, or governance in particular, we are often talking about hierarchy, and we are usually talking about different levels of power. To some, hierarchy and power are fighting words; yet not everyone in a coalition is going to have the same level of ability or interest in taking part. That's just the nature of organizational life. So as long as everyone who wants to can be actively involved, and no one's voice is excluded, it's okay, or more than okay, to have those who are the most interested (and possibly the most talented) take on more of the coalition's governance responsibilities.

The key points are for everyone in the coalition to know what its structure is, to have a say in determining it, and to participate in it as interest and ability dictate. Others will participate, too, but at a somewhat less intensive level for now, or perhaps in a more specialized way.

Governance models. In coalitions and in nonprofit organizations, these governance structures go by different names—steering committee, coordinating committee, executive committee, and board of directors are a few. But can we stipulate what kind of structure is best (not just what it's called, but also how it operates)? Let's look at a few models.

■ Here is one that is about as loose as a governance structure can be:

> *Our Steering Committee has maybe eight or nine members. It's made up of somebody from the hospital, somebody involved with prevention of teenage pregnancy, somebody from the housing authority. But the fact that someone's from the housing authority isn't as important as the fact that it's someone I've known for a long time, and we're friends. She cares enormously about the coalition.*
>
> *It's wide open. Anybody who wants to can become a member. There's no official size. It can be more or less. They're not elected. They don't have a term of office. They can come on and off, and I've put in the newsletter every single month that anyone is welcome. Sometimes I've asked people to consider joining because I just want their kind of thinking on the committee.*
>
> *At least three of the people on there do not ever come anymore. But I don't want to let them off the Steering Committee, because if I need them. . . . They were some of the founding members of the coalition, so they have a big part in the history, and so I need to know that they're on the other end of the phone even though they aren't currently able to come.*

It would be hard for a structure to be more informal than this. Anyone is welcome. There is still a structure, and an inner circle. But anyone who wants to be part of the inner circle can come right in. The boundaries are open.

■ Not far away, there is another community coalition, established around the same time. It's a little larger, and one shade more formal.

> *You get on the Steering Committee by asking another member of the Steering Committee, or myself. Usually, they ask me, because I'm kind of like the designated coalition contact. And then you're on.*
>
> *Can anyone be on the Steering Committee? I don't want to say universally yes. We want people who are engaged and involved in what we do. We also want people who believe in the mission of the coalition and can work*

with all of us. And we don't want to stack it with representation from any one organization—we like to spread it out as much as we can.

But I would never turn anybody down . . . We've been worried about one or two people asking us to join because we fear that they might not fit in and they might be difficult; but we've never turned anybody down.

In this model, there's some nominal screening; though more or less anyone can still walk through the door.

■ It's also possible to keep your governance structure informal while making sure the governing members are invited.

We just call someone up and invite them, and basically, anyone that we want to invite onto the board is invited onto it. It's advisory—it's a community advisory board. If it comes up at a meeting that we think that this person ought to be invited, I call them up and say, "We'd like you to be on the board. . . ."

■ Or you can arrange matters so that a place on the governing body comes not by invitation, but rather by election.

We have an 11-member Steering Committee. We try to maintain representation on a couple of levels: geographically, ethnically, and by age—and we've tried to have young people as well as elders.

They're elected from the general partnership membership, who are the folks who come to the gatherings and receive newsletters. So, we solicit nominations that way. They can be nominated by mail or by handing in a form at the gathering. Terms are for one year, re-electable. Self-nominations are encouraged.

■ Or, you can aim for governance that sounds more formal, which sometimes goes by the name "Executive Committee":

The Executive Committee was set when we set up our structure. Basically it's composed of the officers and the chairs of all the committees. At the beginning, we decided we wanted to have a chair, a vice chair, a treasurer, and a secretary. And it was also decided that we needed some kind of decision-making mechanism, or guidance mechanism, so that there was some cohesion to the coalition meetings.

So the Executive Committee had as its first job to set the agenda every month. And also it exists to follow up on things between meetings, to identify issues for the coalition to discuss in more detail, or refer to another committee, or whatever. It's also the group that is referred to if people have questions, or if I have questions.

We meet once a month before the coalition meeting. It doesn't usually go very long. But it's just a way for everybody to touch base about the various things that are going on. Because like at any given month there might be four or five things that come up that are more or less unexpected. Like, for instance, that RFP on teen pregnancy prevention. . . .

. . . Even though executive committees don't always work that way in practice:

But generally only three or four people come. It's basically the same people. Particularly the chairs of the committees. I think they forget that they have this responsibility to be a part of the Executive Committee. So Jim [the coalition chair] needs to do reminder calls to all of them.

■ Or, more formally still, you can put together a bona fide board of directors, which can look and feel like a capital-B Board in the larger nonprofit and for-profit worlds.

Ever since I've been there, we've had a Board of Directors. The details of who can be on the Board are very specifically stated in the by-laws. Twenty-five percent have to be recipients of services, no more than 25 can be from one agency, there has to be geographic diversity, and so on.

It's a formal office. You get your name on letterhead stationery, if you like that kind of thing. To get onto the Board, you have to run for election, and depending on the year, this has been very competitive, with voting, paper ballots, serious stuff. Anybody could be nominated, and there were some self-nominations, but there was also a nominating committee who looked around and came up with names of its own.

The elections were held on the day of the Annual Meeting. Everyone who wanted to be on the Board was supposed to get up and make a two-minute speech about why they wanted to be a Board member. One year we had I think 20 or 25 candidates for something like 10 seats, so this took a long time, and it was a big deal. It took almost an hour just to count the ballots alone. A lot of good candidates actually lost.

I know that other groups like ourselves in other communities are often called steering committees, or some other name, and maybe they are looser than we are. But a "Board of Directors" makes everyone feel the position is important, and maybe makes Board members take it more seriously. Anyway, nobody here has ever wanted to call ourselves anything else but a board.

These are some models of governance that coalitions have used. Does this mean the more structure the better? Should your coalition be as formally structured as the one just above? No, not necessarily. There are downsides to formality, as one coordinator points out:

Our Steering Committee is functionally a board of directors. But it is informal. I think the formality might scare people. It might change the kind of relationships we have and how meetings are conducted.

If we were a Board, we'd have to have officers. If we have to elect those officers, then suddenly it creates a hierarchy, and the power struggles or the political struggles that one can have within any kind of formal organization. We really don't have that. We all have equal say. . . .

Ultimately, coalitions depend on relationships. Formal structure can impede relationship development, or erode relationships once present. And it's important to note that some coalitions can function with next to no structure at all. Here's one that did—for several years, it operated as a group of total equals. Only after a major community incident did it very reluctantly form as much as a loose coordinating committee.

[Speaker #1]: *I felt a coordinating committee was needed. But I didn't forcefully push it. We said okay, let's talk about it.*

[Speaker #2]: *The issue was that a Latino person had been abused by the police in Worcester and had died. It was pretty brutal. I mean, the guy died. And it happened in the summer, when we don't meet. We were not mobilized. The coalition had not made a statement.*

#1: *So, like for everything else, we went back to the coalition (laughter) and discussed it at a coalition meeting. "What do you think about this kind of small group?" We didn't even want to use the words "steering committee." But we'd use the term "coordinating." And it was discussed and rediscussed and disagreed on, and—I'm trying to remember what the consensus was—there was some real skepticism. Did we even finish at one meeting, or did we come back to it?*

#2: *No, we never finish anything at one meeting.*

#1: *So we had to talk about it more than once, at a couple of meetings, to really discuss it and make sure that there wasn't going to be too much structure somehow being imposed, or the potential for too much power to get centralized.*

It really got talked out, and first of all, we said, "This is an experiment." It's really to be a response to issues; it's a way to stay connected in between our monthly meetings. We're going to try this. We'll kind of look and evaluate it at some point. And if it looks like it's working, then we'll continue to use it. Now, it's working well.

#2: *I've been in a lot of boards through the years. There's nothing like this coalition. . . .*

So what type of governance is best for your coalition? Some guidelines do exist. There are certain specific conditions that favor looser or tighter governance, and the following list notes what they are.

A looser, less formal, less rule-bound governance structure is usually favored when:

- The coalition is just starting out.
- Many trusting relationships among members already exist.
- Many positive working experiences have occurred among members.
- Member motivation to be part of the coalition is high.
- There is a single coalition issue or task.
- The coalition is small.
- The leadership is experienced.
- There is no particular urgency to take action now.

But in contrast . . .

A tighter, more formal, more rule-bound governance structure is usually favored when:

- The coalition is in later stages of development.
- Few trusting relationships among members already exist.
- Few positive working experiences have occurred among members.
- Member motivation to be part of the coalition is relatively low.
- There are multiple coalition issues or tasks.
- The coalition is large.
- The leadership is inexperienced.
- There is strong urgency to take action now.

But as you may have guessed by now, there's no one completely uniform answer. In general, we subscribe to the Goldilocks model of coalition development—which here means finding a structure that is neither too soft nor too hard, neither too big nor too little, but the best fit for who you are right now. As your coalition evolves, your needs may change; you may want to sleep in a bigger bed, sit in a bigger chair, or eat from a bigger bowl; and that is just as it should be.

Voting

We're going to let you in on a secret: Most decisions in most coalitions (and informal community organizations in general) are not made by voting. They are usually made by general agreement, and sometimes made when the agreement is not very general at all.

Next time you are at a coalition or grassroots community meeting, check this out for yourself. What percentage of all decisions are made by formal vote? In a great many cases, this percentage is relatively small. It's more like, "Okay, do we agree that . . . ?" or "Let's do it, and move on to the next topic," or "X, can you take care of that?" or "How about if we try it, and check back next time?"

No actual vote is taken. No formal consensus is reached. Instead, the "sense of the meeting" is that the members agree. Sometimes, they don't even necessarily agree; a topic comes up, the chair proposes a course of action, no one says otherwise, and that's it. The members here don't so much agree as acquiesce. Often they will go along, because it's not personally worth it to them to speak out, or because there are more important topics on the agenda, or because they want to go home.

But what's for sure is that they don't vote. This isn't necessarily bad. Voting can slow things down. Voting can make the coalition's work seem too stiff and impersonal. Voting may be less necessary when everyone is pretty much on the same wavelength, and everyone knows it.

Having let this cat out of the bag, does this mean we forget about voting? No. At some point not too far down the road, it is worthwhile to spell out voting procedures for the coalition. This means asking and resolving at least two questions: (1) Who is a voting member? and (2) What are the conditions when votes are taken? Your answers can save you a lot of disagreements, hard feelings, wasted motion, and all-around aggravation in the long run. Without these answers, it's not as if you are looking for trouble; it's that trouble is more likely to find you:

> *Our coalition had general membership meetings, and it was the larger general membership that approved all actions of the coalition. Voting rules? We didn't have any. If you showed up at a meeting, you voted, as simple as that. This usually worked out okay until it came to an election for our board of directors. These elections were sometimes competitive, and one time this organization, the visiting nurses, wanted one of their candidates on the board.*
>
> *So they packed the meeting—they brought 30 people into the room. No one had seen any of them before. And by our rules, or lack of rules, they had a vote. It was really outrageous.*
>
> *The irony was that their candidate was well-regarded, and would have won anyway. So their packing the meeting didn't do them any good. It just created ill will toward that organization, which would never have happened if we had clear voting rules.*

Once you start thinking about voting, you can get in fairly deep. Voting procedures in coalitions are not as simple as they sound. For example, does each person at the table have one vote? Or, since people at the table may represent an organization, does the vote belong to each *organization*? (Then, if several people are present from one organization, they would still have only one collective vote.) This can get tricky. Here's one solution:

> *We decided that the voters would be individuals, rather than organizations. But we also said that that no more than 25 percent of the voting membership could belong to any one organization. This allowed us to have the*

best and most interested people as voting members, but gave us some pro-
tection against any one organization having too much voting control.

And should there be mandated voting representation from different constituencies, or from different geographic areas?

> *We agreed that at least 25 percent of the voting members should be*
> *consumers of services. We usually aimed for more. We also said that*
> *there should be at least two representatives from each of the four differ-*
> *ent territories we covered. Sometimes we couldn't get two, and then we*
> *would have to spend meeting time working out waiver procedures so that*
> *somebody else could fill one of the vacant slots. Believe it, this was time-*
> *consuming.*

Voting procedures can get complicated. They can easily lead to squabbles. And it's possible to overdo it, to get so entangled in voting mechanics that the work of the coalition begins to suffer:

> *I was a consultant to another coalition, and this job was tough. The mem-*
> *bers got so caught up in voting procedures that little else could get done.*
> *They would meet, and there would be these intense, personal discussions*
> *about could this specific person vote, and could this other person vote, and*
> *what would happen if that person left—could they be replaced by someone*
> *else?—and on, and on, and on. They not only picked every nit, they put each*
> *one under the microscope. They really held themselves back. Ultimately, the*
> *people didn't trust each other, I think that was the problem.*
>
> *But you know, it wasn't that simple. Because the amazing thing was these*
> *people kept on coming back for more, discussion after discussion on the same*
> *topic. They really were committed to their cause; they just had a really hard*
> *time getting beyond voting procedures, and it cost them, big time. I suggest-*
> *ed they make some simple agreements, adopt them provisionally, get on with*
> *the job, and revise as necessary. But no, voting had to be 100 percent*
> *squared away, even if it took them a year. And it did.*

This story illustrates a principle of timing. When the coalition is just getting start-ed, you probably don't want to get into overly detailed discussions about voting. You want to focus on the issues that led you to form the coalition in the first place, to move forward on them, and to keep energy high. If you get too deeply into voting too soon, or if you force the point, you can easily get bogged down. You could scare some of your best members away. Follow the above consultant's advice: keep it simple at the start. More complex voting issues are likely to come up in their own time; let this hap-pen naturally.

And to make life easier, check out what other similar coalitions are doing, especially coalitions at the same stage of development as your own. Borrow from them; voting procedures aren't patented. And no matter what you adopt, voting procedures can always be changed if needed. The main point is to get the work done. Voting can help, but when it blocks the road instead of opening the highway, then it's time to step back and look at the bigger picture.

But there's still another phase in the evolution of some coalitions. Under the right circumstances, especially when people have been together for quite a long time, it can happen that formal voting may become less important, rather than more. What's your opinion on the arrangements of this long-term coalition?

> *We don't have to think too much about voting. I do make sure everybody feels they've been heard, that there's a consensus if the issue is of a controversial nature, and that just sort of happens automatically. They're all pretty frank people, and they would be quite outspoken—"Wait a minute . . ."— if there was a need.*
>
> *I think there's been great benefit from an informal approach, but I suppose it also has a lot to do with the personality of the people. I don't know how it is in other coalitions. . . .*

Or what about this coalition. . . . Is it really sensible, or just fuzzy mysticism, to "follow the river"?

> *We might ask, "How many people think this is a good idea?" but we're not going to count. If we ask people to vote through the mail, they don't. If we ask them to vote at a coalition meeting—they might. Actually, we do ask people to ask around for opinions. We just haven't used voting as a tool.*
>
> *I guess it's like we're on a river, and we just kind of follow the flow of the river and go in the path that the river wants to go. And in 10 years, we haven't made any serious mistakes, where we've gone in a direction that the river doesn't want to go and have beached our canoe as a result of it.*

There's one more way of looking at voting, and that is to have different decision-making methods on call, using each one as the situation demands. You don't simply float on the river, you steer, and if your steering mechanism is flexible and finely tuned, and if you are a skilled navigator, you will slip through the shoals unscathed.

> *It's mostly consensus. I'd say probably more decisions are made when everyone agrees about such-and-such. But if it looks like there's disagreement, then we've said, "Well, somebody needs to make a motion on this, so we can vote on it. Okay?" So, if we can't get consensus, then we move to that strategy. And the third strategy is if you can't get a motion on something, and people are so emotional, then you might form a subcommittee or a task force*

to consider the issues and bring something back to the following meeting.
So we shift back and forth. Absolutely. But the sense is to get the dialogue
going and yet get a collective sense of the whole.

The general moral of this section is to think about voting, and work out voting procedures at the right time, but not dwell on them unduly. Voting concerns should be kept in proportion to the other concerns of the coalition. The most useful consideration in decision making is that members know they can (and are expected to) speak out, and that their point of view will be listened to and respected. This is at least as important as taking formal votes.

Committees and Task Forces (and their close relations)

Committees. Nobody is dying to be on one. Some members, sometimes your best and bravest, hear the word "committee," and they stare at their shoes. You won't get awards or recognition for being on a committee. A glamour job it is not.

Let's face it: A committee meeting rarely makes anybody's day.

But you've got to have them, or structures like them. Why? Simply because small groups are more efficient than large ones. Large groups can work very well, but small groups get more work done per person-hour. Not always, but usually. Everybody knows this. That's why there are committees in the first place.

So the question becomes, "How do we make coalition committees work most effectively?" And (a related question), "How do we make committee membership most appealing and rewarding for coalition members?" If there can't be glory, there can at least be satisfaction, and possibly even fulfillment.

Coalition leaders tell us how to do it:

First, we can change the language. Instead of "committees," we can have "task forces," or "work groups," or even just "groups."

Why did we call it a task force? I guess there's more power in the words
"task force." Task force to me connotes something that doesn't meet forever,
that's focused for a short period of time, and has results coming out of it.

* * *

The task force has a specific task, and if it completes the task, then it
could dissolve. Sometimes a committee just kind of goes on and on. . . .

The difference is partly—though not entirely—semantic. "Committee" suggests "bureaucracy," "boring," and "forever." (You might even have to be a committee chair.) "Task force" suggests you work on a specific, time-limited task, get it done, and move on. Members like that. But these semantic differences have consequences: *They can determine how people will really act in groups.* Our language choices affect our actual group behavior.

Second, we can make sure that our task forces form on the basis of community need.

> *There was a lot of substance abuse in our region. The issues which came up probably involved more than we could handle at a general two-hour meeting. So we decided to form a group of folks interested in substance abuse to talk about it, and that became a task force we developed. And they would report back to the coalition on a regular basis on some of the ideas and suggestions they came up with.*

That much isn't hard. And when a new need arises, the coalition has the flexibility to respond.

> *Forming task forces is not a conscious effort. It's just something that evolves. I don't think about it too much. If somebody came to a monthly coalition meeting and said, "My God, we've got an incredible problem, because they're going to put a nuclear waste facility right in the middle of downtown North Adams," or something like that, I bet a task force would develop out of the coalition meeting to address that issue.*

Third, we can review the committee or task-group structure every so often, or (better yet) every year. We can get rid of the ones that are no longer necessary, keep the ones that are, and add new ones if they are really needed. The sun sets every day. Some work groups can set every year.

> *I mean, every once in a while, I feel you kind of have to shake people up and go, "Now, do we really need a substance abuse prevention committee?" or "Do we really need an information and referral committee?" In fact, this year we actually got rid of a committee because people weren't coming to the meetings, and there really wasn't a need within the group to have that kind of response mechanism.*
>
> *Things do tend to come and go. Which is not bad. To me it just kind of speaks to where people's interests are shifting. . . .*

* * *

> *We've learned that it's okay to take on something and have its life end or at least go in quietude. I know we once had a HIV/AIDS task force and the group was very energetic and productive. They put together a directory of services. They got some HIV/AIDS education plugged into both the big schools, in Athol and Orange. They were involved with a weekly support*

group, but once those things were done, they couldn't see any reason in continuing. If it ever becomes an issue again, I can see them coming back and saying, "Look, we've got to reactivate that task force."

There are alternatives to a graceful departure, however. Instead of dying, the committee can lie low for a while. It can hibernate, and return to life another season.

I'm perfectly willing to let committees go dormant for six months. You get things that happen in committees' and people's lives. The Public Safety Committee is dormant because members have been sick. I can accept that. After all, that committee brought a $525,000 community policing grant into the city. That doesn't mean that at some point we might not bring it back.

Another alternative is for the original committee to create something completely new, and then set out on a new direction.

We had a task force that came along around issues of homelessness, and ultimately what spun off from that was the Interfaith Council for the Homeless. So, that's an outcome you might come up with, a response or a program or a service that could be institutionalized and spin off on its own.

More generally, this type of committee review and revision is healthy for the coalition. It stimulates conscious planning and action. Metaphorically speaking, it's like thoughtful pruning. And it's more than just getting rid of the deadwood. It helps assure that the surviving branches will be stronger, and will better contribute to the overall hardiness of the tree.

Fourth, we can rotate the committee leadership, and its membership, too. Committees shouldn't be life imprisonment without parole. If you join a task force, you can sign on for a one-year hitch, or until the work is done, whichever comes first. At the end of the year, you might have the option to enlist again. But if you don't, someone else will be available to take your place. That's part of the bargain, up front.

One variation of this concept is to have co-chairs:

We have co-chairs, too, which I think works. Each committee is chaired by two people coming from separate places in the community. For example, Public Safety is chaired by a police officer and a neighborhood leader. The Health Committee is chaired by somebody from the Spanish Center and from Pro Health. So it isn't just one person—you've always got somebody.

Fifth, we can make sure that everyone in the coalition has a piece of the action. If there are 20 members in the coalition (or 30, or 50, or more), *everyone* will have some kind of task, group assignment, or the equivalent. *Everyone* has something to contribute; another part of the up-front bargain, right from the start, is that they will contribute in some way, however small. This expectation can be gently conveyed, but made crystal-clear. (Some coalitions set it in writing.) Everyone is needed. "Everybody is a perfect something."

That sounds fair and sensible enough, yet putting that philosophy into practice isn't always easy. How, specifically, should the work be divided? Yes, you divide according to community need, but needs abound. So what's the right number of task forces, or committees, and how can you tell? This question deserves careful thought.

One coalition chose a structure with five working groups:

> *We have five—Executive, Economics, Public Policy, Youth, and Health. Four are standing committees, one is ad hoc. It's about the right number, I think, for all the concerns the coalition has right now. Any new topic that comes up could probably fit under one of those five broad categories. But if a newer group wanted to do something different, you know, if it was environmental, they could form another one. They could do that. . . .*

And in fact, the number five, plus or minus one or two, seems to be the subgroup number most frequently cited. Sometimes, there is pressure for fewer:

> *Right now with five committees, people will say, "That's too many committees. You're trying to do too much." Especially given the fact that we have only one part-time staff person, and a membership that for the most part is overcommitted with their work. Anyway, "Five committees is too ambitious," and all that kind of stuff. . . .*

On the other hand, you could argue for more, as long as you can populate them:

> *There are people in the city who think we're too big already and that we need to refocus, cut down on the number of issues we're working on. But I think it's the more the merrier.*

That is, why limit yourself, especially if you've got the people? And another reason for stretching the numbers, pushing the boundaries, is that you want to respond not only to community need but also to personal interest. That is, if you've got a passionate member who is burning to charge ahead, why not provide a fire lane and pull off to the side?

> *I think some of our work developed because there were people inspired within the coalition. Family violence is a real problem in our region. And Steve just pushed this issue with the coalition. He was relentless. And he was wonderful. Because he really helped us to recognize the need to talk about family violence and about what we could do to prevent it. He led our task force. He helped create products, and helped us secure a grant to disseminate them. And then he got a promotion and moved away. And after he left,*

these things kind of languished, because there was no one to fill the gap. The group really needed someone who was inspired like Steve was inspired.

* * *

There are plenty of issues to be addressed in the community. So anyone who is interested, has the expertise or desire—if someone comes and says, "Yes, I want to do that," we say, "Yeah, yes, do it please. We need somebody to be a part of that." That's an easy agreement to make.

But—and here is the crux of the issue—to "let one hundred flowers bloom" brings problems of its own. Each blossom may be beautiful, yet someone needs to be the gardener. The gardener is typically the coalition leader or coordinator, and the amount of yard work involved in cultivation may be just too much:

The vehicle for getting things done in this coalition is to form task forces. That's the vehicle. And in my enthusiasm as coordinator this past year, all of a sudden we've emerged with multiple new task forces, to the point that I'm really overextended. So believe me, I'm not looking to set up any new task forces. As a matter of fact, what we're looking to do is examine where our task forces are now and see if we can pull back some.

Is that the best alternative, though? If you did cut back, would the coalition be more productive? Not necessarily:

Our coalition had 14 committees on the books. About six or seven were meeting at all, and maybe three or four were getting anything done. So there was a movement to combine everything into those three or four committees, even though when you asked people in a survey, they had more than three or four separate interests. But we did combine. And when we did, those new three or four committees became less productive themselves. They were probably too broad. Myself, I think it would have been better to have more committees, as long as each one was doing something, which I guess is the responsibility of the leadership.

Which brings us to our sixth key point about setting up work groups. They need support. Not only support from the participants, but also logistical support, backup, someone to do the small in-between tasks needed for any group to work.

You need a chairperson to chair the meetings. You need people to type and mail the minutes and the other correspondence, to send the meeting notices, to make the follow-up calls, to promote the work and activities of the task force, to evaluate the progress and the outcomes, to carry out the activities. These are all the things that make a task force work and go forward.

A question: Where is this support going to come from? This is another challenge. Once again, the most likely candidate is the coalition leader or coordinator. ("I'm at every committee meeting"; "It's me pushing the committee chairs.") In an active coalition, this can take an enormous amount of both physical and psychic energy. That energy can be quickly drained. No wonder leaders don't want more committees!

But the coalition leader doesn't have to run the whole show. Much of the solution (in concept, very simple; in real life, not always so easy) is that a large part of the task group responsibility has to come from the task group chairs. With wise leadership from the top, this can happen. (*See Chapter 6 for more on this topic.*)

> *You need good committee chairs. If you're going to run a coalition that's addressing six or seven issues, the coordinator or the organizer has got to understand that you can't run six committees. You can't organize and drive six committees at the same time.*

* * *

> *The coalition coordinator and the administrative assistant have been carrying out most of these tasks for most of these task forces. And now it's abundantly clear to me that not only for my benefit but also for the benefit of the task forces that we need to be sharing these responsibilities—even though it's very easy for busy people who are very committed in their own work to have the coordinator take them over.*

This isn't a panacea. The committee chairs may fall short. (Remember, there's no glamour.) It's more of a large step in the right direction.

> *We've had it both ways. Sometimes it hasn't worked. The chair isn't as conscientious, perhaps, about keeping in touch on a monthly basis. Meetings get out of sync and people feel frustrated about what's going on. But I've learned that I don't have to be the chair of every task force. I think it's been proven that sometimes these task forces can do quite well with another facilitator.*

These are some guidelines, among others, that will help work groups work better. Just as in other aspects of coalition structure, the trick is to find what best fits your coalition at this point in time.

The best fit will vary; that's helpful to know. Usually, though, you'll want a structure that's not too loose, but not overly tight. Not too fancy, but not necessarily the plainest model in stock. You'll want a structure that's suited to the personalities, tastes, and activities of your coalition members. It should be comfortable and pleasing, easy to care for, with a little give in the right places. It should look good on you.

Lessons From The Field

The Necessity of Structure

■ All living things have structure. A coalition will have some structure, too, consciously chosen or not.

■ A coalition will be better off by intentionally choosing its own structure, rather than living with a structure that exists from tradition, inertia, historical decision, uncritical borrowing, or from following the path of least resistance.

■ No one structure is uniformly the best for everyone. What's best for Coalition **A** may not be best for Coalition **B**.

■ And what's best for Coalition **A** at one point in time—say, early in its development—may not be best for that same coalition at another point, a little farther down the road.

Key Principles of Structure Development

■ All organizational structures contain common elements—some type of governance, some rules for decision making, some more general operating procedures (implicit or explicit), and some division and delegation of responsibility.

■ What should determine the structure for a given coalition? Some main factors are the age and history of the coalition; the background, previous relationships, and personalities of its members; the coalition's present and intended size; its goals and objectives; and forces acting from the outside environment.

■ While coalition structure should take active thought and planning, the time spent should not take away from real-world action. Coalition accomplishments in the outside world can and should occur at the same time as coalition structure is being developed.

■ More generally, the time put into developing structure should be proportional to other coalition activities. If structure becomes all-consuming, it defeats the purpose. Or, in other words:

■ The structure of the coalition should serve its members, not the other way around.

The Structure-Making Process

There are also commonly desired features of the structure-making *process*, over and above the structure content or "product" eventually arrived at. Among them:

■ All coalition members should be able to participate in creating the structure, and then in changing it when they so choose.

■ The structure should allow for selection of key decision makers, either through election or voting. Those roles can rotate, *but—*

■ All coalition members should also be able to participate in making coalition decisions, directly or indirectly, *and*—

■ Each coalition member should be strongly encouraged, and possibly required, to take on some specific responsibility relating to coalition operations, so that each member has an optimum chance to participate.

Tips for Developing Your Own Coalition Structure

■ At the beginning, a small group of coalition members can be charged with drafting a coalition structure and presenting its draft recommendations to the full coalition for discussion.

■ The full coalition can make revisions. After revisions are made, the full coalition should ratify the structure.

■ Coalition members should not only accept the structure, they should feel comfortable with it. They should like it. They are the ones who will have to live with it and abide by it.

■ The structure should include a process so that the structure itself can be changed as conditions warrant. A designated subgroup of coalition members (such as a "policy committee," serving on call) can take the lead in developing such revisions.

■ The overall coalition structure should be reviewed from time to time to ensure that it still meets the coalition's needs.

HIV CONSORTIUM OF CENTRAL MASSACHUSETTS

We are glad you are interested in becoming a candidate for the H.C.C.M, Board of Directors. We appreciate your interest in us and the work that we do. The role of a Board member is an extremely important one, because Board members determine our activities, and have responsibility for seeing that they are carried out.

Therefore, we have listed Board member roles and responsibilities below, in written form. Please read them carefully. When you have done so, please sign at the bottom. This indicate that you understand the roles and responsibilities involved, and that you are prepared to carry them out. Thank you, and welcome!

Member of the Board of Directors: Roles and Responsibilities

Board members serve and act as individuals, rather than as formal or official representatives of any agency or organization. Elected for a two years term as stated in the HCCM By-laws.

Roles and Responsibilities:

* Attend all regular Board and General Membership meetings, except for compelling personal or business reasons.

* Act as a point of contact between General Membership and the Board of Directors, and vice-versa.

* Join and participate on at least, one HCCM committee and/or task group.

  •
  •
  •

The Consortium welcomes any and all participation from each member and the roles and responsibilities were developed to ensure that each member would be able to enhance the mission of the organization. This is a growing list and will continue to assess as the needs develop.

I have read this job description, I understand the responsibilities of this position, and agree to carry them out to the best of my ability.

_____   _____
Board Member Signature   Date

_____
Board Member (Print Name)

When you become part of the governance of a coalition, you should know what you are getting into. This coalition asks new board members to review and sign off on a detailed statement of roles and responsibilities before officially starting work. (The statement is abridged from its original version.)

Protocol for Ad Hoc Committees/Task Forces

The aim of a Task Force is defined as specific actions consistent with the mission, goals and by-laws of the Lower/Outer Cape Community Coalition.

Mission of the Coalition

The Lower/Outer Cape Community Coalition is a community-wide alliance committed to improving the quality of life for all of those living on Cape Cod.

Coalition Goals

* To mobilize and maintain broad based community development and collaborative problem-solving initiatives around health and human service issues.
* To insure the availability of and access to basic opportunities and services.
* To provide leadership in developing policies, practices and programs that are effective, responsive and accountable to those they serve.

Task Force Guidelines

* Ad Hoc Committees/Task Forces will have very clear action-oriented goals and objectives (May to May) and evidence of broad-based membership.

* The Task Force shall appoint a chairman to facilitate meetings and a secretary to maintain minutes.

* The Task Force will send a member to the monthly Advisory Board meetings to make a progress report and also allow for discussion of policies and actions. Minutes of Task Force meetings will be provided to the Board at the monthly meetings as a tool for communications and for inclusion (edited) in the Coalition newsletter, The Catalyst.

* As Coalition membership is diverse, the Task Force Chair (or other designated representative) will meet with the LOCCC Coordinator to keep her informed of potential issues that could impact the Coalition and membership.

* Communication with the media is the role of the Chairperson in consultation with the Coalition Coordinator. All press releases, TV releases, and public demonstrations must be approved by the Coalition Coordinator who may consult with the Advisory Board on policy issues or controversial matters.

* Objective evaluation of accomplishments and progress toward stated goals will be conducted in May of each years and submitted for inclusion in the Coalition Annual Report.

* Membership is open to any person willing to promote the purposes of the Task Force and the Coalition. Task Force membership conveys membership to the Coalition.

Similar guidelines can be created for committees and task forces even though there's no sign-off in this particular case.

COALITION OPERATING PRINCIPLES September, 1994

1. Purpose and Policy :

Section 1. Mission :

To organize people and resources which are dedicated to improving the quality of life in Northern Berkshire.

Section 2. Coalition Goals :

• To study and recommend ways to address and meet community needs.

• To collaboratively solve problems regarding issues in health, human services, and quality of life for the area.

• To offer a forum for health and human services in the Northern Berkshire area.

• To promote greater cooperation among all agencies delivering services to the Northern Berkshire area.

• To provide information to community providers and residents to increase accessibility and visibility of services and to facilitate the maximum effectiveness of area resources.

• To expand representation from all segments of the community in the process of improving the quality of life in Northern Berkshire.

2. Membership

Section 1. Eligibility

Anyone who works or lives in the Northern Berkshire area and is interested in the work of the Northern Berkshire Community Coalition is considered a member of the Coalition. Voluntary contributions from members to help defray expenses are requested, but they do not affect membership in the Northern Berkshire Community Coalition.

Section 2. Meetings

Monthly meetings of the Northern Berkshire Community Coalition are generally held the second Friday of each month. Meetings are not held during July and August unless there are special circumstances. Notices of the meetings are printed in the Coalition News. The Coalition Annual Meeting is held each June. All meetings of the Coalition, including the Steering Committee and Task Forces, are open to the public.

3. Governance of the Coalition

Section 1. Steering Committee

The Steering Committee guides the Coalition in its operation with input from and feedback to the Coalition membership. Final decisions for the Coalition will rest with the Steering Committee.

The Steering Committee operates by attempting to reach consensus on major issues. If the steering committee cannot reach consensus :

• The issue can be brought to the next coalition meeting and discussed in order for the Steering Committee to get a "pulse of the membership" and/or

• The Steering Committee can use a questionnaire in the newsletter as a means to survey the membership and/or

• Attempt to get any additional information needed to allow the committee to reach consensus.

Section 2. Composition of the Steering Committee

The Steering Committee is a volunteer committee of Northern Berkshire Community Coalition members who serve two year terms. Annual terms for the Steering Committee commence at the Coalition Annual Meeting in June. There are no limits to the numbers of terms someone may serve. The Steering committee should be no larger in size than fifteen. The Coalition Coordinator and Director of AHEC are permanent members with voting powers.

It is the hope of the Coalition that the steering committee has fair representation from various segments of the Northern Berkshire community. Neighborhood groups and consumers of services are encouraged to serve on the Steering Committee.

A nominating committee recruits committee members. Three consecutive unexplained absences from steering meetings will cause the nominating committee to contact that member to determine interest in continuing to serve. No more than one voting member fromn any agency is allowed on the Steering Committee.

Section 3. Task Forces

The Steering Committee may form Task Forces to study and make recommendations addressing specific issues. Task Forces utilize a similar decision making process as the Steering Committee and have a floating membership (vote with their feet). The Steering Committee should be represented on all task forces either through the Coalition Coordinator or a representative of the Steering Committee

Section 4. Coalition Coordinator

The Coalition Coordinator acts on behalf of the Coalition in consultation with the Steering Committee and Coalition membership. If there is disagreement about the functioning of the Coalition Coordinator, then this is brought to the Steering Committee for resolution. If disagreement continues, then the issue will be brought to the AHEC Director of Community Development.

NBHHSC• North Adams State College •Box 9075 • North Adams, MA 01247 •(413) 664-4511x 519

To formalize their structures, some coalitions develop bylaws (not that hard to do, since many models are available). But as an alternative, you can create a short statement of operating principles, as this coalition did. It's written in simple language, but accomplishes the same goal.

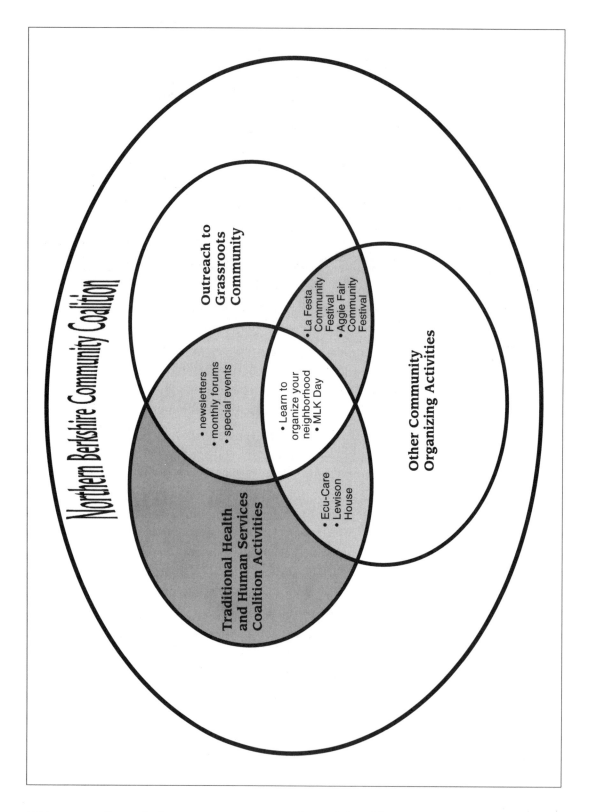

This example and the next are structural models of how a community coalition can relate to other key elements in the community. In this first model, note the separate overlaps with community organizations and with citizens, and the intersecting common interests.

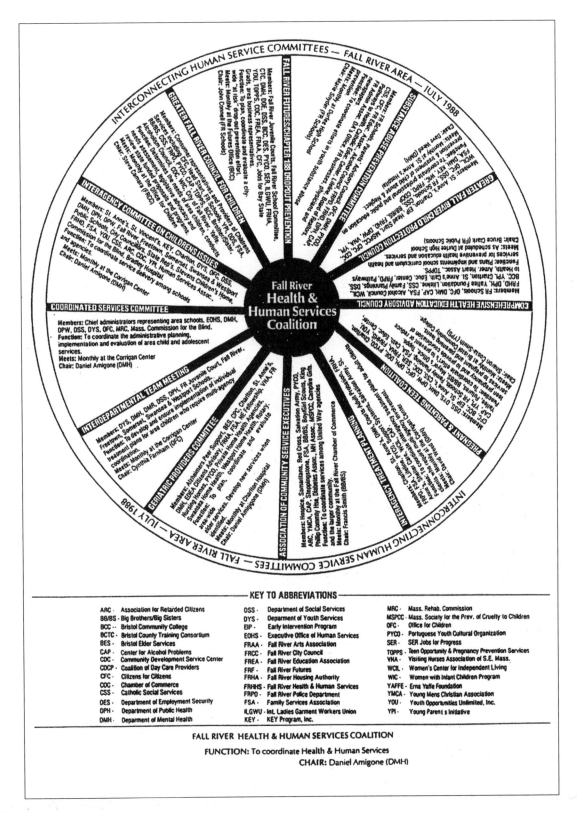

KEY TO ABBREVIATIONS

ARC · Association for Retarded Citizens
BB/BS · Big Brothers/Big Sisters
BCC · Bristol Community College
BCTC · Bristol County Training Consortium
BES · Bristol Elder Services
CAP · Center for Alcohol Problems
CDC · Community Development Service Center
CDCP · Coalition of Day Care Providers
CFC · Citizens for Citizens
COC · Chamber of Commerce
CSS · Catholic Social Services
DES · Department of Employment Security
DPH · Department of Public Health
DMH · Department of Mental Health

OSS · Department of Social Services
DYS · Deparment of Youth Services
EIP · Early Intervention Program
EOHS · Executive Office of Human Services
FRAA · Fall River Arts Association
FRCC · Fall River City Council
FREA · Fall River Education Association
FRF · Fall River Futures
FRHA · Fall River Housing Authority
FRHHS · Fall River Health & Human Services
FRPD · Fall River Police Department
FSA · Family Services Association
ILGWU · Int. Ladies Garment Workers Union
KEY · KEY Program, Inc.

MRC · Mass. Rehab. Commission
MSPCC · Mass. Society for the Prev. of Cruelty to Children
OFC · Office for Children
PYCO · Portuguese Youth Cultural Organization
SER · SER Jobs for Progress
TOPPS · Teen Opportunity & Pregnancy Prevention Services
VNA · Visiting Nurses Association of S.E. Mass.
WCIL · Women's Center for Independent Living
WIC · Women with Infant Children Program
YAFFE · Erna Yaffe Foundation
YMCA · Young Mens Christian Association
YOU · Youth Opportunities Unlimited, Inc.
YPI · Young Parent s Initiative

FALL RIVER HEALTH & HUMAN SERVICES COALITION

FUNCTION: To coordinate Health & Human Services

CHAIR: Daniel Amigone (DMH)

And in this model, the central community coalition is at the hub of a wheel. Other more specific planning groups and smaller coalitions are at its spokes.

Chapter 5

Coalition Meetings

How are coalition meetings different from other meetings?

How can relationships among coalition members
best be developed?

How businesslike should the meetings be?

What should you do if you run into trouble?

ost meetings aren't memorable. We don't usually jump out of bed in the morning saying, "Gee, I can't wait for the meeting today!" Quite the contrary; many of us go to meetings out of compulsion, or duty, with half a heart. Or worse: One coalition member (not one interviewed here) told us, "Meetings fill me with a sense of dread."

It doesn't have to be that way. Here's one example of a coalition meeting. It's a long example, which we'll present in extended form. What do you like about it? What don't you like? What parts of it might be adapted to your own situation?

I'm here early. I'm usually here about 7:00 a.m., just because I'm a worrier and I just want to make sure. And besides that I need some help with the table, and I know that my friend George, the custodian, is going to be leaving, because he gets here about 2:00 in the morning, so I need his help with the big coffee pots. And so he and I have a fine old time, putting up all the chairs and getting the coffee plugged in.

Muffins I make first thing in the morning, before I come, and they are homemade. It's important to me because I know then what the ingredients are. They're very healthy. Well, they vary. The basic recipe is always the same, but they're whole wheat and sesame with an orange—they have an orange rind.

I get up normal time, about a quarter to six, and it only takes me 10 minutes, maybe less, to make the muffins—the time factor is waiting for them to bake, which is 15 or 20 minutes, but that's fine, and then we usually have apples or oranges, depending on the season, and good orange juice, fresh orange juice. That kind of thing comes out of the coalition expenses. It's a refreshment cost.

I bring flowers from home. This month it will be cosmos because the garden is just full of beautiful cosmos. They're very beautiful colors, and I'll be glad to share them. I do collect the flowers. I happen to love growing flowers and arranging them is a big thing. That's what I will do in my next life, is to do that full-time. But anyway, there's homemade muffins and tea and coffee and juice and fruit so that sometimes people know that they could miss their breakfast if it works out that way, and there will be food for them. We encourage that kind of atmosphere so that everybody feels on the same par, and then the networking starts right away.

I'm at the door usually. They'll walk through this door, and I'll be right at the door, and I'll say "Good to see you," depending on who it is. We might even hug. It certainly happens, because they're friends by now, and I have met some perfectly wonderful people as a result of this work. And if I'm meeting somebody for the first time I make sure that they are meeting the next person, and the person nearest to them, especially if I feel that there's a connection that should be made: somebody from Family Planning and the person from the schools or something.

I will introduce people, absolutely. First of all, it's sort of an automatic thing, but I think about it afterwards and realize, of course, that it was very essential. You can make that connection pretty quickly: "Oh my gosh, that's right. So-and-so needs to talk to somebody else." And I'll go over and just say, "I'd love to have you meet . . ." yup, and then what also happens is that you will see them then exchanging addresses or telephone numbers or making an appointment—or "Could I see you after the meeting?" or something like that. And I think it's probably one of the biggest benefits for people, yeah.

Even though the meeting is supposed to start at 9:00, we maybe start at eight after, eight to 10 after, just because you don't want to break the feeling. Then we gather in our sitting mode, and after a welcome we introduce ourselves and each person says a little bit. They might just say, "I'm Barbara Corey, and I'm with the North Quabbin Community Coalition." That's it for that first go-around, so everybody just kind of gets a feeling for who's who.

We usually average about 30, but we've had up to 55 here. Most of them are regulars, and then it changes depending upon the issue. Basically I'd say there are agency people, and certainly a smattering of community people, people on our task forces, like people who have been the victims of domestic violence, and they want to come to this main meeting.

Then we have announcements. I might make an announcement about the Community Partners conference in Worcester in October, and that usually encourages some questions; and then the next thing would be for people to give updates on what's going on. So the local mental health agency has merged with a larger group in Greenfield, and our group needs to hear how that's going to work out, how is that going to affect our population. Will we still be able to go to 100 Main Street for an appointment, or do they have to get transportation solved and get to Greenfield? Is it more than a satellite office? Is it fully functioning? That kind of thing, and it's an important thing for people to hear.

There will be updates from the Domestic Violence Task Force because some important things have been happening there. All through the summer there was a training done for members of that group who wanted to go out to service organizations, church groups, any kind of community group as a speaker, to talk about domestic violence, about what it means in this community, and so other people need to know that those folks are available to be called upon.

And then some people have called me in advance and said, "Could I have seven minutes because I want to do a big pitch about mediation?" Because there's a group that's starting a mediation project here, and now they're looking for referrals. Mediation can certainly have seven minutes; they can have 10 and it may take that, because there's going to be quizzes. People are going to say, "If I have such-and-such a situation, are you going to be able to do family disputes?" or "Are you maybe going to do training of teenagers?" because there's more stress on having people learn these skills at a much younger age.

After the updates, then we usually get into the main focus. It may be transportation. It's not going to be this time, but it will be announced in the newsletter what it is. We'll tell everybody who is going to be there. Is it going to be the Transportation Secretary from Franklin County, or the Chamber of Commerce President, whoever? We'll tell who the players are that are going to be sort of special guests.

But now at this meeting in September, it's really a time for people to elaborate, to talk generally about what it is that you see. What is it that's worrying you? What do you see that needs attention, some prioritizing? Is it street violence? Do we need a task force to address the acting out on Main Street, or . . .? If there's interest in setting up a task force, then people would send around a yellow block of paper and ask if you're interested in pursu-

ing this. That doesn't happen every time. If out of a gathering comes this expression, then that's what we we'll do.

We'll encourage everyone to call or write if they have a concern or a question. Oh, we've also circulated another pad of paper that has on it an attendance list with addresses and telephone numbers, so that I don't really lose anybody that I should have met here at the door. Obviously, you can come in even if I haven't got my hand out to you. But we have a column that asks if you want to be added to the mailing list, so that's another way we have of not losing track of people.

The main focus comes to a close at 11:00, and in the meantime people can feel free to get up and get another cup of tea or coffee or juice or whatever. I mean, it's pretty informal. It's not a scary place at all. One thing we work hard to guard against is somebody coming in at maybe 9:30 and taking a chair and kind of starting a second row, and that really bothers me because it feels very exclusionary. I understand it, to a certain extent. They probably just don't want to walk past another person to sit down, but we'll widen the circle as opposed to having that second row, because I don't think it's the same. I bring them in, and they know I feel very strongly about that, because I'm—maybe even bossy. No, I just let them know because we want them to be part of it, and it makes it seem as if we really mean it, but isn't it a tendency of human nature maybe to go to the back of the hall? Everybody wants to sit out back, nobody wants to sit down front.

We end at 11:00, and the bulk needs to leave, but there are always some that stand around and talk for another half an hour. People chat and hang around until 11:30 sometimes, depending upon who gets connected with whom. But we do have to be out of the room by 12:00, because there's an aerobics class that starts exactly at 12:00.

Then the dishes get done. A couple of people help to clean it up, because it's earthenware. It's not always styrofoam cups, so there's a little dish washing, but that's fine because I think sometimes things get said over the sink, too—people just relax a little bit and they like to be helpful, so the place looks pretty spic and span.

I think you've got to feel that you like this. If it doesn't feel like fun, then you probably ought to probably start thinking about another form of activity or something.

Principles

This is a good meeting. And the evidence bears this out. This coalition is in its 12th year, a long time as coalitions go. People wouldn't stick around, or keep coming to meetings, unless something there made it worthwhile.

What makes it worthwhile? Ultimately, it comes down to four basic elements:

1. Preparation. A good coalition meeting usually doesn't happen all by itself. It takes detailed, prior, internal thinking about the meeting environment and what should happen within it, along with detailed, prior, external work to bring that thinking to life.

You don't need fresh flowers. You don't need homemade muffins, or fresh-squeezed orange juice, though we would never deny these add to the effect. But you do need to make sure the room is ready, the chairs are set up as you want them, the agendas are distributed—all those little planful things. Choreography is involved. Improvisation may be needed, and improvisation definitely has its place, but complete improvisation in meetings is usually not the way to go.

2. Comfort. Physical comfort, sure, and an attractive physical environment, too. But here we mean primarily psychological comfort, comfort of the emotions. A good coalition meeting is one where each member present feels welcomed, accepted, valued, and at ease, and where efforts to sustain those feelings are made and made repeatedly. Wanting to feel accepted and valued are needs we never outgrow. This is human nature. Put the other way, if we feel unwanted or unwelcomed or left out or out of place, we won't come back.

So Barbara, in our example, starts and ends meetings (roughly) on time, a mark of respect. But especially, she welcomes people. This pays off. She stands at the door, introduces people around, makes sure no one sits on the outside of the circle. Or as another coalition coordinator puts it:

> *I will greet people as they come in, with a handshake and an "I'm glad you're here." Because I sincerely feel that way, so I feel like I want to share that with people.*

3. Relationship. If one major theme occurs time and time again in our experience and in these interviews, it is that *strong coalitions are built upon strong personal relationships.* We can't emphasize this enough. People will stick together, and act together, and keep acting together, when they know (and then) like (and then) trust each other.

As we know, sometimes all too well, relationships take time to build. So a wise coalition will allow time for their construction. And coalition meetings are a primary place, sometimes the only place, where that can come about.

> *Our meetings are not just business meetings, they're very grass rootsy. Joey's wife is pregnant, so for 10 minutes it's about Joey's wife. Vito's taking a graduate course at UNH, it could be about Vito's course. I sit on a lot of boards, and this isn't like a board meeting—you come in, you've got an agenda. People from the business world have a sense of time and task—when it's business, it's business, and when it's play, it's play. The grass roots people, it's all stew.*

Would it be better if the meeting were more businesslike? Maybe, but that depends on what you're sacrificing:

> *I think it's fine for people who are paid to attend the meeting, that it's business. But when it's volunteers and community members, then their needs are more than that. They are building relationships, they are coming to this meeting because they care. They want to be acknowledged as human beings. The agenda is secondary to who they are; there needs to be enough decency for them to say, "You and I have been doing this for three years, and I want to acknowledge the fact that your father died, or that your wife is pregnant."*
>
> *I don't think that approach works when business comes first. That's one of the areas where my doubt lies. I'm not always sure that if you've only got an hour and a half, that the best use of that hour and a half is to do all that informal stuff; but I have learned over time to trust that.*

4. Accomplishment. A coalition is social, but not a social club. So the obvious point must be stated: The meetings (eventually) must be action-oriented, and the coalition has to get things done. Some standard business rules do apply. And for one coalition leader at least, the softer, relational stuff is just something you've got to live with, medicine you've got to swallow:

> *At a substantial number of these meetings, 52 percent of it will be nonsense and ritual that you've got to put up with. There's some folk that would say 82 percent. But that's fine, that's okay. That's the price for realizing your goal. If I can get something out of it, it's worth it. It's worth the investment. Yet that's not where the deals are cut. The real deals are cut in the one-on-one meetings, to get the buy-in.*

And true, a lot of the real dealing is done at separate tables. But the coalition provides the venue, the big room, for those deals to be made.

Variations

These are the core principles, the meeting basics. They will generally apply to any meeting setting; and they will work, sometimes with modifications, in any coalition.

In coalitions of youth, for example; maybe even especially with youth:

> *We've trained the youth to organize meetings and facilitate meetings. It's actually an enjoyable two hours. You know, something's bothering them, they're just going to say it, and they deal and get over it. There's not like lots of resentment and bitterness that you carry on your back for years and years and years. You know, if it's mostly agency people, you're always protecting your own place, so you don't ever want to be too honest, because*

sometimes you may think, "Well, that person's going to take my idea," or take my funding, or whatever. Youth are much more honest and much more open than adults are.

In coalitions of tenants in public housing:

What I do in a meeting is usually say, "Okay, let's look at all the things that need to be done." And we would have a flip chart, and we would flesh it out, even down to who's cooking the hot dogs. "Okay, we need someone to do this, we need someone to do that, how are we going to work it?" And someone might say, "Well, I don't know." Well, if they need help, explain that role. The goal is not for you to do all the work, the goal is just to make sure it gets done, and it's the role of all of us in the meeting to help.

And—another variation—in rural coalitions. When people live so far apart, sometimes they can choose to meet by phone:

Phone meetings are very important in this area, because to drive from North Adams or from Sheffield for a meeting from, say, 6:00 to 8:00 in the evening, and then to drive all the way back, it's very late at night by the time they get home, you know, 9:00 or 9:30. There's no family time. Whereas if they're taking the phone call from their home, they're there. I think the conference call costs maybe $50 or so, which is probably what it would cost for food, if we were meeting in person. So, people can stay at home and have dinner with their family.

We set a meeting time, and I set up the call by calling AT&T. The telephone company calls all the people, gets them all on the line, and I'm the last one called. They call off everyone's name in order, and you say, "here." Some of us are silly and say some other crazy things. We have a lot of fun in our meetings.

And then we meet. A key to having these kind of meetings, I think, is having a very specific agenda. We go through the agenda, just as we would sitting around a table.

In the beginning, I thought, "How is this ever going to work?" Because as a facilitator, I'm so used to relying on people's body language. But I found that people develop a telephone personality through these teleconference meetings, and we really—we laugh as much over the phone as we do when we're sitting around a table. So it's really—it's really good.

We try to keep it to an hour. We often go to an hour and 15 minutes, but no longer, so they are shorter meetings by phone. But we tend to zip through the agenda, and get it done in that amount of time. More than that, your ear gets tired. . . .

Problems and Solutions

Let's note the basic fact: When a diverse group gets together, they won't necessarily pull in the same direction. The very diversity and inclusiveness of a strong coalition present potential and often real problems. For in a coalition, and in a coalition meeting, people are going to be of different minds, precisely because they represent different constituencies, with different styles and expectations and needs and ways of doing business.

So a good meeting has energy, but that energy will not necessarily propel the coalition down a straight course. You might meet white water. You could head for the rocks. Yet while unforeseen obstacles may arise, they do fall into common categories. If we know what those are, we can look out ahead for them, and steer around them.

Here are a few, with some navigation instructions:

- People may not show up. In that case, you can work with those who do.

> *I always tell my staff that even if there are five people at a meeting, you still hold the meeting. If that group of five people wants to do something, like clean up a park or whatever, then that's what you do. We say, "We've got five people here, you are interested, let's move on." Then we will figure out how to get more people involved. The worst thing to do, I think, is to lament the fact that there are only five people at the meeting, because then everybody gets really depressed and then nobody wants to come anymore.*

The common belief of strength in numbers may be misleading anyway.

> *The idea that you need a lot of people is not always helpful, because the reality is, and our reality here, is that you are not going to get a lot of people mobilized to do anything. I think the hopelessness is really high. There are all kinds of reasons why people don't come. In some cases, I think five people could be much more effective, because if you have 50 people then you have 50 ideas, and you've got to work all that stuff out.*

- If people do show up, they may not be getting anywhere. One choice is to be patient.

> *You've got to be prepared for a long haul. We invited every health care professional and everybody concerned with health in the city to a table. Twenty people were there and they said, "What are we here for?" And we said to them, "Well, we're just here to sort of talk about the health of the city."*
>
> *People looked at each other across the table, and it was deadly. Nobody knew what to talk about, so the first couple of meetings, we talked about having nothing to talk about, and we lost a lot of people in the process. But it ended up working. I think that process built a lot of relationships that would not normally have been built.*

Maybe (or probably) this group would have gotten somewhere faster with clearer goals at the beginning. But the lesson in the example above, and in the one to follow, is to keep the faith and keep on meeting.

> *I firmly believe you set monthly meetings, and you meet every month whether there's an agenda or not. And if there's no agenda, you meet that month and talk about what your agenda is going to be the next month. I think a mistake a lot of organizations make is that they stop meeting because they don't have anything to meet about. Again, it's not what happens at the meeting this month, it's what happens six months from now; and in order for that to happen, you've got to meet every month.*

■ Sometimes, people may not know each other well. Then if naturally occurring social time doesn't do the job, there are more structured and "artificial" approaches.

> *We went on a retreat. One of the things we did, everyone had to learn five new things about each member, and bring them back. And you would think, "I've been living near this person for the last 50 years." But it would be funny that everyone would come back with five things—whether he likes to wear red socks, or eat chili peppers—no matter how long they've been together. Which means that they had to sit down, and talk to each other, and say, "I have to find out something about you that I don't know." It made you dig a little bit deeper, it forced you to know people more than on the surface. And that's been successful.*

■ Sometimes, people may say things you don't particularly want to hear. Even so, you need to listen.

> *Two years ago, we spent some time talking about violence in the youth community. We would invite kids from the schools along with guidance counselors and some teachers to talk about this with the regular coalition audience. I remember this one kid from a high school in Williamstown, he had this baseball cap that was just kind of pulled over his eyes. He was looking down at the floor and he started talking, and he basically says, "You know, you're full of shit. You guys don't know what it's like when you haven't been there. You're talking at us, you're not talking with us, and you're not really hearing what we have to say." And he went on to talk about what his experiences were like. And I think that moved a lot of people.*

■ Or, from your point of view, people may act strangely:

> *Last year we had a series of meetings about welfare reform and how that's impacting people. And this one man came to our meeting who no one*

ever saw before, just a citizen who wanted to talk about receiving resources from the Welfare Department and what that was like for him. He started talking in a very soft voice, and he got everybody's attention because he was different. He kind of went on and his voice got louder. And his eyes started getting bigger and bigger. And there was a moment when—we froze.

I mean, I think that people were scared, because we didn't know where this guy was going and what this conversation was about. It was as if we were sitting in a room and a storm came upon us and everyone was looking at everyone else to figure out what to do.

And here the coalition gets tested. If it really wants to be inclusive, and to hear different views, then at minimum it will have to hear them, if not actively embrace them, and try to transform them into something positive—as did happen above.

We were able to get some other people to talk about their own experiences with the system and what it was like. That was an atypical event. . . . And actually, all the events are atypical. . . . I'm not sure there's any typical events that occur. . . .

Blending the Ingredients

So simply getting through a meeting, putting in the time, isn't usually that hard—"This, too, shall pass." But running a good meeting isn't always that easy. And running a great meeting requires acute concentration and sensitivity. It can happen, though. It does happen. And if it happens once, it can happen again.

Meetings are art and craft as well as science. They aren't fully predictable, which makes life interesting. Still, you can maximize the chances of great meetings occurring. For more often than not, those meetings will include the four basic elements we have spoken of before:

■ A focus on accomplishment, on getting things done:

I've been through some disastrous meetings simply because there is no agenda. Or because people are not sure why they're there. Or because there is nobody to run the meeting. I mean, I've sat through meetings going, "I know what this place needs; it needs somebody to teach them how to run meetings."

■ And on building relationships among the people there:

I think the affiliation stuff is a real strong part of it. I would consider people in the coalition more as colleagues than most of the people here in my workplace. I have been through thick and thin with them. They've been com-

ing on a consistent basis, and there have been things we've done together. There's a shared history. "Family" is probably a little too strong, but these are people you care about; it's not just another meeting. So another way of putting it is that a lot of people come not because of what's on the agenda. They come because of who's there.

■ And on making people feel comfortable:

Comfort level is very, very powerful. The first meeting that somebody comes to, lots of times they won't know what to expect. And they make a judgment from that meeting. Lots of times we lose people, actually, because they may not have felt comfortable at that first meeting. Sometimes they'll try it again. But unless there's some contact made that ensures them that over time they're going to have a voice—if that's what they're looking for— or that there's a specific something that they're going to get out of this meet- ing, they're going to stop coming, because time is too precious.

■ And all of this takes preparation, forethought, or "advance planning," if you can accept that more formal phrase. Careful planning of meetings is almost always reward- ed. When it isn't, it's often because we get so caught up in our plans that we lose sight of events taking place right in front of us. Flexibility, then, is a complementary virtue. As one leader puts it: "Coalition meetings have to be very fluid, and you have to be able to go with what presents itself." In other words, sometimes the best plans must willingly be tossed overboard.

To blend planning with flexibility (being warm and friendly all the while) takes skill and grace. The skill part is largely learnable; perhaps grace is, too. One might compare a coalition meeting to a small jazz band. There is diversity of sound. Each instrument gets a chance to solo. Improvisation is valued, yet the sounds blend well together. The leader makes sure the group starts on time, and ends on time, while keeping track of time. With practice, things get tighter and easier. And at some point, the group may say, "That was beautiful. Let's play again."

Lessons From The Field

In General . . .

■ People come to meetings, including coalition meetings, for two overarching reasons: They want to get something accomplished, and they want to have a good time.

■ So a meeting should be enjoyable and productive for everyone there. If you're going to have meetings anyway, why set your sights any lower?

■ Coalition meetings are often different from other organizational meetings because the structure is looser, the requirements to attend are lower, the members are more diverse, and the goals may be less clear. Coalitions are delicate. In meetings, therefore, special attention must be paid to building relationships among different members of the group.

■ One bottom line, often *the* bottom line, is whether people show up. If the meeting is valuable enough to them, they will be there. If it isn't, they won't. A very simple measure of your meeting's value is how many people are seated when the meeting starts.

■ To help them be seated, it's best to prepare. Pay attention to detail. Especially if you're just starting out, preparation time and meeting time should be no less than equal.

The Social Side

■ Pay close attention to the physical environment where you meet. Is it attractive, light, airy? Is the temperature controlled? Does it simply feel good to be there?

■ Build in some time to mix and mingle. You can do this before the meeting, during the meeting (by having a break), or after the meeting ends.

■ Help make people feel at home. Greet them, smile at them, say hello. This is especially true for new members—think of them as your special guests. If this doesn't come naturally to you, practice may help. Or ask someone else to assist you.

■ Food and drink are assets, no doubt about it. What makes them assets is that they keep people around and talking. Talking builds relationships.

■ At the close of the meeting, thank people for coming; show your pleasure at seeing them; say how you are looking forward to the next time. End on an up note.

The Business Side

■ Have an agenda, distributed in advance. Not too thick. Not too thin.
■ Assign each agenda item a designated amount of time.
■ Stick to the agenda items and the agenda times.
■ Follow up on decisions made. For each decision, be aware of a) how it will be implemented, b) who will implement it, and c) how will you know?

■ At the end, ask members for items they want to include on the next meeting's agenda. And ask who would like to take the lead in presenting them.

If Thorny Patches Appear . . .

The meetings of any group will hit a snag once in a while. Here's some general guidance:

■ If someone speaks strongly in opposition, or with a contrary tone . . . Respectfully acknowledge the point of view or feelings expressed. Can they be incorporated into the meeting discussion or decision? If so, that's preferred. But if not, maybe that viewpoint or feeling can be positively developed in other ways—at the next meeting, or in another forum. That's certainly fine, too.

■ If discussion goes well past the time allotted . . . Point out that the meeting is running overtime on this item, and ask the group whether it wants to keep discussing it now, or to move on to the next item of business.

■ If you simply don't know how to proceed—if an issue is very complex, or if emotions run high . . . Draw upon and trust the wisdom of the group. Spell out some of the options available. Solicit others. Ask group members how they would like to proceed. The chances are good they will guide you effectively.

■ One summarizing principle is that each member's ideas need to be heard, acknowledged, and responded to as best as possible. Still, most of the time, don't hesitate to steer the meeting back to its main focus—gently, but also persistently. Most members really do want to stay on course and leave the meeting knowing that they have gotten something done.

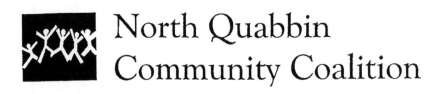

NEWSLETTER

Next Coalition Meeting

FRIDAY, NOVEMBER 15, 1996
ATHOL AREA Y - MAIN HALL
545 MAIN STREET
9:00 - 11:00AM

I. WELCOME, INTRODUCTIONS, ANNOUNCEMENTS

II. Part I - First Hour - **COALITION SHARING** - What's on Your Mind? Questions? Concerns?

III Part II - Second Hour   COMMUNITY CONNECTIONS UPDATE - JOANNA FISHER, ET AL

SUBCONTRACTOR PRESENTATIONS

GAAAFSN (Greater Athol Area Advocates for
Families with Special Needs)
School Linked Services - Athol and Orange
NELCWIT (New England Learning Center for
Women in Transition)
Community Health Service

IV. OTHER?

V. ADJOURNMENT

INSIDE:

Juice, Fruit, Coffee, Tea and Muffins Provided
Bring a Friend!

To have a good meeting, you'd like a good turnout. How to encourage members to come? This coalition puts its meeting notice right on the front page of its newsletter.

You're Invited to the

Lower/Outer Cape Community Coalition

Annual Meeting

Friday, June 10   12:00 - 2:00 PM
Eastham Methodist Church   Rte. 6, Eastham

FEATURING:

Presentation of Community Service Awards

Luncheon and Special Entertainment

A Community Roast of "Retiring" Coalition Coordinator, Mary Lou Petitt

Luncheon catered by The Cheese Corner -- $7
Free child care and free luncheon on request

Call 255-2163 to reserve your seat at the table!

Food and festivities are also excellent motivators. The premise is very simple: People like to eat and have a good time.

HIV CONSORTIUM OF CENTRAL MASSACHUSETTS
PO BOX 2623
Worcester, MA 01613
(508) 767-1812

**BOARD OF
DIRECTORS**
Greg Anderson

Kate Angilly

Sandi Carlson

Jerry Cheney

David Ellis

Lauren Flewelling

Jonathan Heins

Michael Howard

Noreen Johnson

Donna Keegan

Leo Negrón Cruz

Joyce Ryan

Susan Sereti

Wilma Sánchez

Anibal Sosa

Mary Sotiropoulos

Sandy Stern

Jim Voltz

City Representative:
  Maria Reeves

...Let's update ourselves on recent activities, add any new business you have, and perhaps take some time to do some planning for the months ahead. Here's our starting agenda...

H.C.C.M. BOARD MEETING

TUESDAY, JUNE 11, 1996 3:00 P.M. PHELAN CENTER

I. Call to Order   II. Approval of Minutes

III. Old Business and Updates   *(40 min.)*
    A. Policy on Board Member Leave of Absence (**Noreen, Lauren**)
    B. Voting Eligibility at General and Annual Meetings (**Next steps?**)
    C. Consumer Advisory Board (**How best to resolve?**)
    D. Spending of Unexpended Consortium Funds (**Finalize!**)
    E. Training Programs (Updates: **Chris, Lisa**)
    F. Outreach to the Community (**More on this?: Greg, Lauren**)
    G. Follow-ups: (1) Bridges Conference; (2) Community
            Connections, from 5/21 Meeting (**Any next steps?**)
    H. Other Old Business

IV. Committee Reports   *(20 min.)*
    A. Membership & Publicity
    B. Public Policy
    C. Education and Prevention
    D. Ryan White
    E. Nominating Committee
    F. Treasurer's Report
    G. Other Committee Reports

V. New Business   *(40 min.)*
    A. Scheduling of Fun Day
    B. Board Self-Assessment (We agreed to postpone this and revisit
        this item in June: Do we want to pursue it at this point?)
    C. Planning for the Months Ahead (**Possible Major Agenda Item**)
    D. Other New Business

VI. Brief Announcements   (Please bring written materials)

VII. Agenda Items for Next Board Meeting (Please bring them!)

VIII. Adjournment

Once people are at the meeting, a written agenda is of course standard practice. To help coalition members get through this fairly detailed agenda, time guidelines were placed around each part.

V.   YWCA   *(child care)*   30:00 - 40:00 minutes

Problem: Why is the child care program offered at YWCA poorly utilized?

(?'S)

Time offered
Accessibility
Welcoming environment...
        ...for consumers
        ...for children
Trust
Lack of referrals
Lack of promotion needed *(marketing)*
Relocation

Discussion of Alternatives

Varying times that program is offered
Transportation
An open house / Parents day

A welcoming and encouragement for parents
Meetings with...case mgrs...etc.
flyers / ads
Who / Where / When

VI.   NEXT MEETING

            Location   _____
            Date _____
            Time _____

VII.   ADJOURNMENT

Meeting Duration 60:00 - 90:00 minutes

This agenda section (part of a larger document) goes a step further by diagnosing the problem and proposing alternatives right on the agenda itself.

Chapter 6

Coalition Leadership

What leadership style works best for coalitions?

Where can the leader find the time to do the job?

How hard should you push your coalition members?

What personal qualities should the coalition leader possess?

A lot of words have been spilled on leadership. Take a course in health or human services, open any management book, work in the nonprofit or for-profit sectors—discussions on leadership are hard to miss. There's no shortage of opportunities to learn about leadership, and no dearth of sources to learn from.

So what more can we add? Is there anything about leadership in coalitions—as contrasted with leadership in any other group—that adds to what is already known, and that is worth your time reading? We think so. Let's find out.

Here is a preview of the discussion to follow, and a summary of its main points:

■ Leadership in coalitions can be divided into three parts. First, there is leadership at the coalition meeting itself, which guides the events taking place in the room. Leadership at meetings is especially important, because (as mentioned in Chapter 5) members of coalitions might not be in regular contact between meeting times. You may see the members of your workplace almost every day; for coalition members, it might be once a month. So the meetings set the tone for the coalition, usually more so than they do for other groups.

At the same time, leadership of meetings, when all is said and done, is relatively simple and straightforward. We'll emphasize "relatively"; it's not quite a piece of cake.

Still, this part of leadership rests on learnable skills and the accumulation of some experience. The great majority of people can learn to lead groups reasonably well. In this very fundamental (though also narrow) sense, most of us can become good leaders, if we aren't already. That is good news.

■ There's another part of leadership that goes on between meetings, in the 90+ percent of days that the coalition does not meet. This is leadership that connects the dots. It happens in private. It can be lonely. The behavioral content of this leadership will consist of memos and reports, personal notes and letters, phone calls and faxes, and casual contacts, sometimes unplanned. These activities seem routine, and often they *are* routine, but they are leadership nonetheless. They are what bonds the coalition together from meeting to meeting, month to month, across meeting spaces; they are glue.

A carpenter joins wood to wood. A welder bonds metal to metal. A coalition leader links person to person. Leadership here is glue on all fingers, or whatever it takes to hold people together. The complexity of the individual skills required is not that high. This type of leadership is also relatively simple, at least conceptually. In this case, what it requires are the basic qualities of concentration and attention to detail, plus time in the day, together with a commitment to put each detail to rest. This type of leadership, too, is within the range of the great majority. Good news again.

■ Yet there is a third aspect of leadership that has less to do with meetings, less to do with the intervals between, and more to do with who the leader is as a person— with what is sometimes called "leadership style."

Leadership style in coalitions deserves careful review; yet for us "style" is too narrow a term. In coalitions, what's at least as important is the leader's character, that which lies within. A good coalition leader will have the chance to display that character, as deep as it goes. A certain kind of display will motivate coalition members not only to comply with requests, but also to follow that leader's overall vision, and what's more, to internalize and model that leader's overall behavior.

So how the leader's character is demonstrated will make a measurable difference in coalition effectiveness. And because that interior aspect of leadership tends to be less thoroughly explored, and because it is not yet fully charted, that's where we'll spend the most chapter time.

But now, let's consider these three parts of leadership in more detail.

Leadership at Meetings

If you are leading a coalition meeting, what are some of the key skills involved? Here's a short list:

■ To begin with, knowing who the people in the coalition are, and showing them some personal concern:

> *I just make darn sure that I know who people are. I feel it's very important for me to say their name, and so I'm checking my little list here, but it's not hard because I do know a lot of the people. It's an important thing, because I really do think people need to feel a part of this. That is going to make them want to come back.*

■ Creating an agenda—though an agenda alone doesn't do the job. You've got to make progress on your agenda items, or members will stay away:

> *We had an agenda for the meeting, but we wound up going around in circles. People got very frustrated. And at the end of the meeting, one person said, "God, I don't want to come and waste my time doing this again." Probably we needed to have something very, very specific on the agenda, so that even if we went around in circles on one part, there would be other things where we went from A to B or D or G, and where we had made progress.*

That is, the agenda should lead to specific outcomes and clarity of expectations for the next meeting, shared by everyone in the room.

> *I take the responsibility to be sure that we cover the agenda, and also that people walk away with something to do, and that we all know where we're going to go from here.*

■ Keeping track of meeting time, and letting others know it:

> *I don't necessarily say, "You've had your seven minutes," but I'm conscious of the fact they've asked for that amount of time. And sometimes an occasion will arise when someone will take over, and just can't stop, and then you really just sort of have to say, "We've got a long agenda." Or, "In order to get all this agenda covered, we need to hear from others as well."*

■ Giving everyone a chance to speak—if necessary, by calling on them directly:

> *If there's only one or two people talking, I might say, "Well, let's give everyone a chance to comment." Or if I felt there were particularly quiet people, I'll call on them and say, "What do you think about this?"*

■ Keeping your cool if people attack you. While that's rare, it can and does happen, and it isn't easy to deal with:

> *She started throwing racial epithets at me, like, "You Spanish-speaking blah, blah, blah"—and this was a community leader. I got the brunt of her anger that day although I was just there trying to facilitate a meeting. But*

that was where the person was at that point in time, and she's an important community member.

You can absorb a lot of it. It isn't easy. It's not easy at all. But that's where it becomes important that you really know what your role is, as a facilitator for the process. If you personalize it, I think you lose. You start creating barriers, because you don't want to listen to that other person. And then you can't do your work anymore.

■ And—maybe the single most important coalition leadership skill—delegating tasks, with the full realization that delegating is personally harder for some people than for others. Our temperaments differ. We may not be sure how to ask. We may have to summon a little courage to do it:

I do delegate. I could do more. I don't want to stretch people too far—I feel like people are working so hard, and I appreciate the time they take by coming to the meetings so that maybe I don't delegate as much as I should. But I do some.

More on delegating. If delegation seems hard, let's try to make it easier. For one thing, coalition members expect delegation to occur. They're not naive. If they show up, they know that eventually some task will come their way.

We haven't had too many people who are just lumps. I mean, who do absolutely nothing but take up space and maybe eat our doughnuts or something like that. If we're going to do something, somebody's got to agree to head it up. You know, the usual. And usually it's the person that first brought up the idea who gets stuck with it. But that's how it goes.

And sometimes people are actually glad to be asked:

A lot of times people will do things for you because they want to be helpful. And sometimes I've found, surprisingly, that the person was really grateful for having been asked to do that task—they said they felt valued, that it was a wonderful experience for them. So I need to remember that.

Then, whatever gets delegated can be small. And whatever it may be, it should get supported.

My thing is, "Whatever you feel comfortable with, whatever skill you have." I don't care if you say to me, "All I can do is fold napkins in triangles." If that's what you feel you can do, then you have a piece of this pie. I try not to make people feel it's too small and minute.

. . . Because in some coalitions, when members don't come forward it's not because they lack the time, but because they lack the confidence. So you build their confidence, gradually.

> *My approach is, "If you do something this time, we can encourage you to do something else next time. If you don't know how to do it, I'll help you, or someone else will help you. If there's something you want to learn, let me know. If I don't know how to teach you, someone else will teach you."*

By asking something of each member, by paying attention to current skills—that's how a coalition becomes strengthened; that's how future coalition leadership gets built:

> *We had a woman, she was never part of any kind of group, had never gone to a PTA or parent council meeting. Her husband didn't even let her go down and get the mail. Now for the last year she's been the secretary: She knows how to set up the tape recorder, work the Xerox machine, answer the phone, take messages, announce the meetings, do the documentation. We have another one that was very shy, but she was able to take responsibility for the Halloween party. It's something that we've been building. I think it has to do with trust.*

How do you actually go about delegating, and making sure everyone gets a piece of the action? You have to make the decision to ask. And why not ask? It's perfectly legitimate; these are your colleagues and friends. So you can be quite direct:

> *If there's a missing piece, we may say, "Well, everybody has to take a share—now, Rita, you haven't said that you want to do anything. What piece that's left would you like to do, because as a team member we all have to help." . . . And then sometimes I say, "Well, what are we going to do? This is our work, this is our problem. If you guys don't step forward, it can't get done."*

At the same time, delegation works best when the delegator has style and grace, and when reciprocity is built in. Here's how one coalition leader brings these points together:

> *I think I know people pretty well, and I know what to expect. If it was you? . . . I might say, "Listen, Bill, we've written these articles, and I really need somebody who's good at editing, and I know that you're good at editing. And it's going to take some time, and I understand that, but would you give it some thought?"*
>
> *And I'm going to you because I think I know you well enough to know that by the same token you could ask me to do something. In other words,*

there's going to be some even-stevenness here, and I definitely think that's an important understanding. It's not going to be a one-way street. I'm not going to expect you to do this editing and not to be able to be there for you if you want me to do something for you, okay?

Delegation is a learned skill. And actually, it's possible to learn it a little too well, because some you ask will have a hard time saying no. You don't want to twist out a yes, and then have them not come through for you.

If they say no, I'll say, "I understand," or "Maybe next year," or something like that. But there are other people that just because of the nature of their personality, they're not going to say no. They are committed, but then they wind up kind of scrambling at the last minute to try and keep all the ends together. And often they don't do a good job because they don't have the time.

We'll return to this issue of time in a moment.

Leadership Between Meetings

The coalition meeting has ended; the coalition's work now begins. In most coalitions, most of the action takes place between the meeting dates. How much? A good bet is more than half, possibly a lot more than that. Who is going to do that work, or see that it gets done? The leader (or leaders), no one else. Part of leadership, a big part, is follow-up. The devil is in the details.

A good leader is somebody who's not only committed to the mission and goals of the coalition, but somebody who also recognizes that it takes time to follow up on the things the group identifies as being important. And agreeing that they have the time to do that.

What the group identifies as important will vary, but the actions needed for progress are very much the same, no matter what the particular issue. On the next page are some examples of tasks that might go on between coalition meetings. It's a composite "to-do" list, based on actual coalition experience. (What others might apply to your own coalition?)

Taken one at a time, these tasks are small. They may appear trivial, but they have to be done. Someone has to do them. The person who does them, or delegates responsibility for their being done, is the coalition leader. And getting these tasks done is crucial to coalition leadership. If the devil is in the details, then so, too, may be Godliness.

Would you agree that these tasks, taken singly, are reasonably easy? They are nothing you or most of your colleagues couldn't do with a little bit of motivation, and with

A Post-Meeting Checklist: Items for the Coalition Leader to Handle This Week

1. Deposit this month's checks in our account.

2. Write a thank-you note to the guest presenter at our last meeting.

3. Call the news editor of the local paper. Where was our press release last time?

4. Review the notes from the last meeting.

5. Draft the agenda for the next meeting.

6. Call all committee heads. Make sure they've got something to report. And if not, why not?

7. Call the person who agreed to draft an amendment to the by-laws. Where is it?

8. Make sure the first-time visitor at the last meeting gets a follow-up call.

9. Get the name of the new agency head. Write a welcoming note. Call a week later.

10. Proofread the new coalition brochure.

11. Make a lunch appointment with the head of the interfaith council. Possibility of more church participation? What benefits can we give them?

12. Call State House for information on new grant RFP. Consider applying.

13. X (coalition vice-chair) seemed angry/annoyed at the last meeting. Call to check.

14. Y (long-time member) hasn't shown up the last two times. What's going on?

15. ~~Check to see if we can afford new graphics software.~~ Yes, we can. Pick it up. Learn how to use it.

16. Evaluation of coalition—Someone brought this up at our last meeting. Do we really have to do this? Check to see if they would lead task group.

17. Route legislative alert received today to head of Policy Committee.

18. Get fax machine fixed (again).

19. Call PTO head to confirm our appearance at next parent meeting.

20. Come up with possible locations for coalition social event and "Fun Day."

concentration of effort (both of which are basic leadership qualities). No other overpowering ability is called for. What is called for, though, is time.

Time, pure and simple. Here is an unadvertised fact about leadership: You can't do the job if you don't have the time. Coalition leadership, in large part, depends not so much on charisma or masterful technique or inborn skill. It instead depends on having the minutes in the day to follow up and execute a series of small tasks with competence and reliability.

It's that uncomplicated. If you don't have the time, you're not going to be able to lead very well, no matter how skilled you are:

> *Our treasurer is somebody who's been very actively involved with the coalition from the beginning. This year, though, I must say she's not spending any time. She's missing meetings. So that means very often our treasurer's report is something that just gets faxed to us. And that's been a problem, because if you're going to be an officer, you really have to have the commitment of at least making the regular monthly meeting, if not doing even more.*

Conversely, if you've got the time, or will make the commitment to find the time, you've got a leg up on effective leadership.

> *Armanda, who is the chair of our multi-cultural committee, is very self-conscious. She's really embarrassed to speak. She's from Portugal. She feels like she doesn't have good English, but her English is fine. And she's very organized, very committed. She's taking the time, she's making the time. And because of that, that's probably the committee that's doing the most.*

Part of "having the time" is simply making yourself *accessible.* ("People know they can call me 'til about 10:00 at night.") As for the skills, the skills can be learned. As for "charisma," it's nice, but not required.

> *The overarching vision, the charisma, it is helpful. But I don't think it's necessary. I mean, the whole thing about having skills in terms of running meetings, that stuff can be learned. That's where I would see my role [as a consultant]. Like for instance, Cheryl [not her real name], who coordinates our local partnership. She doesn't have great facilitation skills. But she's bright, she can learn that stuff. If she has the time, and the commitment to do the job, those are two things that make a good leader.*

But having or finding the time to lead a coalition may not be a simple proposition at all. It can be very difficult. Who, in real life, has the time to take this on—especially since many of the logical candidates have day jobs and/or daytime responsibilities?

> *People don't want the job because they feel they don't have the time. And in a way I don't want to argue with that, because it does take time. Just by nature, people can only spend so much time in being committed.*

* * *

In our coalition, everybody says, "Oh, we need to have more access to health insurance, and more health information, and all those things." Everybody feels strongly about that. But when it comes down to actually putting in the time to make that happen, it's like these people aren't doing it because they're not getting paid. They're getting paid to work 9 to 5 for somewhere else. They see a lot of clients coming in their door who don't have adequate health coverage, and it is a big problem, but that's not what they're getting paid to do. And they can't really figure out how to come up with the extra time to do it.

Even worse, if there is a true time shortage, the coalition might have to settle for second-class leadership. Here is reality biting:

My feeling is, with the coalition, usually you're not going to get the best leaders. Because the best ones are being grabbed to do something else that they're going to get paid for, or get some other reward for. That's my feeling, anyway. For instance, I felt like Brenda [not her real name] was a very good leader. But right now, her time is going into presentations to get corporations to donate to the United Way. And I understand that's her job. But, you know . . . .

So how do you manufacture the time? There are no time factories, as far as we know. So personal time creation must be a home enterprise, from the basement workshop, a result of patching, stretching, occasional corner-cutting, and general making do. Specifically, there are almost always spare minutes to be found, some efficiencies to be gained. There's usually something to squeeze from the tube; this can help a little.

There is a point of no return, though, when there's literally nothing left, and at this point a leader may want to delegate more tasks to current members (*see discussion earlier in this chapter*), recruit new members (*see Chapter 3, on Membership*), groom new leaders (*see Chapter 10, on Maintenance*), raise money to buy or expand coalition staff time (*see Chapter 8, on Funding*)—or simply reduce the amount of coalition work. But another option is available, which is to reflect upon and modify one's way of leading, from the inside.

This is the topic of our next section. Is there a certain type of coalition leadership which goes with getting more things done?

Leadership from Within

The third element of leadership has to do with things that go on within the person, one's personal qualities, or at least those personal qualities that are displayed. As a leader, someone out front, you must show who you are. And who you are counts.

What counts in particular resembles "leadership style," which in discussions of leadership tends to mean how much authority you choose to exert, and how you choose to exert it. That is, in a group, a leader can be soft or hard, directive or non-directive, democratic or authoritarian or laissez-faire, or some finely and variably calibrated combination of them all. In actual practice, should you guide the group toward consensus, or let the group find its own way, or grab the group by the horns and say, "This is it"? And, a harder question: If the answer depends on the particular situation, what do you do when?

If there were one fixed answer that applied all the time, we would state it, close up shop, and move right along. But there isn't one answer, which is why leadership demands constant agility. Leadership of a group takes sensitivity and receptivity, a feel for what's going on. You have to be able to feel the pulse, then know what that pulse means. And then you have to have a wide repertory of behaviors on call, to deal with different prescriptions for your own different diagnoses. Human nature is complex enough, one human at a time; why should group nature be less so?

There's no single answer, and few universal leadership rules. You learn how to lead by watching experienced leaders in action, by reading and reflection, by taking many pulses of many different groups, and by trial and error. And so far so good. But having said all that, coalitions are a little different from other types of groups, which has consequences for how one ought to lead them. Coalitions are different because they are more voluntary, less formal, and less norm-based. The leader of the coalition, compared to other leaders, has less official power. He or she cannot usually discipline or fire, threaten or sanction, promote or give material rewards, even if these were desired. Influence and power must usually be exerted in kinder, gentler, more subtle ways, all of which are conducive to a more nuanced and less directive leadership approach.

So for much of the time, there is a possible irony or paradox in coalition life, in that the coalition may work best when the leader does not cling to or strive for one particular fixed outcome, but rather sees and guides the group as it is. If you drive the coalition too hard, you can run aground. Perhaps this is not irony at all, but simply a truth about voluntary groups; that part of leadership means releasing and letting go.

We have heard this viewpoint over and over again:

> *There's clearly an ethic of "We're all here because we want to be here."*
> *If someone leans too hard, then the option is, "See you later." So, I mean, it*
> *demands a certain degree of civility. Otherwise, it won't work.*

And driving too hard can lead to personal disappointment as well:

> *John was leading the coalition for a while. He had ideas about what he*
> *wanted the coalition to do, but I don't think he got a lot of consensus. Once*
> *we had a speaker series; John put a lot of time into that. It was a good series,*
> *but it took a lot of work, and a lot of that work fell on him in terms of con-*

tacting folks and arranging it. And it wasn't always appreciated. I mean, I can remember four or five meetings where it's 10 after one, and you've got four people in the room, and those were always the meetings where the speaker had driven for two hours to get there. . . .

I think John wanted the coalition to have a lot more clout in the community, to be more of a determining factor in how human resources were configured, and that it would be the source of a lot more actions and activities. When he left the position, he left the coalition, and I think part of it was disappointment that the coalition wasn't more ambitious, that it couldn't be more than what it was.

So you let go of your controlling impulses; you trust the coalition to chart its own course. A lot of coalition leaders have come to believe this, even if they didn't start out that way:

I think the most important thing I've learned is that I am most successful when I leave my ego at the door. When I bring my agendas to the meeting, then I become the center, instead of the issue becoming the center. Sometimes I hate to lose, I hate not to see my point being taken seriously. That's when I'm bringing my ego to the table. When I leave it at the door, and really just put faith in the group to make the best decision possible, I think that's when our meetings are the most productive.

* * *

A lot of time I think the organizer or the coalition leader tends to do too much, and in order not to do too much sometimes you have to pull back. It's not what happens today or tomorrow, it's that the effort continues. You've got to realize that the members aren't paid. You've got to let them work at their own pace. That means if it takes them three months to get something done that I could get done in three weeks, then that's what I've got to do.

Sometimes they seem like they take a long time, but that's good. If it takes them six months to get something done, it means they've been around for six months. The important thing is at the end of the six months, they have more people doing it than they did when they started. So it doesn't matter how long it takes. What matters is that they keep working at it.

There are those who not only choose not to drive the coalition, but who see any attempt to do so as being counter-productive:

They [the members] have to do it. They have to come forward. There are times when they set agendas I will sometimes question. But my role is to do their bidding. If I suggest or they suggest that I'm in a leadership role, that defeats the whole coalition aspect. It really does. I mean, it's something that they have to sustain; they can't rely on one person to do it.

The same noncontrolling theme appears in a coalition of neighborhood residents:

> *You've got to talk to the people in the neighborhoods to figure out what needs to get done in the neighborhoods. I'm not going to tell you that you've got to organize a clean-up. You tell me. You work with residents, you have a meeting with the residents, and they decide what the priorities are, blah, blah, blah. But I am not going to tell you what the priorities are, because that is not my role. If I did, then it would be my coalition or my set of agendas.*

And letting go is what you are *supposed* to do, for the often-voiced reason that it empowers the members of the coalition:

> *Some folk need the ego shot like dope. But if you're the leader, you've got to have a sense that you've got a larger goal that transcends your ego. If you want to build a coalition, and you want it to be a **coalition**, as opposed to simply a chorus line of followers whose function is a backdrop for your ego needs, you've got to learn how to let go. And then you have to be genuinely committed to empowering other people, if you're going to build an authentic coalition. That's the price of an authentic coalition.*

So, in plain language, sometimes as leader you keep your mouth shut:

> *I have tried to keep my personal issues in control. I could have said, "No, we are not going to do the by-laws first, we are going to do this," and really kind of push my ideas. But I didn't do that, I said, "Okay, this is what they want to do, I'm going to do that." I'm not going to say, "Look, I've tried this before, it doesn't work." I'll say, "Let's try it again, let's do it again, let's try a different approach, whatever." That is what it takes.*

And yet, if you think that letting go (or even keeping quiet) is easy, or that all you have to do is let the coalition go its own way, take a second look. Letting go has consequences, and one of those consequences is that less may get done.

> *I feel like I'm stuck in second gear sometimes, because I would like to have seen things gone further. If I did certain things, I think it would have gone further. I feel somewhat frustrated that we have not progressed as far as we could in the five years. But it would have been me doing it, me pushing it, and me doing all the work. That's not what I wanted to do.*
>
> *I feel like where have the five years gone? It's almost like July is right around the corner. I am a passenger, when I could have been the driver.*

100

And the leader, one might say, is *expected* to drive the coalition, to get it to act, to deliver the goods. If you don't, then what are you there for?

> *If you didn't keep pushing, things would gradually grind to a halt, to an end.*

* * *

> *My leadership style has always been tied around action. I mean, I wouldn't be involved in something that didn't lead to action. It's counter-productive to me, and I guess at my age I don't want to just spin gears.*

* * *

> *Somebody's got to lead. I'm a lot less unrealistic about that. Somebody's got to lead. It often means the exertion of power and control. I mean, there's no magic, there's no juju. This is as old as hard work and focus. I'm here almost everyday. I work early, I work late. I make some decisions about things. I'm not a razzmatazz kind of person. I'm focused, focused, focused. Sharpen and improve your efficiency. Do what you got to do.*

How, then, do these viewpoints get reconciled? Maybe by choosing not to drive the coalition, you keep your sanity, in a way:

> *Overall, I think it was better to do it like this and keep my own sanity instead of being crazed trying to do everything. Because ultimately it is up to the coalition or the partnership to move things on, and it's up to me to continue what I'm doing.*

But then again, maybe not:

> *I came in being so enormously dedicated to process and to getting group consensus that I thought that Mary Lou [the previous coalition leader] was going to slit her wrists. She was like, "Oh my God, when are we ever going to get to do anything?" I mean, she said, "I'm just too old, I've been to too many meetings, I can't sit through one more meeting where we just talk—I can't stand it." And she was just going cuckoo.*

So the leader is supposed to let the coalition make the decisions, but also to drive the process and the coalition's agenda. To release one's ego, but also to exert power and control, at least from time to time. To sit in the back, but also up front. This is a tall order. Its magnitude is compounded by real-world pushes and pulls coming from multiple directions—and in a lively coalition, they are coming a mile a minute. Leadership exposes you, sometimes too much. When someone declines a leadership role because "I don't have the time," he or she may also mean, or primarily mean, "I don't want the aggravation."

The fact is that in complex organizations good leadership is always a cliff walk. You can fall. You've got to keep your feet on the ground. You need to keep your balance. Yet you probably also want to keep on moving, and not dwell on the chasms below, even if the downside risks are pretty steep.

But a complementary fact, possibly just a bit reassuring, is that any important human relationship is a balancing act, too. Marriage, to pick one. Or parenting. Or supervising people. Or even assigning priorities to different parts of your own life. We learn to keep balance, more or less, ever so slowly, through trial and error. The same applies to coalition leadership:

> *There's a balance. There's a real balance for me that I feel I have to strike between offering solutions and yet also eliciting solutions. And you have to have some of both. I mean, I now know that I have to be prepared to offer some solutions for discussion purposes, you know? I had to learn that you just can't open up the floor and start from zero, because people sit there and look at you.*
>
> *Okay, so now I can come in and I can offer options and say, "Well, we could do this, or we might do this, or let's look at this." It's a basis to begin thinking and working with ideas. And we'll probably end up someplace altogether different, but they need those kernels to start with. So, it's been painful—believe me, it hasn't been without some pain, some of these lessons. But I now feel very, very comfortable, where earlier on I felt very uncomfortable.*

It's possible that this idea of balance goes further. A good coalition leader is not only balanced in terms of initiating actions within the coalition, but maybe also balanced personally, within one's full self. It's that personal, internal balance that keeps you steady, un-crazy, gently moving forward, and not blown off the cliff.

Think about it. Do you agree with what this coalition leader has to say?

. . .What makes it crazy?

The scheduling, the constant meetings—not only with your own coalition or partnership, but with school meetings and neighborhood meetings, and other things in the community that it's important to stay in touch with. So I think a lot of meetings makes it crazy.

How do you deal with it?

By taking time for yourself. Who was it that said that life is more than work and work is more than a job? That's really true. I need to remind myself that there's more to me than just the work I do. As much as I love it, I really need to remember that there's a person inside of me outside of the work.

When you say "take time for yourself," like what, for example?

The personal side, you mean? Spending time with friends and family, and doing things like going for a walk, appreciating the beauty of where I live.

You might do something like that in the middle of the day?

That would be nice.

Do you actually get a chance to do that? Or maybe once you're in the office, it's intense, and you don't get a chance to do that type of stuff?

Certain times of the year, it's crazier than other times. During the summer, it seems to slow down. And so I spend a lot of time then sitting on my deck and enjoying the lake and going for a walk and reminding myself of what fun things I like to do, and doing them.

Does that help your work?

I think so. I think that you really need to maintain a balance. I think I've learned a lot about how to maintain balance; and a lot of it is recognizing when things are getting just too crazy and taking a walk, or taking a really deep breath and maybe doing breathing exercises.

Literally?

Literally, mm-hmm. A balanced leader is calm, relaxed, and confident. There are things you can do when you're out of balance to bring yourself back to the balanced position. And for everyone, it will be different. For me, it may be to take my calendar out and just draw a line across a day so that I don't schedule anything and do something just for me. Someone else might spend time with their kids.

So a balanced leader, a calm, relaxed, and confident leader, is a more effective leader?

I believe so. Because when you're doing your work then, you're coming from a more grounded place. . . . The heart and soul of what we're trying to do, I believe, is really a spiritual thing.

To be a good leader, then, is no harder and no easier than being a good human being: balanced, focused, sensitive, internally strong. Which can be comforting, but certainly also soul-stretching, because it is another daunting assignment to be a full human being in more than isolated corners of the day, to have your full humanity always present, not to mention in public view.

But there is a more difficult and threatening problem, which complicates the picture, for a complete and balanced human being does not necessarily make a very good leader:

> *I was in a coalition where the leader was a truly wonderful person. She received all kinds of awards and recognition. She was full of life and joy; people loved her. When she called me, sunshine poured right through the telephone. I would walk on my knees for her. In meetings, she listened to and cared for everyone; she was a consensus-builder par excellence.*
>
> *The only problem was that the coalition didn't do much. Her success, and in a way it was a success, was getting people into the same room. Once they were there, it didn't seem important that much of anything else happen. And it didn't.*

This time, the speaker above is one of us [BB]. And maybe our judgment is a bit too harsh. Sure, we want joyful and compassionate people to be our leaders, men and women of the highest character, with consummate sensitivity, grace, charm, and tact, fully evolved humans in all senses of the word; and, in addition, at the very same time, leaders who are superb meeting facilitators, who love little details, who have time and commitment to spare, and who are also totally engaged in the task at hand and won't let up until the last objective is nailed down.

All this may be too much to ask of a single person. We can hope for it, and we can move in that direction, but to expect it . . . maybe not yet, at this stage of our development. A talented leader should be treasured beyond words. But leadership also rests with each coalition member. The best coalition leaders know that leadership is everybody's business, and work at developing new leaders to take over the reins.

Good leadership? It's within the grasp of almost all of us. Excellent leadership? It's within the reach of more of us than we might think. Truly distinguished and transformational leadership—that is a goal for many of us to aim for, while honoring, valuing, and maximizing the leadership abilities we currently have available, and finding ways to promote those same abilities among all of our members.

Lessons From The Field

Leadership at Meetings

A meeting is a performance. The meeting room is the stage. The leader is the director. And, like most performances, the meeting will go well when leaders:

- Prepare before the meeting.
- Anticipate the different responses that might occur, and how to deal with each one.
- Stick to the agenda, but not too rigidly.
- Play to the audience; draw everyone in.
- Keep things moving. Watch out for slow spots, when interest may be waning. Change the pace, and if you need to, step on the accelerator.

Leadership Between Meetings

- Identify the tasks that need to be done between meetings.
- Put these tasks on a list. In coalition work (and elsewhere), blessed are the listmakers.
- Prioritize the tasks. This can be very simple. For example, "What most needs to get done this week?"
- Delegate the tasks. First, ask yourself, "What do I need to do personally?" and "Who else can do what?" Then, ask others as needed. Be specific. Get commitments. Agree on timelines.
- Follow up on your delegation, by phone call or note. A good leader has mastered the art of gentle reminding. When the task is done, cross it off your list, and move on to the next one.

Leadership from Within: The Qualities of the Leader

- There is value in guiding the coalition to make its own decisions at its own pace, without direct suggestions from you. A good leader, in this sense, spends the most time steering.
- But there is also value in making direct suggestions and taking direct action, occasionally without full coalition support—for example, when a deadline approaches, or when you have special expertise, or when no one else is available. A good leader here picks up an oar and rows.
- Whether to steer or to row, or to drift for a moment, depends on your perception of the group at this point in time. Who is involved? What are their commitments, availabilities, and talents? What is the history? What is the mood of the group right now? A good leader will take in all this information and be thoughtful before responding.
- And a good leader will be able to respond in many different ways. Not only that, the best response tomorrow may be different from the best response today. Good

coalition leadership not only requires thoughtfulness, flexibility, and versatility, but also draws upon the full range and depth of one's character.

■ Yet a leader cannot be all things to all people all the time. So part of leadership is to stimulate and leverage the talents, interests, and motivations of other coalition members in the service of the group. Good leaders know which switches will turn on the power; the best leaders make each member a power source.

Leadership Qualities, in a Nutshell . . .

Three coalition leaders sum it up:

■ "You need a sense of humor, a willingness to applaud the process as it goes along, to be welcoming, to be upbeat, to be a cheerleader whenever possible—and what's really important, to help people leave their suits at the door."

■ "I think you've got to really feel it in your bone marrow that you want to make a difference, that you believe a difference can be made, and that it's not a 9-to-5 kind of thing. It isn't a job. It really isn't a job."

■ "Leadership can be developed. But there has to be a desire on the part of the person to be a leader. The idea that anybody can do it is not necessarily true. I mean, there has to be the desire. But that person doesn't have to have all the right personality traits. . . ."

Job Description
Coordinator of the Lower/Outer Cape Community Coalition

The Lower/Outer Cape Community Coalition is a community-wide coalition whose purpose is to:
- Develop a forum for health and human services in the Lower/Outer Cape.

- Develop a planning body to study and recommend ways to address and meet health and human service needs.

- Promote greater cooperation among all agencies delivering services to the Lower/Outer Cape.

- Collaboratively solve problems regarding issues of health, human services and quality of life for the area.

- Provide information to community providers and residents to increase accessibility and visibility of services and to facilitate the maximum effectiveness of services.

- Monitor successful implementation of plans developed by the Coalition.

To fulfill these goals, the Coalition Coordinator will:
- Organize all Coalition activities
- Chair monthly meetings of the Coalition/interact with Board members on an ongoing basis
- Set agendas for Advisory Board meetings
- Work closely with Statewide AHEC/Community Partners office to coordinate with other AHEC Coalitions across the State
- Develop position papers, press releases, reports and regular newsletters on behalf of the Coalition
- Develop and monitor Task Forces with membership around specific Coalition issues
- Recruit and maintain membership
- Provide contact with the media about health and human services issues
- Chair special events for the Coalition
- Serve as a link between the Lower/Outer Cape communities and the health and human service community
- Play an advocate role around issues of human needs
- Coordinate programs and agencies
- Generate and provide resource materials on Coalition issues to members of the community at-large, legislators, etc.
- Act as Coalition liaison to various organizations, Boards, etc., where appropriate
- Search out grant and funding possibilities to implement Coalition administration and/or program implementation
- Be Coalition/human services spokesperson (or pointperson) to towns, media, civic groups, religious bodies, etc.
- Be responsible for overseeing any administrative/clerical staff hired to implement programs
- Serve as Lower Cape human service liaison with Cape legislators
- Work to encourage, through Coalition membership and programs, the empowerment of community residents in human service activities
- Establish the Coalition as a leader in prevention activities, coordination, publicity, funding, etc.

The Coalition Coordinator works under the supervision of the Statewide Area Health Education Center's Director of Community Development.

Much of leadership is intangible and hard to capture in written documents. But when searching for a new leader (a coalition coordinator, in this case), a specific and well-written job description certainly helps.

Resume Screening Sheet for Lower/Outer Cape Community Coalition Coordinator Position

Candidate Name_____

Please circle the most appropriate number for each item listed where 1 means little, 2 means somewhat and 3 means very.

Little---Somewhat----Very

Organized individuals	1	2	3	4	5
Facilitation skills	1	2	3	4	5
Advocate/passion	1	2	3	4	5
Writing skills	1	2	3	4	5
Interpersonal skills	1	2	3	4	5
Financial/fund-raising skills	1	2	3	4	5
Work with media	1	2	3	4	5
Work with legislators	1	2	3	4	5
Conflict resolver	1	2	3	4	5
Verbal skills	1	2	3	4	5
Organizational skills	1	2	3	4	5
Knowledge of human services	1	2	3	4	5
Community outreach experience	1	2	3	4	5
Community involvement experience	1	2	3	4	5

Your name_____

Send changes or suggestions to Mary Lou Petitt
P.O. Box 797
Eastham, MA 02642

...Then, when applications come in, you'd like a systematic way of screening them.

CLARITY IN COALITIONS

Coalitions often find it helpful to examine the clarity with which their purpose, structure and operations have been defined. A check on the coalition's clarity may be done by a single officer or coalition coordinator or by the entire coalition membership. When an area is in need of more clarity, specific actions may be taken by the leader alone or the entire coalition membership may choose to work together on the issue. To quickly check the charity in your coalition, register your opinion regarding each area by placing a number selected from the scale in the parentheses under the name of the area.

very unclear   very clear

I. Statement of Purpose–Is the mission statement for the coalition focused enough?
    (   )

II. Criteria for membership–how official **voting** membership status is determined?
    (   )

III. Representation–The number and level of representatives expected from member
    (   )   organizations?

IV. Authority–The degree to which coalition decisions are expected to be binding on
    (   )   member organizations?

V. Leadership–The officer roles and responsibilities?
    (   )

VI. Selection procedures–The means of choosing officers, committee chairs, etc.?
    (   )

VII. Meetings–scheduling and expectations for participation?
    (   )

VIII. Meeting management–ground rules for conducting business (e.g. rules of order)
    (   )   written agenda, etc.

IX. Decision making–procedures for making official decisions (e.g. quorum,
    (   )   consensus, voting procedures)

X. Work responsibilities–documentation of who will do what, by when?
    (   )

XI. Fiscal management–procedures for receiving and disbursement of funds?
    (   )

XII. Accountability and evaluation–reporting responsibilities and criteria for
    (   )   evaluating success?

A good leader will check the health of the coalition every once in a while, preferably in some structured manner. (Think of it as a coalition tune-up.) This simple self-assessment can help the leader and others learn more about how members perceive the coalition; adjustments can then follow. [Thanks to David Chavis for originating this document.]

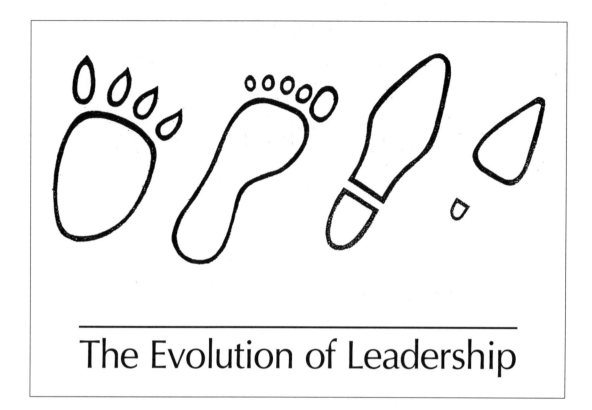

The Evolution of Leadership

Would you agree?

Chapter 7

Promoting The Coalition

How much attention should be given to publicity?

How can a coalition best get the word out?

Should publicity be low-key and casual, or formal and planned?

What are the key principles to keep in mind?

In this conversation, where do your sympathies lie?

So how is your coalition going?
Not too bad.

Specifically, people are coming to meetings?
They are, actually.

The committees and task groups are doing their jobs?
More or less.

Leading the coalition, how's that working for you?
Better than I thought. They haven't kicked me out yet.

And you're getting things done in the community?
I think so. Why do you ask?

Because I was checking around, and not too many people in the community even know you exist.

It's not been a problem. Those who need to know, they know.

Wouldn't it be better if more people knew about the good things you're doing?

Maybe. If we could handle it.

You don't want to publicize your work?

Occasionally, we do. But not in a major way. We don't have the time or the resources. And I'm not sure it's that important to us. We're pretty happy with things the way they are.

You don't think you'd be better off if—

Sorry, but I've got to be going now. . . .

Is Promotion Worth the Effort?

How about your own coalition? Would it be better off if it spent more time publicizing its activities and ideas, in reaching new audiences, in getting the word out? We hope you will give yourself enough time to answer that question thoughtfully.

We don't know what your answer will be. It might not be an unqualified yes or no. You might indeed be happy enough with the way things are. The coalition will not stand or fall on whether the press release goes out. And really, who cares if a few more people have heard about you? And who has the time to tell them?

The status quo is not always bad, nor is growth always good. Inertia has a place in the social world. Organizational energy can expand only so far, which sometimes is not very far at all, and a large investment in publicity may mean a smaller investment somewhere else. If you blow your own horn, you may run out of breath. And why blow it anyway? If people want to hear, they can come close and listen.

But there are real reasons for turning up the volume, even just a little:

■ Publicity attracts members. Members (*see Chapter 3*) are the lifeblood of any coalition or group. But—and there are few surer laws of group life—members don't stay members forever. They change jobs, move away, get sick, have children, lose interest, find themselves with fewer hours. Even if they stay on the membership rolls, they may become inactive, no longer lending their talents nor pulling their weight. You need to publicize the coalition so that new members will fill their places.

■ Publicity attracts community resources. A well-publicized coalition is better positioned to tap into other community assets. Money, for one. Grants, awards, contracts—all flow to groups who are known quantities. But resources mean more than dollars. If you are well-known, the local college might send an intern your way. The print shop might give you a price break. The office supply company might make a donation, or the bank a contribution. The media will call on your perceived expertise. When groups need speakers, your phone might ring, and that engagement might lead to more opportunities. Recognition begets recognition; publicity can snowball; and there is more:

■ Publicity is needed for growth. You may have to publicize just to stay in place. But if you are interested in growth, of membership or resources or community clout, all the more reason to get the word out. Yes, sometimes strangers will wander through the door, and conceivably, through dumb luck or circumstance, you may get attention (not always of your own choosing); but that is rare. Most of the time, members (and resources, and clout) must be sought after, which means others must know and value who you are, which means someone has to tell them. Hence, publicity.

■ Publicity can mean more gets done. The more members and resources you have, the more talent is available to act, especially if the structure and the leadership of the coalition are both operating smoothly. You can form more objectives, create more task groups, and list more actions on your action plan, for there will be more actors available to set plans into motion. And while bigger is not always better, if other things are equal, the more members you have, the more accomplishment possibilities there are, because each new member will have his or her own network of contacts in the community. Whatever your needs, the chances are greater that you will know someone, or know someone who knows someone, who could fulfill them.

But the most important reason comes last:

■ Publicity can help you reach the people you want to and need to reach. Those on the receiving end, those who need the service or who can benefit from your action, must know about you and believe in you before they will take advantage of what you have to offer. These people are probably busy, just like you. They may be overloaded. They may also be suspicious, cynical, cautious, unaware, and not particularly motivated to change. They may never change. But if those people are ever to be reached and changed, and possibly helped, they must first be informed. It's as simple as that.

Publicity is a way, and one of the only ways, to get your message out to the people who need to hear it so they can benefit from it. Seen in this light, publicity is not a burden one must shoulder, nor an extra added frill, but it is rather a coalition necessity. A coalition imperative might not be too strong a phrase.

So here are the major questions we want to take up in this chapter:
■ How should the coalition's work be promoted? and
■ How do these methods work in practice?

Methods of Promotion

What methods should you use to get the word out? Well, how many stars can you see in the sky? You can pin, tack, glue, or emboss your message on almost any object, in almost any location, in almost any manner, with almost any content. The possibilities are limited only by your imagination.

Below are some examples of how coalitions have used promotional methods in practice. They start from the familiar, and move toward the less usual:

Newsletters
Our monthly newsletter arrives a week to 10 days in advance of our coalition meetings. We have a mailing list of about 440, and that includes a lot of people who do not come to meetings, but who need to read it, legislators and clergy . . . .

Letters to the Editor
In one community, the newspaper never liked to publish any of our news releases. So we became regular letters-to-the-editor writers, because we discovered that was the best-followed form of publicity in that town. Everybody would flip right to the letters that got written. . . .

Brochures
We were making up a brochure for our coalition and wanted to make sure that it got attention. So we found a guy in town who a lot of people in our audience knew. He was a recovering addict, a nice guy, and good-looking too; those who knew him liked him. We invested in a professional photographer, and posed Tommy on the cover talking with two local women in a natural setting. That brochure got a lot of recognition in our community. . . .

Cable Television
FATV [the local community access channel] *will film anything we want. If we put on a half-hour press conference, they'll film the whole thing and then play it 10 times. They'll play it to death. We do that on a regular basis. We have coffee and donuts, and 50 people show up. We put on the show, and then we all hang around and talk to each other.* [Publicity for this coalition becomes a social occasion.] *It's good to get together. There have been a lot of relationships established through the TV shows. . . .*

Board Memberships
One way you spread the coalition is by serving on other boards. I'm on the legal services board. I stayed on the interfaith board, the CDC board. And I'm on the Eastham Housing Authority. I talk frequently about what the coalition is doing as part of that task. . . .

Bullhorns

We had people doing door-knocking for the election, letting people know, or handing them a flyer. And then the day before, we had someone walking around with a bullhorn, reminding them that the election is coming up, come out and vote. We had the highest turnout. . . .

The Town Census

The coalition was supported by town government, so we had a flyer about the coalition sent to every household along with the annual town census, about 19,000 households. And then we asked people to respond with their own interests, the areas of our work they might like to get involved in. We got 1,400 responses back in the mail, and had all these responses computerized, by interests and by census tract. . . .

Shopping Mall Kiosks *The Health Committee has plans for a kiosk at Searstown Mall, the major mall around here, in which they would identify the health issue of the month, and bring agencies in, so there would be health education going on continuously, each month changing over. . . .*

Parades

There's a parade on Sunday, and a prize is given for the best activity in the parade. It's a good opportunity because there are quite a few human service groups there. One program said that's one of their best ways to do outreach. They're raffling off a quilt and they're giving out some freebies, magnets for the refrigerator, things like that. It's a very good way to communicate. . . .

Videos

[This coalition did a community video in connection with its application to become an All-America City. The value was not just in the video itself, but in bringing people together.] *We got 30 people, ranging from the head of the Chamber of Commerce and the heads of two banks and the mayor and the planning coordinator, and we matched them up with the neighborhood leaders and the neighborhood youth councils and we had them work on a project together for six weeks. We helped fly them out of state to present what they had done, and then let them relax and get to know each other better for two days before they came back home. When you do that, it clearly creates a different community when they come back. Just the bonds that are created by getting people to meet—it's just phenomenal stuff. . . .*

Almost every week, it seems, we run across another new way to get the message out: We've seen coalition messages on lollipops, water bottles, and billboards, and other organizational messages on plastic shopping bags (in bilingual comic-strip form), on trading cards (photographs of your local police), and on shoes ("grafeeties"). We won't dare to predict the future.

Core Principles

Whatever method you use to publicize, some common general principles apply.

■ First, it helps to communicate to people in everyday, natural language:

> *We've always been trying to lessen the jargon. We try to get down to a level that people understand. When we are talking to funders, we talk about healthy communities and empowerment. But when we are talking to people in communities we say, "Can we help you solve some of the problems that you have? What is it that you want to do?"*

■ It helps to offer specific benefits that address stated needs:

> *You have to give them something very concrete. You have to determine what their interest is, and then respond very concretely. For example, 300 people responded to a survey. Most of them said that public safety, personal safety was their primary concern. We didn't understand why people were thinking that; all the crime statistics had dropped. So the challenge for the coalition was, well, what do we do about this?*
>
> *We then had two safety workshops. The Boston Police and Tufts University Police came in and did workshops in the neighborhood for residents. They would be very specific: "If you're elderly, don't travel alone. You see someone who looks threatening, change sides of the street. Don't call 'Help,' call 'Fire!'—that gets people's attention much more quickly." So that's what we do. Very concrete things.*
>
> *If we can offer people opportunities to become involved in activities that address their needs or interests, then over time we can get them engaged on another level.*

■ And it helps to realize that creating community visibility usually takes repetition and time:

> *You need a long-term commitment. In a community like ours, people see a lot of things come and go. It takes a long time to really get your foot in the door. We have been working for a long time, and we know what the issues are, but we are still not totally known in the neighborhoods or throughout the city. We are still not able to really mobilize the numbers of people we would like to. Prevention is such a nebulous kind of thing. It*

just takes a lot more time for people to really understand what we are trying to do.

The overriding principle we want to get across, though, is that publicizing your coalition, or anything else, is not just a mechanical operation. It's not something that operates by setting a production schedule, or by doing a bulk mailing and checking who opens the envelope. *Publicity is also a social transaction*, from one human to another, where you communicate to someone you care about, from a position of truth, something of value that you truly believe can be helpful. That is what publicity should be, anyway.

And because you believe in what the coalition is doing, you, yourself, are the coalition's best publicity agent. And because good publicity is both transactional and personal, the single best way to do publicity, whenever you can manage it, is to reach people personally, face-to-face, and self-to-self. We'll come back to this idea a few pages farther on.

Methods and Principles in Practice

How do these points translate into practice? Let's give a few case examples, identifying and illustrating some more principles as we go along.

Reaching out: Door-to-door. If you want to reach out to people, you go where people are. And as often as not, where people are is at home:

> *We have gone into the neighborhoods. We did door-knocking originally to talk to people, and we have periodically done door-knocking again. The neighborhoods are not that complicated. We know where the streets are and we've got maps and that kind of stuff.*
>
> *The way you do it depends on the neighborhood. In one neighborhood, we just go into a building and begin with the first floor and start knocking. We have developed, for lack of a better term, a survey, or really a series of questions. It could be like five or six questions, and then we will change the questions based on our experience at the door.*

Note that the "survey" in this case is part of the publicity effort. Both the survey and the personal appearance provide visibility, and hopefully credibility, for the coalition. The survey questions asked, though, are real questions with a real purpose, not just make-believe. They help the coalition learn more about current perceptions and needs; and no less important, about people who might like to become active. Publicity can be—and sometimes should be—combined with needs assessment and with recruiting as part of the same social encounter; this is smart strategy.

But won't people slam the door in your face? Perhaps less often than you'd think:

Very few people have actually been angry. Some people may totally dis-agree with what we are doing, or say it's a waste of time, but most people will answer the questions. A few people, they say "Who is it?", and you say who you are and what you are doing, and they don't answer the door. This is a very few.

But we are talking about inner-city neighborhoods. We're not talking about suburbia. There may be more fear in suburbia, but here in the city you get into the building. You say, "I'm working with this group, we are doing this and that," then people are willing to answer. By and large most people will give you their name. Some people are very talkative, and some say they really want to do something.

Reaching out: Visiting natural gathering places. Reaching people face-to-face at home is great if you can do it, but it takes a lot of time and energy. It is labor-inten-sive. If you can't go door-to-door, or choose not to, you can reach people at other places they naturally visit. At stores, for example:

In a rural area like this, we really need to look at creative ways to get the word out. What about the folks who live in hill towns and don't get the paper, or who can't read? So how do you reach them? Maybe it's a flyer hung in the general store. One suggestion was to have a coalition bulletin board, which sums up the announcements in our newsletter every month. And to make thousands of copies and hang them in the general stores, and have them available at the grocery stores and the banks and places where people need to go, and get the word out about services that way.

Using local institutions. Or you can reach people through the institutions com-mon to almost every community—the school, the church, the town government—all potentially accessible to any coalition:

A good contact point can be someone in an elementary school. And par-ents get involved with their elementary school children's educational experi-ence, more so than at the older levels. I've also worked with nurses in some of the elementary schools. A nurse may call my office and say, "You know, someone handed me a partnership newsletter, what's this all about?" It's kind of hit and miss.

The churches, also. I think that the churches are another vehicle in the smaller towns because even the smallest villages have a church. And even the smallest of towns have their annual town meetings. We haven't really tapped into that. . . .

Using social events. Or at naturally occurring social events, when people get together to have a good time. In ethnic communities, it could be a street festival:

At the August Moon Festival, we'll have a booth or a table and we'll be passing out literature, greeting people, doing surveys or petition campaigns and stuff like that. We have to be assertive. We have to go out and grab people and get the stuff into their hands.

So if someone would make eye contact, you say, "Please sign our petition. Please come over and meet us. Would you like something?" Sometimes we also have a draw [raffle]. I mean, the first time we did it we told people if they filled out a survey they could put their names on a card and there'd be a raffle for $200.

Or in smaller towns, it could be a firemen's picnic, a spaghetti dinner, or (as below) an annual fair. You can piggyback onto these natural community events. And your presence there can give you more than simple visibility; it can get important information into the hands of people who need it:

The Oktoberfest is coming up, two weeks from now. And last year it was estimated that between 3- and 4,000 people came, which is like 10 percent of the population of the Lower Cape. So, I mean, you're touching a lot of folks. Our coalition basically put the Prevention Fest together [as part of the Oktoberfest] and sponsors it—last year, I think we had 40 exhibitors from primarily the health and human services community, but also from businesses, like Willy's Gym, and anybody related to health and fitness. We have our herb guys coming again this year. . . .

We have these events on the Cape that are a regular part of our community, like the Windmill Weekend, the Harwich Cranberry Festival, the Fall for Orleans. And I think that the best thing we did, when we wanted to do a prevention fair, was to get connected with an ongoing community event, instead of going off and sitting in a high school gym somewhere and having, you know, two or three people stumble through. I mean, the health and human services need to be perceived as part of our community and what makes it run and what makes it work, so we're an integral part of it.

The Masonic Lodge is the main sponsor of the Oktoberfest. They do a lot of publicity. We piggyback onto that. A printed version of our prevention flyer goes home in the backpack of every elementary school kid on the Lower Cape. So, we'll distribute like 3,000 of those. Plus this year, for the first time, they're distributing 10,000 ad books with our name on them. So, that doesn't hurt.

It's a family day. It's in a ball field, in Orleans, under tents. We're like right field; that's our designated area. Like a quarter of the field, probably, is all of us. And, of course, the coalition also has a table among all the other vendors. And it doesn't cost us a cent. There are two ways the Masons make money at this event. One is at the gate, they ask people for donations. Nobody will be turned away if they can't give a donation, but there's a bucket. And

119

> *then on the field there are games, pony rides, amusement rides, food. So we get 55 percent of the inside-the-gate profits. Last year it was about $2,000.*
>
> *We've lucked out on the weather. It's been a real pistol to set up, though, the night before. It takes a lot of work.*

Sure, it takes work. But anytime you can get 10 percent of the community's population to show up for anything, that is impressive in itself.

Generating social leverage. Yet it's possible to take these principles of outreach and make them more effective still. Your outreach effort can become more sophisticated, operating at a higher level. And what this involves is not simply using the publicity channels and good offices of the school, church, or public event, but actually enlisting those institutions to work actively for you, on your behalf. This is the basic principle of *social leverage*, which can be as powerful as the institution you are leveraging itself. The church, just for example:

> *The Pledge for Peace is our violence prevention initiative. That put us on the map. Pledge for Peace is about getting all the different parts of the city to do something at the same time—not necessarily to do something together, but when everybody does something about violence during the same eight-week period, it feels like you're all doing something together. So Pledge for Peace is about feeling you're connected to everyone else.*
>
> *So you get the clergy to do something, you get the youth to do something, you get the athletic community to do something, you get the newspaper to do something. The coalition just picked the time period and we've got all these people doing stuff, so now we literally have 70, 80, 90 organizations doing something during the period, with 70, 80 events going on, and they're all independent.*
>
> *One year we had a nine-part television series, and the Chamber of Commerce got involved. When's the last time the Chamber of Commerce ever worked with us? The only thing they do is the Pledge for Peace campaign. We had a novena of rosaries. We had nine Catholic parishes coming together every week on Tuesday morning for nine weeks to pray for the success of the coalition and for peace in the community. Every Catholic church.*
>
> *I would love the opportunity to try to replicate Pledge for Peace, and go to another city and say, "Let me try to do this." It just makes people feel connected.*

Though often you don't have to enlist or leverage the entire institution directly. You can instead enlist the support of its leader, and let that leader lead. Through that endorsement, sometimes percolating down through the organization, your work is done for you. This is leverage again, on a higher order:

At our street fair, we found out that one of the biggest draws of the community is the principal of the elementary school, Mr. Wong. Wherever he was, he would be like a little magnet. The kids would come over and say, "Hi, Mr. Wong!" And the parents would come over, and he knew all the families, and he would simply say, "Do this, please." And of course they would do it. It's just using his influence. It's working with the structure that they're familiar with, which was being very respectful and deferential to his position.

* * *

We reached out to the Archdiocese of Boston. Did a lot of work with the Cardinal. Made a major difference in terms of successfully getting other people on board.

The Cardinal loved our 10-point plan. There was no fat on the bone. In other words, this was very tight. The plan itself was practical. It was doable. Made sense. It wasn't flashy or stupid. It was real direct, straight ahead, and we could really move forward on it.

We asked the Cardinal for his endorsement. Then asked him to encourage the involvement of the Archdiocese. No problem. So once the Cardinal came on board, then The Boston Globe editorialized the support of the Cardinal's endorsement. Then we got momentum.

Cultivating the media. Of course, among the most powerful opinion leaders are the media themselves. So it is to your advantage, and (not to be forgotten) also to their advantage, that you develop a close working relationship with people in your community media. Here's the general idea:

If you don't have the personal relationships, then go meet the people, go meet the person who's got the city beat. Tell them about your work, or tell them that if she ever wants a quote on what's happening in human services to give you a buzz. So the paper might get a press release on a change in a health care program. She could write that up, but it would be good if she could find someone who could say what this really meant. And if she knows that you're available and quotable, she'll call you.

. . . And a couple of examples of how the principle works in practice:

The managing editor of the newspaper sits on our Steering Committee, comes as a faithful attendee. Then we have the Ray C morning radio show. Ray C is a radio personality, and we have an open invitation to go on his show any morning we want, and we probably do go on seven, eight, nine times a year. To talk about whatever we want to talk about. If we had some-

thing to talk about tomorrow, I could call Ray C up today and say, "When can I get on?" If I called him up on a Monday, we would be on that week.

* * *

One of my strengths is press relations. It's because I like it. I like reporters. I like journalism. I am a paper person. And I think reporters know it. I mean, I comment to them that they did a really nice job on that particular story—and then they feel enough trust in you to say, "Look, I can't come for the whole thing. When should I show? Can you give me a rundown?"

And we know who the reporters are. We certainly invite them to all of our meetings, and then we do follow up with a phone call, particularly if it's a meeting that you want to get press on. Some meetings aren't as urgent. But some of them really are, because what you really want is to get beyond the meeting to the general public. And we've been, I think, very successful at that. One of the reporters became a close friend. We knew that she and another woman were interested in social services. It didn't hurt that we gave them our awards at the end of the year, either. . . .

Publicity as a Social Transaction

There's an overall point here, a fundamental yet easy-to-lose-sight-of point, transcending and adding to those already made. In getting the word out about your coalition, or about anything else, you are working with people. Your outreach efforts will be more successful if you are successful in developing a relationship with those people, whether they are citizens at home, work, or play, or whether they are organizational representatives, institutional leaders, or the press.

It's not a one-way relationship, nor one where someone is being used or exploited. It's a relationship of mutual benefit, with the mutual recognition that each of you shares interests in improving community life.

We emphasized the importance of relationship building in Chapter 5 on Meetings. We alluded to it in Chapter 6 on Leadership. Here the theme occurs once again:

It's all about relationship, and publicity is about relationship, too. I mean, it's about building relationships with the people who call to say, "Can you show up at this forum, or at this meeting?" It is. People come in many cases because they have formed a relationship with you.

Down here, it's not an us-or-them type situation. Like I think of Debi [a local reporter], and she lives here, she works here, she's trying to put a lifestyle together on the Lower Cape. In the last couple of years she's become a parent and dealt with all the issues around trying to be a working mom, and bringing her son to meetings on occasion with her backpack, and finding out that it's okay to do that, that he's welcome to come.

> *I mean, I think it goes back to that we really are all in it together. So how can I make things easier for her? "Sure, Hunter [her son] could come to this meeting. That's not a problem at all. He'd be welcome at this meeting." Or, "Can I provide you with babysitting?" I've even been known to offer it. She hasn't taken me up on it yet, but I've been known to offer it. . . .*

This speaker comes from a relatively rural area. Would the same principles apply in the big city? Maybe not quite in the same way or to the same degree, but we think the basic answer is yes. To restate the question: How do you go about building these relationships? The wide-scope answer is that it's not about writing a press release or a public service announcement. In a larger way, it's how you act every day, and, as we discussed in the leadership chapter, who you are as a person. Or to put it another way, publicity is in everything you do:

> *I think what I've been learning over the last year is that everything you do is an opportunity for publicity. And that doesn't mean that I get it done at every event that comes along. But it's just keeping your name out there as far as the coalition is concerned, and who we are and what we do. I think we've come to the point now where you just say "the coalition," and people sort of know who it is and what it is. You just keep putting your name out.*
>
> *If we go the store, we might be recognized. Our community is small. So we often meet people in stores who are either clerking or being waited on who know us and know the coalition. When they see me, they have thought "coalition." After all, we've been here how many years?*

The role of personal connectedness. But this leads back to the broader issue of how publicity happens at all. Our suggestion is that good publicity is not simply giving away brochures at an event, but rather being connected to the event in a more personal way, with your self. And this concluding story, which builds momentum as it goes along, is a good illustration:

> *The one health fair we did at Durfee High School is on my list of supreme failures. It was an attempt to get everyone together and do a dog-and-pony show on their own particular kinds of services. The chairperson wanted to make it a big event. A few of us said, "Well, we can do this," but we knew what it would be like. Sure enough, the average Joe Public doesn't come out to a health fair to pick up a bunch of brochures and talk to people working in human service organizations. Come on, give me a break.*
>
> *On the other hand, the community policing event in New Bedford was basically a fair for neighborhood folks. It was neat. It was fun. There were a lot of kids doing a talent show kind of thing, and a community police basketball game. One of the comments from one of the kids was, "I haven't had*

this much fun anytime." They had a barbecue and the whole thing went on all day. It was just a good time.

Food, definitely. Food and entertainment. And the focus was "Let's get together and enjoy one another, okay?" And then along the parking lot were the usual dozen or so tables with the human service brochures. I hope I wasn't too obnoxious, but I was basically saying, "Hey, there's nobody picking anything up, you know?"

Or, "Why are we doing this?" People are obviously here for fun, and if you think they're going to walk over to a table. . . .

We drag all this stuff out and we sit here all day and nobody wants to look. We've got to figure out a different way of doing this. Well, maybe we should do like the old cigarette girl thing, or have a clown outfit and go around and hand stuff out to people. . . .

Brochures are for people who work at other agencies. That's what they're for. I would tell the people in the human service agencies, first of all, don't come as if you're coming to work. Come and grab an edge of the parachute and have a good time. Or get up on stage.

I don't even know if you promote your message. I mean, sponsor the event maybe, or something of that sort. But I get really annoyed with the way we try to force our stuff on people. We ought to work out of a whole context in which people do enjoy getting together, do know one another, do like being together. If you can use federal dollars for hot dogs and hamburgers, it's money well spent. This is the kind of stuff that needs to be part and parcel of what we do. We don't do nearly enough of it.

The hell with the message. You promote a process. This is the Mount Pleasant neighborhood, it's half housing project folks. There isn't anything like the fair that most of these kids go to all year long. The community policing coalition comes out—it just happens to have that particular name, but it's a coalition—they do four or five events over the year, and that is the social life of that community.

If I asked any of the kids there what community policing is, I don't know if I'd get a clear answer from anybody, and I don't know how much difference it makes. The fact that this guy who happens to be a police officer, but he's not wearing a uniform, knows these kids because he plays basketball with them every Friday afternoon—I mean, isn't there intrinsic value in that, and do you have to go beyond that to say you've done something? I have a hard time with it.

But anyway, brochures definitely are out. It just makes us look really awkward, I think, and ties us up. I mean, for God's sake, don't sit behind a table. Let the brochures blow away and get to know somebody there.

The speaker has a point: His comments are a strong corrective. Publicity and outreach rest on human connection. You can't just throw words on the wall, or in the air, and think you've done your job. Fertile ground must be cultivated; so must your audience. Unless it is, your wonderful but depersonalized words have about the same chances as a telemarketer on the phone: slim to none. They won't penetrate. A basic principle of psychology is that people are most influenced by those they know, like, and trust. The development of relationships is fundamental.

That said, don't let the brochures blow away. Our view is more eclectic. Brochures, flyers, and their print siblings and electronic cousins, should not be so easily dislodged. Few of us can spend the whole day doing publicity, nor would we want to. Brochures and their like are your stand-ins, much as books are for in-person storytellers. They can be perused at home, at leisure, at any time or place, and kept for future reference. And they can supplement memory; for unlike a person, a brochure never forgets.

The community world is complex and multi-dimensional. One's outreach approach should match that dimensionality. The personal and the less personal can be combined. A planned publicity strategy, with thoughtful identification of your target audience, with multiple ways of reaching them, carried out by as many as possible, and evaluated as part of an ongoing effort — that is the core of an outreach effort that will best publicize your coalition's activities and help you achieve your coalition and community goals.

Lessons From The Field

Before You Start . . .

- Ask what you would like to accomplish with your publicity and outreach. What are your overall goals? What do you want to see happen?
- Take stock of what publicity and outreach your coalition is doing now. Make a list. How does your stock-taking match up with your overall goals? And how effective has it been in meeting them?
- Decide if more publicity needs to be done. Maybe your answer to that question is "no"; but if the answer is "yes," see if you can:
- Create a publicity plan. Who do you want to reach? How can they be reached? What resources (people, money, time) do you have to reach them? Creating a real plan—even a scratchy draft to start with, but on paper—is time well spent.
- Check your plan with others in the coalition—a publicity committee, if you have one, or members you corral. But some others in any case, unless you are firmly committed to going it alone.

The Principles Behind Your Message

There is a large and expanding number of competitors for your audience's attention. This means that any publicity you present should:

- Be tailored to your particular target group. Who are they? What values and beliefs do they hold? And how can your message be shaped to resonate with those values and beliefs?
- Be credible. Your message will be considerably more effective if it is presented (or endorsed) by someone your audience knows, likes, and respects.
- Capture attention. Messages that attract attention tend to be novel, vivid, colorful, surprising, and different from what's been seen or heard before. And the value of symbols, logos, and catchy slogans should not be underestimated.
- Offer a clear benefit, ideally more than one. Understand what benefits your particular audience most values; then do your best to offer them.
- Request a specific action. Almost every time, you want your audience to *do* something with the information given to them. Make it easier for them. *Tell* them what you want them to do, explicitly and specifically, and make it as easy as possible for them to take that action.

Strategies for Getting Your Message Across

- What methods should you choose? A simple two-part answer is: a) it depends on the people you are trying to reach and b) you needn't rely on one method alone.

Your coalition's outreach methods, accordingly, should usually be planned and diversified. Give your audience many and varied chances to know about you.

■ Publicity should be directed to where people are likely to receive information. A great message is totally useless if no one is around to see it or hear it. Learn where your audience can be found and reached; reach them there.

■ The more personalized the publicity, the more effective you will be. Face-to-face communication is definitely the best.

■ Publicity is also more effective when you enlist the support of opinion leaders in the community and the institutions they represent. If they will actively broadcast the message, so much the better. Their participation will tend to strengthen their commitment to your cause.

■ Publicity is more cost-effective as well when you can link it to something that someone else is already doing. Look for opportunities to piggyback onto an existing event.

■ Publicity, positive or negative, also takes place through everyday actions that are not directly intended to publicize. Others will inevitably make judgments about your work by how you say hello, or answer the phone. In other words, continuous opportunities for publicizing exist, to the extent you want to take advantage of them.

■ Since impressions are always being made, everyone in your coalition can make them. Everyone in your coalition can and should be an ambassador for the work you do, publicizing the coalition indirectly through their personality and character.

When the Message Has Been Delivered

■ Repeat the message. Your message may not sink in the first time around; even if it does, it needs to be reinforced. Repetition strengthens comprehension and the likelihood of favorable action.

■ Evaluate its effects. Who came to the event? How many contributed? Who requested more information? How many signed up to help? Keep records. Then look at those records, and make a truthful judgment if you are getting the results you want. Adjust your publicity efforts accordingly.

■ Create a structure in your coalition so that publicity efforts continue—a formal committee, an informal work group, or one designated person if need be. Publicity is not a one-time effort; it will *always* be needed, since the scene always changes. If you've got that structure the next time around, you won't need to begin again from scratch.

COASTAL VILLAGE FISHING FESTIVAL

A Celebration of Our Fishing Heritage

<u>Admission Buttons</u>
$5 prior to event
$7 at the gate
Kids under 8 free

<u>Local Outlets</u>
CCB&Ts (Including Stop & Shop branches), Chocolate Sparrow, Puritan Clothing, Selected Retail Outlets

TUESDAY, AUGUST 27 in WELLFLEET

10 am-6pm   *at*   *Baker's Field*

<u>FISHING ARTS DEMOS</u>
Trap Building, Net Mending, Fly Tying, Lobstering, How to: Clean Fish, Surf Cast, Shellfish...

<u>FOOD & SEAFOOD</u>
Chowder, Stuffed Clams, Clam Pie, Raw Bar, Hot Dogs, Linguica, Portuguese Pastries, Fruit Salad...

<u>ARTS/CRAFTS/GIFTS</u>
Paintings, Mask-making, Pottery, T-shirts, Photos, Jewelry, Prints, Carvings, Stationery, Caricatures...

<u>FOR THE KIDS</u>
Fish Tales-stories by and about Fishermen, Fish Prints, Chorus, Tank of Fish, Readings by Authors...

7:30 - 10 pm   *at*   *Town Pier*

Listen, Sing, Dance along with the likes of

Cape Cod Fiddlers & Toi and the Verdatones

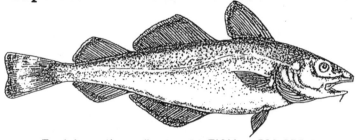

For information call 800 656-FISH or 508 255-2163

Alternate Rain Site: WELLFLEET METHODIST CHURCH
Main Street, Wellfleet

SPONSORED BY AND FOR THE LOWER/OUTER CAPE COMMUNITY COALITION

Publicizing your coalition's work (as vs. leading the coalition, in Chapter 6) lends itself easily to print. On the next pages are five publicity samples from coalitions we have encountered.

In each example, the primary goal is to draw a crowd. And to do that, note again the linkages to food, to festivity, to cultural heritage, to the arts, to entertainment, to acquiring useful information, to plain-and-simple fun, or to more than one of the above. When these benefits are clearly perceived by your target audience, that's what gets them out and about.

ARTS in the community

A County-Wide Gathering
to explore the role of the arts in community life

Thursday, May 1, 1997
6:00 p.m. - 8:00 p.m.

FREE and open to everyone

Reservations Requested by 4/25/97

FOOD provided

at the

Appalachian Bean Cafe
67 Main St., North Adams

An opportunity to meet people, become involved and share ideas

To reserve a place or for more information call:

| Berkshire Prevention Alliance (413) 448-2276 | *or* | Northern Berkshire Community Coalition (413) 662-5519 |

華埠社區聯盟
THE CHINATOWN COALITION
of the
HEALTHY BOSTON INITIATIVE

Invites You To An   誠意邀請閣下參加

經濟發展研討會
ECONOMIC TOWN MEETING

Learn more about the City of Boston's Enhanced Enterprise Community Grant, the Boston Empowerment Center and the financial resources available to community businesses.

來認識有關波士頓市政府提高社區企業活動基金，波士頓強化社區居民中心及向社區內商戶提供貸款的資源。

Date: Saturday, September 30, 1995

Time: 10:00 am - 1:00 pm

Place: Asian Community Development Corporation

888 Washinton Street

Translation will be available
現場提供翻譯服務

For more information please contact Beverly Wing at 357-7079
詳情請電梅雪嫻女士，電話：357-7079

THE FALL RIVER HEALTH & HUMAN SERVICES COALTION
INVITES YOU TO PARTICIPATE IN

RICE & BEANS

A CROSS-CULTURAL DIVERSITY & COMPETENCE PROGRAM

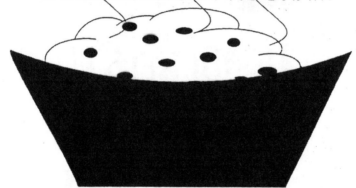

FRIDAY, NOVEMBER 5TH, 9:30am-4:00pm
Stanley Street Treatment & Resources
386 Stanley Street, Fall River

Everyone must eat to maintain their health. People of diverse cultures have diverse tastes. Feeding information to an individual or communicating with an ethnic community is most effective if easily digested. We have learned that culturally appropriate and linguistically competent programs and materials serve well the population it is meant for.

RICE & BEANS, the Multicultural AIDS Coalition's Cross-Cultural Curriculum, is named that way because rice and beans are a basic food staple to most of our world's cultures. There are as many diverse ways to season and cook rice and beans as there are to develop and sustain relationships. Our curriculum shows us how much cultures have in common, and how much variety there can be at the same time.

OPEN TO ANY STAFF OF FALL RIVER HEALTH AND HUMAN SERVICES COALITION MEMBER AGENCIES

**$5.00 COST INCLUDES LUNCH!
REGISTER BY OCT. 22ND**

FOR REGISTRATION INFORMATION, CALL DON SINGEWALD @ 672-2537

FITCHBURG, MASSACHUSETTS
ALL AMERICA CITY PRESENTATION   JUNE 23, 1995
****

(VIDEO SCRIPT)

Wife: Hey! Look! Fitchburg, Massachusetts has a page on the Internet. Didn't you live in Fitchburg.

Husband: Yeah, I was there in 1991. It was like the City was shutting down. The Civic Center was closed, the Planetarium was closed, Coggshall Park had closed for renovations and the City pools were closed and the City didn't even have money for summer recreation programs. Main Street was dying, Gangs were organizing, drive by shootings were common place, a couple of students had brought guns to school for protection and the neighborhoods were filled with drugs and prostitution.

Wife: According to the Internet page, Fitchburg is a 1995 All America City Finalist. Hear what is happening in Fitchburg today.

****

(LIVE PRESENTATION)

Lauren -McNamara,   Vice President Wallace Civic Center and Planetarium
                        Owner, Almac Home Improvement

As a Trustee of the Wallace Civic Center and Planetarium, I am here to tell you about a valuable city asset brought back and maintained by the efforts of our citizens. After years of operating in the red with no public funding for upkeep or capital improvements, this city owned facility had to close its doors. Only through the hard work of many volunteers - young and old, rich and poor - and the generous contributions of local businesses is the center open today. Not only open but flourishing as we now host concerts featuring national acts, circuses, festival, summer camps, skating shows and are home to over 100 hockey teams. Since re-opening last September, the Planetarium has hosted over 6,000 visitors and has become a Science
and Math Learning Center for area teachers.

Elizabeth Watson   Member, Friends of Coggshall
                        Director, Fitchburg Public Library

I am one of over 400 Friends of Coggshall Park and am proud of the renovation of our "crown jewel" 263 acre park. We received a federal grant to complete a facelift and are now determined not to let our park fall into disrepair again. Our group raises funds to maintain the park and provide programs. We run a concert series on Sunday afternoons during the summer. We brought back to Mirror Lake the traditional swans in summer and public ice skating in winter.

Lee Andujar   Member, Fitchburg First
                    Parent Coordinator, MOC - Head Start Program

Fitchburg First works with the neighborhood associations, businesses and individuals to clean and beautify our city. Each spring a clean up effort is held in 7 neighborhoods. Nearly 1,000 people participate over a 6 week period. We encourage and facilitate businesses to enhance our city with flowering traffic islands. 32 Islands are maintained weekly by an army of volunteers.

Three other examples of promoting coalition work: An excerpt from the script of a coalition video.

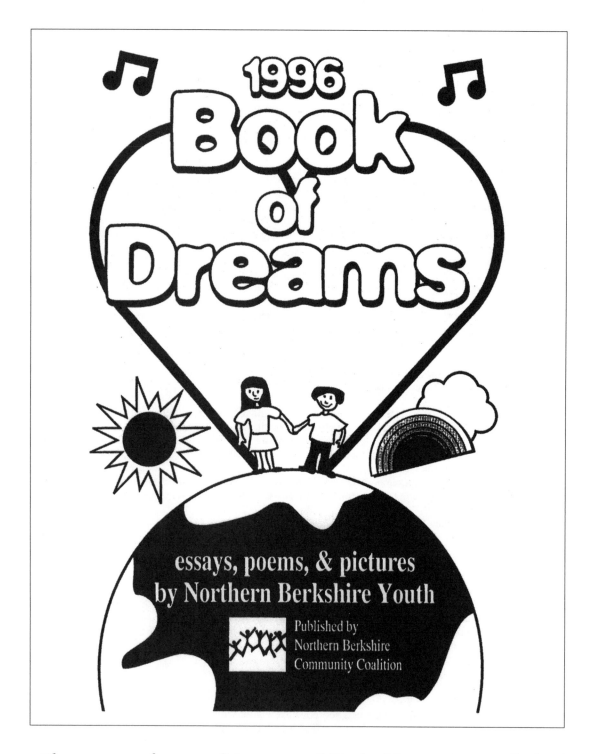

...The cover page from a coalition-sponsored "Book of Dreams," written by local youth and focusing on anti-violence themes. A related version of this booklet was published in a newspaper supplement and reached 12,000 households.

Craig F. Walker / Berkshire Eagle Staff

Jennifer LaPine stands in front of the billboard she designed for a contest sponsored by the Northern Berkshire Health and Human Services Coalition.

Getting a message across
8th grader's dream of peace captured on sign

By Linda Burchard
Berkshire Eagle Staff

NORTH ADAMS — Jennifer LaPine, an 8th grader at Conte Middle School, not only has a dream, she has a message, and it is emblazoned on a billboard for motorists to read as they approach the city on State Road.

Jennifer's drawing shows two youngsters holding hands, with another billboard in the background showing the earth and the message: "Let's Make Peace in Our Community."

It was chosen from among some 250 entries, including essays and poems, created by city schoolchildren expressing their dreams for the community. The "I Have a Dream" contest was sponsored by the Northern Berkshire Health and Human Services Coalition in January.

Accolades from mayor

This week, Jennifer received congratulations from Mayor John Barrett III. She was accompanied by Conte Principal Joseph Rogge and Sister

Natalie Cain, director of Northern Berkshire Neighbors, a community organization.

Said Rogge, "I'm very proud of this lady, and of a lot of kids. We had 20 to 25 kids who participated."

Coalition coordinator Alan Bashevkin said Jennifer's drawing is the first of seven that will be displayed on billboards donated by Callahan Outdoor Advertising through December in North Berkshire.

Jennifer's is the first, said Bashev-

BILLBOARD, continued on B4

…And a similar peace message on a billboard on a major state highway. The coalition sponsored the "dream of peace" concept and secured the billboard donation.

Marketing Your Consortium: A Self-Assessment

Here's a way to help you think about marketing and promotion efforts in your own consortium. What are you doing now? And how does this stack up against what you think you could and should be doing?

For each activity below, place a check if you have done it within your own consortium in the past 12 months. And if you haven't done it, would it be a good idea?

	YES; we've done this	NO, we haven't. Would it be good if we did?		
		I think so	I'm not sure	This isn't for us
1. Published a press release	____	____	____	____
2. Written a letter to the editor	____	____	____	____
3. Been featured in the newspaper	____	____	____	____
4. Written a radio or TV spot	____	____	____	____
5. Been on a radio or TV show	____	____	____	____
6. Updated your media list	____	____	____	____
7. Given a talk at a school	____	____	____	____
8. Given a talk to a community group	____	____	____	____
9. Met with your local or state officials	____	____	____	____
10. Held a special event (any kind)	____	____	____	____

Finally, what do you think about these summary questions below?

On a scale of 1-10, where 1= lowest and 10 = highest, how much marketing and promotion do you think your consortium is doing now? _____

And on that same scale, how much do you feel that it might be doing? _____

Thanks for your feedback! Let's use the results to stimulate discussion and possibly action.

Publicity, like almost all coalition activities, takes planning. This is a short form that can be used to diagnose your coalition's current promotional efforts and to plan new ones.

Chapter 8

Funding The Coalition

> *Does your coalition really need money at all?*
>
> *How should that money best be spent?*
>
> *Where's the best place to find money, if you need it?*
>
> *What traps should you watch out for?*

Is Funding Really Needed?

Most discussions of funding and coalitions assume that funding is necessary for the coalition to prosper—that the one is needed for the other. But let's start this chapter by challenging that assumption, and asking a different question: "Is funding really needed for coalition development?" Think about it:

> *If a group of people gets together, I think the first questions I would ask them are "What it is you want to accomplish?" "Why do you need to accomplish that?" and "Which of those things can you get pro bono or donated in kind, and which do you really need money for?"*

Consider this argument: Maybe money is not a firm requirement. Think, for example, of crime watches or other neighborhood groups; they can function very effectively with just occasional meetings and many pairs of eyes. Okay, then—why are we concerned about funding at all? To some degree, and somewhat paradoxically, because funders themselves have set that agenda. Coalitions, many believe, are not only successful but also economical. As government and foundations began to notice the success of coalitions, they also began to offer funding for projects, with coalitions being required for that funding.

Here's another analysis of the money vs. no-money difference:

> *Many coalitions start because a group of people passionately cares about something and says, "Let's do it." Money is not the issue, because things will be run by volunteers. These coalitions are like other grassroots organizations. They get going on their own, without dollars, and in truth many of them don't go looking for money at all.*
>
> *A lot of the coalitions we see around here, though, are groups of people who are responding to a funding request. They have been stimulated either by foundations, or more likely by government funding, and therefore they start up with someone giving them money or staffing to address a specific issue—HIV, teen pregnancy, substance abuse.*
>
> *So you can get going either way. When you start from passion, it's not like you're sitting around saying, "Let's create a coalition, and now how do we get money for the core staffing?" When money does come up at the start, it's usually because someone else has put forth a Request for Proposals, offering dollars to some coalition that hasn't started yet.*

It is interesting to compare coalitions that were started by grassroots groups, without a budget, to coalitions that started around a specific funding source. In grassroots coalitions, whatever their issues, we usually sense genuine community interest at the outset, despite the lack of money. In contrast, among coalitions drawn together by dollars, we do not necessarily feel the same level of community involvement. On the other hand, they've got money in the bank.

Which works better? In our experience, we have seen the full resource spectrum, ranging from coalitions that are virtually penniless, to those with modest resources, to those with six-figure budgets and up. And in all these categories, we have seen successful and unsuccessful coalitions. Some community coalitions have been highly successful with virtually no funding; some very well-funded coalitions (one might suggest too well-funded) have failed. Money by itself is not the formula for success, even though without that formula the coalition might be poorly nourished.

Put it another way—the presence and the degree of funding, and the way in which decisions about funding are made, create very different sorts of organizations. So is funding always required for coalitions? If so, how much? What should that funding be used for? And what are the problems and dilemmas that funding may create? One goal of this chapter is to explore these questions in greater depth, so that you can gain a better understanding of the proper role of funding for your own coalition.

Funding for What?

One lesson up front: Before your coalition goes looking for money, it should decide—

clearly, thoughtfully, and in advance—what it wants to do with it. This brings us to the question of "funding for what"? To paraphrase, if coalitions can exist on volunteer effort, why add dollars, and for what purpose? Here are some possible answers:

Core expenses. Because some money makes coalition life easier. There are things good will can't buy. The phone company or the post office, sad to say, will not do business on a smile and a promise. At the minimum, you might want a little bit of money for expenses you would otherwise pay out of pocket, or for unforeseen yet half-expected contingencies. If you're serving coffee, coffee beans add up. If you're mailing newsletters, even in bulk, that adds up even more. These are your core operating expenses.

> *We certainly need a pot of money to function. That allows us the flexibility to take care of the immediate issues that come up. If I didn't have a checkbook so that I could write a check for a parent, so they could pay child care for their kid, so they could come to a meeting. . . . You know, we have to have that to be an effective coalition.*

* * *

> *You have to have that little pool of money. You are a coalition. You have to provide coffee, you have to have pastries. You have to fund the doings of an office. A heavy, heavy burden of this office is postage. Heaven knows, when you have a mailing list of almost 400 people for a newsletter that goes out monthly, it is expensive.*

Even those groups closest to the grassroots can profit from a little bit of funding. Without any money at all, it's hard to do substantive community work that goes beyond getting together to swap stories. And even that much can be hard to sustain:

> *Often we see unfunded groups such as human service councils successfully gather together and exchange information on a regular basis. The downside of these unfunded groups is often their inability to do any kind of collaborative problem solving. And over time they can really burn out, because they don't do anything but exchange information.*

Staffing. Coalitions can also use funding because it helps pay for core staffing. One of the primary coalition lessons we have learned is that most coalitions function better when they have a designated staff person they can rely upon, even if that staff person works part-time and is very modestly paid. Even a small amount of staffing serves to catalyze the coalition and the community, and that is one of staffing's main functions.

I have worked with health and human service coalitions that with volunteer leadership can get one or two tasks done well in a year; but if you give them part-time staffing or more, they can really increase their productivity enormously, for what is essentially a very small investment. What you are doing is supporting the catalyst function of a coalition. So putting some money into part-time staff has been our core model, and it is one I like a lot.

* * *

I think you've got to hire administrative support first and foremost, because if you have to do the big-time thinking and then carry everything through right down to licking the stamps, you're going to be fried.

. . . Even though money for coalition staffing is not necessarily easy to shake loose.

Money for staffing is real hard money to find. I think it is one of the tragedies of the system. A good coalition playing a catalyst role for the community is worth a fortune, but it is one of the toughest things to fund. No matter how good the track record—and I think we have some coalitions with extremely impressive track records—getting someone to give you, let's say $25,000, some core money, to keep a part-time staff person going, and the newsletter, stuff like that—it is just a killer.

Projects. Staffing may be desired, even if not required. Yet the money you put into staffing could also go into projects, or "real coalition work." These two functions may compete. Many coalitions struggle with choosing between dollars for projects and dollars for staffing, or dollars for core coalition functions. And their resolutions are not always uniform. Here, for example, one coalition leader speaks quite eloquently about the dangers and conflicts of project money:

. . . Because that kind of money will drive you. Very few foundations will fund just the operating support, but that is what you really need. You don't need project money. The project money distracts you. It will stretch whatever resources you have to implement that project. If it brings in new monies, how much could you allocate to the overall coalition operating support? It is just another set of activities that generates more work and more responsibility.

For example, when everybody sees community benefits from the hospital as being the new cash cow, well, the hospital is going to want a health focus. That is not necessarily a conflict for us, because we want better health care and better health services, but it's just that it wasn't necessarily our first priority.

And yet, for the same leader, money talks:

> *We are going to do it [adopt a health emphasis] because the opportunity presents itself. There is some money attached to it, so we know we have to shift our focus. It is very hard then not to do that, not to let that happen, because we need a certain amount of funding to sustain ourselves. You can get more money for projects—that is the easy money to get. The operating support is the hardest to get because it is not concrete. People like something flashy, funders like flashy stuff. . . .*

Still, in other coalitions, dollars have been used happily and unequivocally to support local community programs. There may be nondistracting and noncompromising ways of doing this. One intriguing solution is simply to give the project money away, through mini-grants:

> *Our coalition has used money to stimulate natural neighborhood initiatives through the use of mini-grants. We put out small amounts of dollars to see who in the community could use $200 to $500 to do a campaign on anti-smoking, seat belts, teen drinking, whatever the cause. This brings in lots and lots of natural community helpers and gives them access to resources they wouldn't otherwise know about. That is a very exciting use of dollars.*

And one particularly promising variation of mini-grants we have seen is to reward neighbors financially for completing a neighborhood leadership training program. Neighbors enroll as a group; if they complete the six-week program together, they get a $300 stipend for a neighborhood project of their choosing. (*See Documents section.*) Worth a try?

Money for basic requirements, for staffing, or for programs? Different coalitions will have different answers, and the same coalition may have different answers at different stages in time. The key point is to reflect and keep reflecting, fully and deeply, about what you need and why you need it.

> *You have to think about it now. You should think about what it is that the coalition needs, short-term and long-term. Your current funding is going to run out, and this is a good opportunity to think about all your possible options—not just the one that you think is ideal.*

Where to Find the Dollars

This is, of course, the million dollar question—well, perhaps the $50,000 question. Our strong belief, borne out in practice, is that the money you may need is ultimately out there. It will not fly into your bank account automatically. It must be sought after, meaning that someone must want to seek it and then do the seeking. Nor is it

141

as simple as "Seek and ye shall find"; it's more like "Seek, and your probability of success will increase significantly."

It is true that funding for coalitions may be tougher to find than funding for an immediate, vivid, and compelling need. If, for example, domestic violence (or child abuse, or youth crime) in a community is rising off the charts, funders will pay attention. They have been educated on the issue; it also touches emotions. These same funders may be less eager to support "coordination" or "collaboration" (a process, not an issue) with real dollars, even though they are believers in principle. Those words seem fuzzier; perhaps they are.

To win the funders over, the coalition somewhere must produce, or at least project, results; all this coordination, collaboration, and communication must lead to something you can point to. That sharpens the focus. And such pointing is possible; funders' hearts have been won. So let's review some funding sources that existing coalitions have used successfully, and then move on to some broader issues that are likely to surface.

Local fund-raising. You can raise money locally, in your own community. A few years ago, residents in a Southern California community faced a possible take-over of park land by a housing developer. They raised $2.5 million in six weeks to buy the property themselves. The annual Walk for Hunger in Boston has repeatedly raised $3 million in one single day. Coalitions don't normally shoot for the moon, but they can soar above the clouds.

Many easily obtainable books will spell out fund-raising details, and a common point among them is that fund-raising is largely a matter of expectation. If you want to do it, and think you can do it, you are well on your way.

> *Any time we needed money to do something, we would just put out a call and we would raise it. We would raise it through the business community, sometimes through bankers, and sometimes the [local] Health Alliance. With Pledge for Peace, we needed $2,500, so I called up the Health Alliance and said I need $2,500, and they gave it to me.*
>
> *So we fund-raise, and we are successful at fund-raising around individual events. The $30,000 we needed for a health study was fund-raised. It was local money. The $50,000 that we are raising for the business plan for the community health center is all locally raised money. . . .*
>
> *But, I mean, I am not a really good fund-raiser. . . .*

We wonder what would happen if this speaker *were* really good. But in fact, this coalition leader does not sit at home and wait for the phone to ring. It takes work. And (once again) it takes relationships.

> *It wasn't quite that easy. I got turned down by several people before I got to the ones that said "fine." I have a personal relationship with them. . . .*

In-kind support. What you can't raise directly, you might be able to get donated. The best strategy, of course, is to be proactive: You need to want the support, you need to know where to look, and you need to do the looking. Sometimes, not always, there are organizations in the community willing to be more helpful than you might ever have imagined. A local college, for example:

> *At the very beginning, the coalition asked, "Can anyone house us?" And one of the early members was a state college professor. He said, "Well, let's see what we can do with the college." So the college from the beginning has donated space, mailing privileges, copying privileges, phone privileges to us. Enormous support. And it's worked very well for them, too. Finding that kind of local sponsor is real helpful.*

Or, among other sponsors we know, there's a visiting nurse association and a chamber of commerce. And one coalition leader is not only based at the local anti-poverty agency, but also gets part-time pay from them to coordinate the coalition. That arrangement has worked well, even though it could be unstable down the road:

> *If you totaled in all the mailings and everything else in addition to half my time, the Opportunity Council probably has a $35,000 annual commitment to the coalition. Because the Council has done it for three or four years now, people expect it to continue. But it's unfair for them to be in a position of coming up with that money year-in and year-out.*

Point well taken. So you might combine local fund-raising and in-kind support with other sources—such as:

The private sector. You can reach out to the private sector. Sometimes the private-sector leadership is approachable and local, which is to your advantage. But sometimes that leadership represents large and possibly distant companies, while you are just a small hometown coalition. What if you don't have the private-sector connections?

Then you go to someone who does, leverage that person's influence, and hang on real tight. The coattails (or robe) in this coalition's story belong to an unlikely sounding, though previously mentioned, source:

> *How do I get businessmen whose time is valuable into a room to raise $150,000 to get a certain thing done? You get someone like the Cardinal, who is very powerful, to call a group of businessmen whose banks hold some of the Archdiocese's money, right?*
> *. . . going to a meeting with the Cardinal, and a bunch of businessmen. We've got to raise some money. We start at 8:00, we go upstairs at 8:30, and at 8:35 we're down and dirty, we start looking for checks. By 8:50 we've got them, and by 8:55 we are out the door.*

> *You get the commitments and you raise the money. Oh, yeah, I mean, it is a sort of dog-and-pony show, but the Cardinal is the Godfather. He cuts the deals. So it is a power-brokering kind of meeting, lots of navy blue suits and, like I have said, in 20 minutes we have $150,000.*
>
> *It may sound easy, but there was a lot of work that went into that. I mean if we didn't have a real program, you can believe that the Cardinal would not be doing this.*

Not only does it have to be a real program, but you have to have some real bravado to knock on the Cardinal's door. But the Cardinal, among other things, is a man of the world. As our narrator says, "The Cardinal knows how to get things done."

Foundations. Another source coalitions often turn to is foundations, sometimes national, but more frequently local. Many communities have some community foundation or local trust whose funds must be spent locally. So you make your contacts, you use your connections, and if that doesn't work the first time, (no brilliant technique here) you simply try again.

> *In our town, there was a foundation that was designated to serve the community. When our coalition started, we quickly wrote them an application, and just as quickly we got a "No, thank you" in return. But then six or seven years later, they had a new fund manager who came to a coalition meeting and was blown away to see 30 people at a meeting who were working together, who knew each other, who collaborated, who exchanged information, and who actually liked each other.*
>
> *This foundation had usually designated $80,000 a year for our geographic area, which they usually gave in small amounts, $3,000 to $5,000. But their board was beginning to feel that this was just doing bandage work, and not making a major difference, so they offered us this opportunity. They suggested that the foundation would be willing to look at providing a large amount of money to our coalition. They said, "What would you do if we offered you a large amount of money? What would be your project?"*
>
> *So our coalition did some problem solving about what we wanted to really focus on, and we proposed to the foundation that we do a four-year program on grassroots child abuse prevention, with a real community development component. And they bought it. They provided the coalition with $240,000 over four years. It was very exciting, and it was nothing that we could have predicted. It was just the result of our good work over time.*

By the way, if a coalition is thinking about foundation support, it can broaden its horizons and think big time. Maybe not for right now, and maybe never; but not to rule out the option, and just possibly to exercise it later:

> *. . . I mean, it'll take a couple of million bucks to do the work. So I'm fly-ing down to Philadelphia to meet with some folk from the Heinz Foundation. And somebody connected with Arianna Huffington; she's got 150 million bucks and she wants to move some of it around.*
>
> *The money's out there, if you've got the programming and you do the politicking. You've got to do all the networking. You've got to do all of it. It takes a lot of work.*

Legislators. If a coalition has done a good job of engaging its legislators—local, state, or federal—then these elected officials are also a potential funding source.

> *In the very beginning, what we did is we went to our state legislators— they had been the ones who invited us into the communities to help start these coalitions. So because the time was politically right, we suggested to them that they put a certain amount of money into a state account that would fund the coalitions. And they did it. That baseline of $70,000 per year has been the core funding for three of our coalitions for a decade.*

This point is worth highlighting: It is possible to work through your legislators to get public funding for your coalition on an annual and regular basis. If your work is deserving, it may legitimately be deserving of public support. (In fact, after this inter-view took place, these same coalitions were successful in getting an even larger amount of money placed into the state budget, targeted for them.) It can be done, and it has been done. That certainly gives coalitions one less thing to worry about. (*For more details on how to do this, see Chapter 9, on Coalition Advocacy.*)

Grants and contracts. You can write grants: a huge topic in itself, but quite defi-nitely a learnable ability. You can start small and learn on the job:

> *We have written grants—well, the radio program was one. We had to write a grant to staff it. So now we have a weekly radio program called "Getting to Know Our Health." Basically, we have an invited guest who talks on a certain topic, say, substance abuse.*
>
> *One of the radio grants was written by a graduate student. We told her what to do and she learned through it. She had a project where she learned the process of grant writing, and as a result we got a product.*

Another bright note is that many public grants, as well as contracts, are announced around a specific initiative. That is, a funding source may put out a call for proposals in violence prevention, or tobacco cessation, or peer mediation, to name some areas. If your coalition is working in these areas (or has a serious and credible interest in doing so), you can respond to such announcements, which might fortunately be tar-geted toward what you already do.

Then, once you've gotten a taste of success, you can aim higher. If you want, a lot higher:

> *We do grant writing to everywhere, foundations, the Feds. We actually have a pretty good track record. We are a $1.7-million operation right now, and we are on target for the next couple of fiscal years. Money is a major issue if we start talking more long-term, but in the short-term we are doing okay.*

Not bad for this coalition, which not so long ago wasn't even a gleam in the eye.

Membership dues. But grant writing is an acquired skill and an acquired preference. If for whatever reason you would rather not reach outside the community, and if formal fund-raising is not your style, you can always look toward dues. (*See also Chapter 3.*)

The key advantages:
- Dues are usually simpler to generate.
- Because they come from your own members, dues test commitment to the coalition.
- Membership dues increase coalition self-reliance.

The main drawbacks:
- As a rule, dues yield less money than outside sources (though you may not need more).
- Sometimes people simply cannot afford to pay enough dues to make collecting them worth your while.
- Dues may make money a condition of membership, which may be contrary to your original intent:

> *People don't pay dues or anything like that. We didn't want them, and we feel we don't want them now. We don't want to close the door by setting up dues, or criteria as to what makes you a member.*
>
> *A fee structure would be a lot of money for some of the people in our group. It would be a lot. That would eliminate our coalition real fast. I mean, we were talking about having a Christmas party, and it was $25 per person, and people were saying, "We really can't make that."*

Some coalitions get around this point by calling dues "donations" or "sponsorship fees"; a sliding scale can lighten the financial burden for some, as can having separate support expectations for organizations and single individuals. Though these strategies are imperfect, they make it easier for anybody who believes in the purpose of the coalition to become a member.

>Certainly we have always asked that communities generate some local fees. We have pushed hard for this not to be a membership fee, because we really believe that membership should be open to anyone who buys into the mission of the coalition. If the mission is to improve the quality of life, that generally means most people in the community.
>
>So you do want to have supporters of the coalition, but you don't want to exclude anybody based on dollars. We have seen communities raise up to $3-, $4-, or $5,000 per year by generating dollars from supporters. One coalition has a donation envelope they pass around at coalition meetings; or they send out letters. Others put requests in their newsletters. Even though that all comes to only a few thousand a year, it is very important money because it is local money.

"Creative techniques." The coalition leadership can choose among all these fund-raising alternatives. They're not mutually exclusive; they can be combined. *And more alternatives can always be created.* There are always new ways of doing business; that's the beauty of the work. Here's an example of one coalition that decided to distinguish between its "active members" and "passive supporters," and came up with a way of trying to enlist the latter:

>We are going to start a household affiliation campaign this winter. We have a subcommittee working on a household affiliation package. There will be 5,000 of them, ready for 5,000 households. In this package will be a variety of household products we think will be helpful, plus community information, a survey, a bumper sticker or window sticker, or a lapel pin—ways for people to say, "I am a passive participant in the coalition's efforts." The household package will have a sticker for your telephone with emergency numbers, and a refrigerator magnet that is also a towel holder. We also have a vial of life for elders that has a little logo on it somewhere.
>
>We are going to charge for the packets. We will go to the community and say, "If this is valuable, give us a $5 check." Our hope is that we can recoup our costs. Our steering committee said that $5 is important because then people are demonstrating support, and that if you just give the packets away, everyone will accept them, but it won't mean anything. So if 5,000 people pay $5, that is $25,000.
>
>One of the challenges that we have is identifying the passive support that is out there. And this is also a way for the family to step up. We are inviting them to do that, though we have never invited them in this way before.

To dream up a fund-raising and community building method like this, you've got to think creatively. But aren't we capable of one creative thought a year?

Two Questions to Resolve

1. Who is going to raise all this money?

If a coalition does decide it needs money, and what kind, and how much, the next questions that emerge are, "Who is going to take responsibility for raising that money?" and also "What will the costs of that effort be?" (in human energy, not in dollars).

> *Fund-raising is just something that I don't have the time to do, and do everything else I am doing. We don't have a mechanism in place either to do fund-raising on a local level or to seek out grants.*

For there are such costs. Coalitions can't afford professional fund-raisers. Unless there is specialized talent, nearby and on-call, the fund-raising responsibility is likely to fall on the coalition coordinator, or someone else in a leadership role. But when leaders spend time in raising money for the future, they take time from meeting needs in the present. That is, unless they choose to sleep less at night, which comes with costs of its own.

And even if you can find the dollars and live on less sleep, that's not the whole job. You've now got to handle the funds you have so successfully acquired. Life's little ironies: The price of financial success is that you have to manage your money. This is not always joyful work.

> *What do I do during the day? Actually, I find myself getting more into financial issues, and trying to track the finances, and sticking to a budget. I've got to know how much money we have, and what we need to spend to keep us going. I'm becoming a mini-administrator in that way.*

This particular coalition gives out mini-grants. Be assured they don't get granted by themselves:

> *We have given out over $22,000 in mini-grants, and I am the staff person to the mini-grant committee. I come in, and we look at the applications and make decisions, but I am the one that writes the letters and sends them out, and helps track the financing of the applications that we end up awarding. I need to be responsible for all these things.*

You can turn that money management over to a third party or lead agency, but that can have costs of its own.

> *When you run your dollars for a coalition through a big bureaucracy, the flexibility you need to do good local stuff virtually disappears. It becomes so harrowing to get reimbursed for your daycare expenses for a meeting. It requires forms in triplicate, and waiting six weeks to get reimbursed. When*

that happens, people either pay out of their pockets or they just don't do it. We need to have fiscal systems that are user-friendly for doing neighborhood and community coalition work.

Such user-friendly arrangements are worth finding, though not easily found. We do know of a few, and even of coalition leaders who have gone full-time into nonprofit fiscal management. This is an important and useful function—even though these people are no longer doing coalition work.

2. How much funding do you need?

We have argued that coalitions often need a certain amount of funding just to sustain their core functions of coordination, collaboration, and information exchange. The basics include money for duplicating, postage, supplies, and possibly rental of a meeting space. With a little more money, one can pay for part-time or full-time staff support, a model we favor. Such support can be secretarial, to do the clerical work that goes along with the coalition—mailings, minutes, and newsletters. Or it can also involve highly trained staff to assist with coalition planning, facilitation, mediation, and leadership.

But when do you stop? As we've seen, some coalitions go beyond the basics, and beyond staffing, and begin to seek funding for specific programs. The danger here is reaching too far too soon. We all know what happens when you fly too close to the sun.

We have moved quite a bit of money into the city, but we haven't figured out how money can come into the coalition without corrupting the process. . . .

* * *

I have watched a lot of coalitions go after huge chunks of money early in their development and then self-destruct. That happened with one small coalition. It was a brand new coalition. This was about big money, hundreds of thousands of dollars, and there were bitter, divisive battles, just a lot of real animosity and bitterness among people that used to be friends. And that is sad.

And over-reaching is not limited to the young and inexperienced:

. . . But I have also seen some groups that have been around for a while get a lot of money and burst into flames on a variety of levels.

You and your coalition may be mature enough not to crash and burn. A different danger, though, is losing your organizational soul. Coming into money can do strange things to people, no less to coalitions. It changes the organization; the coalition takes on a different persona.

149

> *We have also seen coalitions form around dollars and get large amounts of money, sometimes hundreds of thousands of dollars, sometimes millions, who begin to provide a wide variety of programs. Then they start to resemble large human service agencies, as opposed to organizations committed to increasing collaboration and coordination, which is the true function of a coalition. It gets hard to distinguish them from the next agency on the block.*

"So you have to be careful," this leader says. Yes, and highlight that last sentence. How much money? What is enough? As before, these are questions that every coalition must answer individually; and as before, the best answers will come from careful coalition planning.

And Two Dilemmas to Ponder

Dilemma #1: Competing with Your Own Members
- *On the one hand:* You need money to sustain the core work of the coalition.
- *On the other:* Your coalition members may themselves need money to sustain the core work of the services *they* deliver, in their non-coalition roles.

If available money is strictly, or even not-so-strictly, limited, the coalition then can wind up competing with its own members. This is not a pretty sight.

Suppose, for example, the coalition decides to hold a fund-raiser. Sounds harmless enough, until you think more clearly where the funds raised will come from:

> *Regarding our fund-raiser: Basically I think it puts us right into that same game with everybody else in town. It's another organization, another agency, that is coming to people asking them to put out money to do this or that. It is pretty much the same issue about being competitive with our membership again.*

Because of that competition, everyone can wind up spending so much time raising money that they have less time for doing coalition work, or service work in general:

> *The other piece of it is that all the members of the coalition are involved in one way or another with fund-raisers in their own agency, and it is taking up a lot of their time. Every one of these groups are into this constant local fund-raising—and it is easier for them than for a coalition to do that kind of thing. They have volunteers, too. . . .*

And the community's pockets go only so deep:

> *Everybody is having fund-raisers. So what do we tell our people? Do we just say, "Well, put this money into this pocket, and next month take it out from your other pocket?" I am not averse to doing this, but sometimes we don't know when the pockets are going to get empty, or if people are going to feel like they can't keep giving.*

In the long run, it doesn't work for Peter and Paul to keep raising money from each other. It's not only the competition. Too much life energy goes into money changing hands, while not enough hands go into changing the situation that made people need to raise money in the first place.

Coalitions facing this dilemma must look for new sources of revenue, possibly outside the community. And coalition members must unite to create larger systemic change, to break the cycle that encourages members to devour each other, and to redirect social and economic resources to stated community needs. That's largely what a coalition is for.

Dilemma #2: Competing with Yourself

■ *On the one hand:* As in Dilemma #1, you want to find dollars to fund the coalition's core work.

■ *On the other:* You also want to find dollars to support the work of coalition-related programs in the community.

It's tough enough if the coalition finds itself competing for funds with its own members. But here we mean something even tougher, because the coalition runs the risk of competing with itself. That is, you may want money for staffing. But how can you weigh that against the importance of money for a program which the coalition itself got off the ground?

Which comes first? And what are the criteria for making the judgment?

In the example below, one coalition coordinator started initiatives in the neighborhoods, which turned out to be more effective than the coordinator himself envisioned. Now suppose the coalition comes into some money. The coordinator might see it as salary. But don't you think the neighborhoods would want a piece of the action? They sure would.

If you had to make a choice, it could be, "Whom would I like to hurt least?"

> *I'd personally be better off if I didn't have to worry about raising money. But if someone gave us $30,000, no strings attached, it would cause a problem. It would disrupt our relationship with our neighborhoods. The neighbors would go through the roof, because they would be saying, "Time to pay the piper here. You said that your commitment is to build neighborhoods. Now you have $30,000. How much of that is coming to the neighborhood people?"*
>
> *They don't understand what it takes to run the coalition. I keep going back to postage [not to mention salary], because it is a major sore point.*

151

If you want to keep people involved in the coalition, you have to spend a lot of money sending out notices.

On the other hand, I think the neighborhoods have come a long way. When we first found city money for the neighborhoods, they didn't want to hear that any of the money was going to be spent on anything but neighborhood people. Today I think they are much more understanding. . . .

Okay, but it can get even more problematic. Who do you think has to worry about raising both kinds of money? You are right: It is usually the coalition coordinator.

If you believe you really need money for the core staff, and if the person in the coalition most responsible for finding the money is the core staff, then that person is trying to find money for their own job. It puts them in a quandary when they try to raise money for their own positions. It's a real dilemma.

It becomes especially tricky because a lot of people who run coalitions, and who do this work best, are people who feel like they should be paid considerable amounts of money, and that they are more deserving of that money than someone who is delivering services. . . .

The trick here is finding a skilled fund-raiser, program developer, and leader with low salary needs, all in one package. Funny, we were looking for just such a person ourselves. . . .

So we can see that, just as for people, money issues play a significant role in the life of a coalition. Concerns about how much money, where it should come from, and how it should be used can take up enormous amounts of coalition time. But money and funding concerns also provide an opportunity for coalitions to develop clear missions around sharply defined goals, and to build significant funding partnerships that will not only help support the coalition financially, but in numerous other ways.

For most coalitions, money is a simple fact of life. Facts by themselves are neutral. When not dealt with carefully, money issues can give you headaches beyond number. But when used wisely, money can enrich your coalition's work, even beyond your own expectations.

Lessons From The Field

The Whys (and Why Nots)

■ Do you need money to run an effective coalition? Many times, no. Great community work can be, has been, and will continue to be done with very little money—or no money at all.

■ Will money help you run a more effective coalition? (A very different question.) Generally, yes. *Other things equal*, you can get more done with a moderate-sized budget and some cash on hand.

■ Why seek money? To buy you assets and resources, including staff time; to help you convey your message on a larger scale; to give your coalition more stature, visibility, and independence; to free up your energy for larger concerns.

■ Then why not always be seeking? Because money can erode coalition cohesion. It can create competition among members. It can take time to spend, and to monitor that spending. And money can be addictive; you can easily become preoccupied with getting more money, diverting you from your original goals.

■ What criteria should guide your choices? Think in advance what your true coalition goals are, and what it will take to achieve them. They may or may not involve money. Any activities directed toward gaining money should follow from those goals—not the other way around.

The Wheres

■ The first principle: Start with what you've got. This means taking an inventory of the resources you have, much as a household would. What are your liquid assets? The other material assets you can call upon? And the intangibles?

■ The next principle: Look close to home. Begin from the center and radiate out. This means you might look first to your own coalition members, and their contacts and allies. Only when their resources will not be sufficient might you need to search outside your immediate circle.

■ The next step out from the center is holding community fund-raising events of one kind or another. These events can bring new people into your network and increase community visibility for your cause. They can also be creative, engaging, demanding, morale-boosting, and fun.

■ You can also find funding through legislative appropriation, public contract or grant, or through private foundations or corporations. The skills involved in getting such funding can be learned.

■ In reality, you can also adopt a mixed funding strategy, looking for and accepting money from several different sources, which may vary from year to year. Seeking funding is then always something of a scramble, never fully certain—just like most things in life.

The Hows

The basic steps, in their usual order:
- Identify funding goals for your coalition.
- Identify available funding sources, including those from your own members. Prioritize those sources, primarily in terms of a) possible rewards if you succeed, b) the best clear-headed guess that you will succeed, and c) the probable costs of making the effort.
- Develop a funding plan, based on your needs and your prioritized sources.
- Then take Step #1 in your plan, which will quite possibly involve applying to a top source on your priority list, and possibly more than one.
- And then stay with it. You persist, knowing that your proposal might not be funded now, or that you may otherwise fall short. You learn from experience, and you don't give up.

Four More Tips

- It always helps to network, to stay informed, and to develop connections with others. By doing so, you'll find out about funding opportunities and meet people who can help you in all kinds of unanticipated ways.
- Some coalitions hire others to write grants and proposals for them; a good grant-writer can be a great investment. One next best alternative: Find a sympathetic and knowledgeable local professional to review your proposal for form and content; follow that person's advice.
- You can often find some other like-minded, tax-exempt organization to be the formal applicant for you, if tax exemption is needed and if you don't want to or can't apply for tax-exempt status yourself. That same group may also manage grant funds received.
- Successful fund-raising also depends upon your being in the right place at the right time, over and above the actual merits of your proposal. And funding deadlines are often short. These are all the more reasons to stay connected with possible funding sources, and to have ideas and action plans developed so that you can move quickly when the right opportunity comes your way.

BUDGET - F/Y 1998

Source	AHEC	Public Health Foundation Grant	Dept of Public Health	Outreach Grant	Dept. of Social Services	Fees	Total Allocated	Total Needed	Surplus (Deficit)
Personnel									
Coalition Coordinator		3,800	31,802	4,026			39,628	39,628	0
Fringe		761	6,420	808			7,989	7,989	0
Administrative Assistant			6,320	1,028			7,348	7,348	0
Fringe			808	148			956	956	0
Office Expenses	1,050	480	650	5,972	3,680	700	12,532	12,532	0
Travel		524		1,400			1,924	1,924	0
Special Projects		18,000					18,000	18,000	0
Administration (overhead)			4,000	1,367	320		5,687	5,687	0
Carryover to F/Y 1999				1,833			1,833	1,833	0
	1,050	23,565	50,000	16,582	4,000	700	95,897	95,897	0

A budget should be the centerpiece of your coalition's financial planning. It serves several purposes: clarifying your needs, focusing your energies, increasing your accountability.

RESOURCE DEVELOPMENT PLAN
LOWER/OUTER CAPE COMMUNITY COALITION

SOURCE	WHO?	GOAL
GRANTS		$12,000
Foundations, Private		
*Investigate foundations that fund Coalition activities:		
Community Development/Empowerment		
Prevention		
Possibilities include:		
Associated Grantsmakers	Anne to investigate	
Attendees at AGM presentation?	Mary Lou	
*Explore possibility of developing proposal to support		
existing Coalitions to do what we already do		

Membership

		WHO?	GOAL
1. Begin with Advisory Board	11+12/95	Anne McManus	$4000
Goal: 100% participation by agencies on Board		Ellen Jones	
Stick with current fee guidelines		Charlotte Miller	
2. Previous Coalition supporters--Follow-up phone calls	1/96	Freddie Fitzgerald	
3. Other agencies that participate in the Coalition	2/96		
4. Generalized plea to mailing list through newsletter	2 +3/96		
5. Community Service Organizations	4/96		
6. Other Community Groups	4/96		
7. Businesses			
8. Others			

Fundraising

	WHO?	GOAL	
Events	Cici Schoenberger	$6000	Summer '96
Storytelling *Series* about Fishing	Michael Collins		
At "salty" location	Margaret Van Sant--?		
Storyteller to tell/read tales of seafarers	Jim Wolff		
Fishermen to tell their stories			
Summer or off-season?			

To reach your income goals, no matter how modest, coalitions (like people) should have an income plan. This is part of such a plan one coalition developed. Note the income targets, the timelines, and the assignments of responsibility.

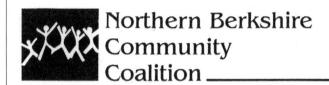

Northern Berkshire Community Coalition

Fall, 1997

Dear Friends of the Northern Berkshire Community Coalition:

Once again we are asking for your help. All of you who know about the Northern Berkshire Community Coalition know the impact we have in the Northern Berkshire region. As we begin our twelfth year, we are asking for your contribution to help the Coalition maintain its community presence for the next year. Since its inception in 1986, the NBCC has been a forum for the planning, development, and coordination of health and human services as well as other events and projects for our region. The Coalition has been the catalyst for:

- The creation of Northern Berkshire Neighbors, a project that supports five local neighborhood organizations.
- Four annual community-wide celebrations in support of Martin Luther King Day.

The Coalition Steering Committee has initiated the following sponsorship fee guidelines for agencies, health care organizations, businesses, individuals, and community organizations involved with and benefiting from the Coalition. It is based on .1% (one tenth of one percent) of an organization's budget with a maximum $500 contribution. Remember, these are guidelines. If you can't give the recommended amount, please give what you can.

- Budgets over $500 000..$500
- Budgets from $100,000-$500, 000 (one tenth of one percent)...................$100 - $500
- Budgets under $100, 000 (one tenth of one percent)..............................$ 25 - $100
- Individual Contributions can be from.......................................$ 10 - $500

We are committed to continuing to promote an exchange of ideas and resources that enhances the quality of life for all of us in this area. Thank you for all you do to support the Northern Berkshire Community Coalition.

Sincerely,

Alan Bashevkin, Coalition Coordinator, on behalf of the Coalition Steering Committee

Nurit Berman	Greg Betti	Maggie Bittman
Gail Bobin	Steve Green	Amy Hall
Marie Harpin	Maureen Hegan-Gigliotti	Paul Hopkins
Chris Meehan	Al Nelson	Janice O'Keefe
Mary Sugden	Ken Swiatek	

You might start implementing your plan by raising money from your members; you'll need a good fund-raising letter, as well as personal contact. This particular fund-raising letter, reproduced in part, was effective.

Thank you for your contribution to the Northern Berkshire Health and Human Services Coalition. Your contribution helps us to publish our monthly newsletter, continue the work of Northern Berkshire Neighbors, provide a monthly forum for a discussion of health and human service issues, and work with others to improve the quality of life of Northern Berkshire.

From:

**Northern Berkshire Health &
Human Services Coalition
North Adams State College   Box 9075
North Adams, MA 01247**

And it goes without saying, you want to make it as easy as possible for people to make the decision to give.

The following strategies have been identified as priorities for these grants:

❖ Increasing Community Awareness
  ◆ about alcohol, tobacco and other drugs
  ◆ about substance abuse prevention
  ◆ about community building activities

❖ Training people who influence youth, for example: peers, teachers, parents, neighbors, and other adults

❖ Early intervention and prevention

❖ Providing alternative activities

❖ Affecting public policy

❖ Building life skills

Proposals must clearly address one or more of the strategies listed above and answer the following questions:

Mission: What is the purpose of the program or activity?
Goals: What do you hope to accomplish?
Objectives: How do you plan to achieve this?
Evaluation: How will you know if you were successful?

How to Apply:

Proposals should be:

• Typed or legibly handwritten.

• No longer than 3 pages, double-spaced.

• Clear as to how funding requested will be spent, and if it will be used in conjunction with other grants.

• Submitted by **January 28, 1997** to:
  Berkshire Prevention Alliance
  305 North Street
  Pittsfield, MA 01201

NO EXTENSIONS WILL BE GRANTED.

• Awardees will be announced at Alliance Annual Meeting, to be held Feb. 6, 1997.

• Projects must be complete by **September 30, 1997.**

The Berkshire Prevention Alliance provides grants for community projects to improve the quality of life in Berkshire County.

How these grants are to be used:

◆ Any project which you believe will make your community a better, safer, healthier place to live may be eligible.

◆ Collaboration among two or more groups is strongly encouraged.

◆ Outreach efforts to parents and businesses are especially encouraged.

◆ To help community and youth groups organize special projects.

◆ To organize new community or youth groups.

◆ Proposals may range from $250 - $1500.

◆ Approximately $11,000 will be awarded.

◆ Every effort will be made to ensure projects are funded in all parts of the county.

◆ If you would like assistance in preparing your proposal, please call us at 448-2276.

◆ A grant writing workshop will be held on Monday, January 13, from 6:00-8:00 p.m., at the Alliance storefront - 305 North Street, Pittsfield

One productive way coalitions can spend the money they receive is to give it back to others in the community. Above is part of a brochure describing a mini-grant program which one coalition ran successfully.

Athol-Orange
Health and Human Services
Coalition _____

March 29, 1989

Kay M. Seivard
Executive Director
Greater Worcester Community Foundation, Inc.
44 Front Street
Worcester, MA 01608-1705

Dear Kay:

On behalf of the Coalition, we want to thank Greater
Worcester Community Foundation for your $4,500 grant for
the coming year. You are our savior!

We are indebted to you for your support for the last three
years. The Coalition has been strengthened greatly in its
efforts to help solve the issues of housing, child sexual
abuse, youth, day care and transportation. You benefit our
programming enormously.

We all send our grateful thanks.

Sincerely,

Barbara Corey, Coordinator, A/O Coalition
Tom Wolff, Ph.D., Statewide Coalition Coordinator

Barbara Corey, *Coalition Coordinator* • 545 Main St., Athol, MA 01331   508-249-3703

*And not to forget, when you are fortunate enough to receive a grant, it's both good
practice and good manners to thank the awarding organization.*

Chapter 9

Coalition Advocacy

> *Should my coalition get involved in advocacy?*
>
> *How should we choose the right advocacy technique?*
>
> *Is it possible to advocate without taking risk?*
>
> *What are the principles of advocacy success?*

Should coalitions advocate? Should they speak out and try to change public opinion on matters they care about? Should they get right in the middle of local issues of the day? Should they assume positions of community leadership? Should they take stands based on principle, and hold onto them despite potential cost?

The Positives and the Negatives

The positives. Of course they should. How could it be otherwise? Coalition leaders themselves agree, without exception or reservation:

> *We all get involved in it. We really do have to get involved in it. It's something that needs to be done because no one else in the community may do it.*

* * *

> *It's an important piece of the work that we do. It's important for us to work at that level. It makes the impact of what we do longer-lasting—you*

know, if you have a law which is passed and it's on the books, it may outlast your funding source.

* * *

I think coalitions have no choice but to advocate. Because very often they're working on a local issue, and they're either going to become the passive victim of those laws, or they're going to act to influence them. So they don't have much choice. Although coalitions don't understand that very often. I mean, a lot of times the coalitions just bitch and moan about what's come down to them, and especially in the beginning, they don't have much of a sense that they can have an impact. But they've got to. They've got to do it. They've got to advocate.

Correct. How can you not speak up for what you believe in? How can you not advocate and still lay claim to being a coalition or community group of any ethical or effective standing? A coalition should have a finely tuned social conscience. A coalition is there to provide moral as well as substantive leadership, to be progressive in thought and action, to be out in front of others. If it isn't going to do those things, what is it there for?

The negatives. But—hold it just a bit. Maybe we shouldn't speak quite so fast. It's not quite that simple. There are downsides.

When you advocate for a particular position, you can lose support. You can lose support within your own organization. And you can lose the support you had within the community, that same support which originally contributed to your success and upon which your success may depend now. The more strongly you advocate, the more support you stand to lose. This is especially true if your coalition is new, or vulnerable, or a group without an established track record, or if you formed in the first place because of issues that not everyone (or hardly anyone) saw your way.

It gets worse. If you advocate too vigorously, you can lose not only community support, but support from your funding sources as well. Funders, public or private, tend to be conservative. They want to see you make progress, but noiselessly and without waves. They are not crusaders. They want to make sure your issues and actions are supported by the community; for if they aren't, they may reevaluate the support they are giving to you.

Lastly, advocacy in some cases may also go against the explicit guidelines of your funders, as well as state or federal regulations or laws, especially if your advocacy is overly political. There are legal restrictions on advocacy by tax-exempt nonprofit groups in lobbying and in political campaigns. These restrictions may limit or prohibit advocacy of some or all kinds. To fly in their face, openly or covertly, is to risk losing your financial backing. That would hurt you.

162

Proceeding, with care. So there's a potential and possibly real difficulty here. Coalitions are supposed to lead, and have a moral voice, which suggests they should advocate. But to advocate, *by its nature*, means to speak out on a topic on which 100 percent of the community does not necessarily agree. It can mean taking a minority position, or a controversial position, or even a majority position where there is strong minority feeling. Advocacy, *by its nature*, involves risk.

At the same time, community coalitions are also consensus-builders. By *their* nature, they are supposed to bring different sectors of the community together in common cause. That's the very essence of the coalition. But should it advocate, the coalition itself threatens that core principle, and risks losing the support and accomplishment which prompted its origin in the first place.

And further: Often, the very thing that makes an issue important, and *worth* advocating for, is that some people have something to lose if you win. Or think they do. They have their own interests, which they will protect if they feel threatened. They will oppose you. And why *shouldn't* they oppose you, if their interests, on this issue at least, are different from yours? You don't own their opinion, or their allegiance. If the roles were reversed, you'd be fighting back, too.

And that's why if you advocate—when you advocate—you should be careful. If you're going to do it—and we think you should—you should know how other coalitions have done it. Before you head into deep waters, you should know how to swim.

So in this chapter, we'll cover three areas: First, we'll offer some specific advocacy techniques, then some general principles, and then raise some broader issues about advocacy that you and your coalition may want to think about before taking the plunge.

Some Advocacy Techniques

All right: how do you do it?

Suppose there's an issue in your community. You want to speak out and sway others to your side. Those you want to sway could be members of your own community who don't know much about the issues, or they could be known community opponents. Yet many times your targets may be bureaucrats or politicians, living *outside* the community, and with more power than you—the institutionalized power to make decisions that will get you what you want. Persuading them will not necessarily be easy.

But . . .

An important first thing to remember is that you and your coalition have power yourselves. You can mobilize your own supporters, and bring your own strength to bear. To do so, you have many techniques at your disposal, which you can modify to suit the occasion.

Specifically, for example, and starting very simply:

Laying the groundwork. Before people will advocate at all—write a letter, sign a petition, or do something more involved—they first need to know a) what the issues are, and b) what positions on the issues will best help them. Then they will be primed to act. So good advocates lay the groundwork before advocacy actually occurs, and prepare their members early. Here's one coalition that does this well by making up flyers, then knocking on doors to spread the word in advance. (Word of mouth helps, too.)

> *We've done flyers where we'll walk through every hallway, and hand out the flyers, and hang them on the walls, and in the mail room. Then later we'll knock on every door, and people will talk to us because the flyer said we're coming. And people will know what we're talking about, because of the flyer, too.*
>
> *Then there's always word of mouth. The board members are always telling people, people that we know, "Oh, did you get such-and-such? There's going to be a _____." For particular things, we know which people really come out, so we make a special effort to talk to them one way or another; by phone, or running into them in the street, or whatever.*
>
> *You're always talking to people, letting them know what's going on— "How do you feel about this?" "Well, we're going to try to be doing this, so look out, we need your support on this."*

Letters, phone calls, petitions. You can adopt the time-tested techniques of writing letters, making telephone calls, and signing petitions, directed either to decision-makers, or to the media, or both. But these simple techniques can be blended into an "advocacy menu": You list the menu options; you give your advocate a choice.

> *We designed some very concrete things that people could do. If they didn't have the time, they signed a postcard and sent it in. If they had some time, they got a petition that they could circulate. If they wanted to do something more self-generated, we gave them sample letters that they could replicate. Or actually gave them telephone numbers and sample things to say.*

This coalition's message was, "We need your help on this. Here are some ways you can help us. What works best for you?"

Hearings. You can seek out public hearings, stand up, and testify—sometimes with genuine impact:

> *At the hearing, the Governor's representative said, "Well, we're going to do away with welfare as it stands." But then a welfare mom came forth and said, "Look, it's very simple. There are 300 people on welfare in this community. You're saying that they all should work. Tell us where the 300 jobs are, and tell us where the day care and transportation for those 300 people are going to be, and we'll support your bill."*

That was a profound moment of truth. I heard that debate referenced in many places around the community.

Naturally, many people (make that almost all people) don't feel comfortable speaking in public at a hearing. It's formal, it's often far from home, they're out of their element, and it can be scary. So you prepare them. You can orchestrate the proceedings in advance. You can give people scripts:

> *Like if we're having a meeting with some of the officials, people all want to say something, but they don't know how to say it. So we sit down and talk about what they want to say. Then I write it up, and I'll give them their piece, and it's really what they have said, but written down so they don't get nervous.*
>
> *I'm just going, "Okay, now here it is, you read it." And Carmen would say, "Okay, my question is . . ." and get an answer. You know what I mean? Number one, this takes away their fear. Number two, it makes them feel that they're important. It was structured. But it was structured based upon what people wanted to say.*

Showing the facts. You can show others what the facts are, in no uncertain terms. When you put the facts right before someone's eyes, the truth is hard to deny.

> *To get lighting in the area we've met directly with the mayor, after we wrote him a letter. But even before we met with him, we had the city department come out and we showed them all the spaces that used to have lights, poles that had been removed. We found out there were 19 removed, that had never been replaced. Then when we went to meet with the mayor it wasn't just something blowing out of our ear—we could show you where the poles were, and now it is dark. So we had 11 of those 19 replaced with new lights.*

Collecting the facts. If you're not certain what the facts are, you can go out and collect them. That can be a good role for a coalition. True, sometimes the facts are all **too** well known, and sometimes fact collecting avoids the real need at hand; but not always. Facts shape policy, and a coalition is well-poised to do some fact-finding research. Here's one reason why:

> *We've got the time to step back and look at the bigger picture. For example, welfare reform has direct impact on the clients that our agencies and organizations are dealing with. So the coalition allows us to do all the moaning and the whining that we all need to do, but then to say, "Okay, now what can we do that's going to help?" So our task force chose to try to get a profile of our welfare recipients. What are their capacities? How are they going to be able to respond to new requirements—do we really know that? Do we really know how it's going to impact these folks?*

> *And so we decided to do a survey. And because we have the luxury of being a small community—we've got a welfare population of about 150 people currently—it's really possible to describe this population pretty completely. Then we can be in a much better place to plan and advocate with them on how we're going to address this welfare thing.*

Other techniques, and variations. You can call into talk shows, send faxes, and (more and more) send e-mail. You can develop fact sheets or phone trees, set up public information tables, register voters, hold candidates' nights, or even "reverse candidates' nights" (the citizens speak; the candidates listen and report on what they've heard). You can picket, boycott, parade, demonstrate; name your action verb. Of course, this is a partial list. When you think about it, advocates have many tools in their tool kit.

None of this means that you become too satisfied with any one technique, or that you overuse it or over-rely on it. A technique can become shopworn and wear out its welcome. The users may no longer fully believe in it. The recipients may become tired of receiving it. Advocacy is a process of constant adjustments, because times constantly change. That's why you always need to be looking for new techniques, or variations on the old, to help you get what you want.

In other words, good advocacy gives you plenty of room for creativity. The two not only go together, they go hand-in-glove. You need fresh, clever, creative, custom-tailored techniques to get your point across. And while you are being creative, keep in mind that your advocacy doesn't have to be heavy-handed. Sometimes a light touch is best:

> *We talked about how we could educate the community more about the legislation. How could we convince them to sign the petition if we couldn't have Mr. _____ [a respected school leader] standing there? And we'd laugh and say, "Why don't we get a giant blowup picture? We'll make him into a cutout and we'll have a tape recorder there saying, 'I'm sorry that I can't be here in person. I'm taking care of the children in school. But these are good people. They're working on this project. Please won't you sign your name to this petition? It's okay.' "*
>
> *I think the next time anything comes up like that, we'll probably do it because it's so much more fun for us.*

Other community groups have really used cut-outs of kids on front lawns to slow down neighborhood traffic. The coalition above never actually tried the cut-outs, but it could have. They might work, for them or for you.

Do these techniques work? Not automatically, for sure. Not every single time. Not always to the degree you would like. But the experience of our leaders, and our own, indicates that these techniques customarily do work when intelligently applied. They work because they derive from basic rules of persuasion, which have been successfully demonstrated from the time of Aristotle's *Rhetoric* (4th century, B.C.) straight through to the lab experiments of modern social psychology. Minds get changed according to tested principles. You can learn them. *(See the next section for more on this topic.)*

This viewpoint is factual, but also optimistic. For when it comes to coalition advocacy, you have to be somewhat optimistic. It's an occupational hazard. You have to believe that something is going to work; otherwise, why are you in business? Why are you taking the trouble to advocate at all?

Choosing your technique. Of all these techniques and variations, which to choose? This question has three helpful answers. The first answer is that you can choose more than one. The second answer is that you can choose different techniques for different groups of supporters. And the third answer is that you can choose different techniques for the same supporters at different stages of the advocacy process. These statements are positives. They mean you can be flexible, that you have a number of options at your disposal, many ways of doing business.

To choose your specific techniques, you need to know your targets. Who are they? What do they know? What channels of influence are they exposed to? Decide on that basis. If they don't read their mail, then don't write them a letter. If they don't listen to the radio, forget about radio spots. But if they show up every Wednesday at the bingo hall, or read every note their child brings from school, that's where you want to direct your efforts.

And you want to know your own resources—people, money, and time. You want to take stock of how much time you have to advocate, who can help with the mailing or phoning, what kind of money you can muster, and whether that much will do the job. You might also ask, "Who owes me a favor?" or more politely, "Whom can I call upon?" Finally, you want to assess what power you have, real or perceived, that you might use to turn your target around.

After the diagnosis, there is the treatment. So when you've completed your analysis, and drawn your conclusions, you probably want to shape your conclusions into a plan. When you advocate, it's better if you have a plan worked out in advance, rather than going in with a scatter-shot approach, or picking a technique simply because it's lying nearby. We hope you have noticed that we are serious believers in planning, as well as in subsequent evaluation of the impact of your work.

Some Basic Advocacy Principles

Using basic concepts of persuasion. Having made life a bit complicated, we can now make it easier. The basic concepts of advocacy can be grasped by almost anyone. There are general principles of coalition advocacy, of any advocacy, regardless of type. These principles transcend specific techniques. You probably already know what many of them are, because consciously or not you have used them before, but it may be useful to recall some of them here.

This time, rather than making a list, let's do so by hearing a story. It's a simple and localized story, which in this down-to-earth instance had to do with getting a new heating system. Watch out for the check marks; a principle follows just after each one.

> *What we try to do is ✓ identify the issues and then meet with the appropriate folks, trying to work it out. We sit down, and we ✓ present what the problem is. If that doesn't work, then we may have to ✓ force the issue.*
>
> *Once we wrote a letter, saying we wanted the officials to come out and meet with us. Well, they met with us, but they said, "We don't know, blah, blah, blah." So then we thought—"Well, okay, what are we going to do from here?" We decided to do the petitions again. We ran around, got a petition signed from everybody, and said," ✓ "This is what we want, this is what we demand; it's our right to get a new boiler system."*
>
> *But we had to ✓ do the research, because if you don't, they can blow you off. We had to read back through documents, and find documents to show them five years ago, by their own statements, the boiler was outdated and beyond repair. Then we requested, with that petition, a ✓ short-term resolution and a ✓ long-term resolution. We wanted ✓ timelines.*
>
> *And we had to ✓ meet with people who were responsible. One thing we found with everything we do is that the chief in command, or the second in command, has to be there. I'm not going to work with someone and have them say at the end, "Well, I can't do it." You need to be there with the person that can say, "It's going to be done."*
>
> *So you have to ✓ pick your battles, so that you will be successful, and that's why I think we are. Some people say, "You're slow; you only do one thing at a time." But we complete that ✓ one thing at a time.*

What made this advocacy attempt successful? We believe it was the intelligent and persuasive use of advocacy principles. Once again, in somewhat different order:

1. Identify the issues.
2. Do your research.
3. Meet with the decision-makers.
4. Present the problem.
5. Make your request.
6. Get a resolution.
7. Get timelines.
8. Force the issue (if necessary).
9. Pick your battles.
10. Work on one thing at a time.

These principles, presented here in bare-bones form, are not tremendously difficult to learn, nor to use in practice. The coalition members in the previous example were not professionals. In this example, they were tenants in a public housing project.

The key point, we think, is to be thoughtful about these principles, to be mindful in advance about what you want to accomplish and how to accomplish it, to enter into an advocacy situation with technical but also mental preparation. If you go into the room knowing just what you want to do—and how and why you want to do it— and if your mind is calm, clear, and focused, that can make all the difference in the world.

This is a start. Now, let's put some more principles out on the table.

Developing relationships. However effective this testimony was, however effectively these principles were used, they would have been even more effective had there been a good working relationship between the communicators and their target audience. This does not mean that the audience members or decision-makers are going to be your friends—much as we value friendship. It means more that your relationship is based on mutual respect and trust.

The decision-makers may not like what you and your coalition have to say. They may oppose your position, and privately (or even publicly) wish you would go away. But if you have developed a working relationship with them, if they know you are credible and straightforward, if you mean what you say and you'll stick to your word, you are much more likely to get a fair hearing and get what you want.

You've seen this principle before. The principle of building relationships is perhaps the most fundamental principle in this book, about as close as we can come to a law of human nature. Other things equal, people are more likely to pay attention to the arguments, and be swayed by the arguments, of someone they know, like, trust, and respect.

> *At the heart, coalition building and collaboration is really about people. It really is. So I think you start by building a relationship.*
>
> *Because suppose something comes up and you need to advocate with some department in the system, where you don't have a relationship. Then you use much more of a power strategy. But in general, if coalitions are gonna be around for a while, then very early on you want to start to build a relationship with that department. So it becomes much more a question of letting their office know that you're really concerned about the changes they are proposing. A lot of it is just relationship building.*

* * *

> *. . . And that is certainly true for the media. On the Cape, the coalition has developed wonderful relationships with the media. We get very good coverage on a regular basis. And the same is true of* The Transcript *up in North Adams—for at least the first three or four years of the coalition, we had a newspaper reporter there every meeting. So I think in the small communities especially, it's all based on personal relationships. And from what I know about people who get coverage at* The Boston Globe, *it's because they know some reporter who calls them regularly.*

Using your relationships: Making personal contact. Once these relationships have been developed, an effective advocate will use them. Just to be clear: We're not talking about putting unfair pressure on people, and certainly not about threats or worse. Rather, it's about using your relationships to make sure your point gets across. It's not unethical to request a favor, nor to ask your contacts to get you through the door. Your target audience may still not agree with you, and eventually may not decide your way. But if you've got a sympathetic ear, why not make sure you get heard?

So good advocacy also means direct, interactive contact with the people who can make decisions in your favor. You want to go to the source. You want to seek out the decision-makers and talk to them, to state your case face-to-face, up close and personal.

For a simple example, you can pay your decision-maker a visit:

> *You talk with various business people. You talk to business groups. You talk with CEOs. You meet with Sam Gerson, President and CEO of Filene's Basement [a discount clothing store], and say, "Sam, listen, I've got some kids I need to get hired for the warehouse." He says, "Gene, send them down to me, we'll see what we can do." That's it. Yeah. I'm on the board of the Urban League and Sam is chair of the board of the Urban League. So, it's straight ahead that way.*
>
> *It's contacts, it's developing contacts, working your contacts, developing networks. See, there are a lot of people out there that want to do the good things. They just need to know what needs to be done and what works. And that's really where they are. So, there's a lot of good will.*

And when you visit or phone, if you have influence or power of your own, here's your chance to use it. What else is it there for?

> *If we want jobs, we get on the phone, with the governor, the mayor, the state reps. And I say, if it's the mayor, "Tommy, hi, how are ya? Listen, we need 40 jobs for the summer for the kids." And they say, "Okay." Yeah, that's exactly what it is. Yeah, absolutely. And it means calling the governor and setting up a lunch meeting with him in about a week or two, to sit down and talk about what can be done on the job side for the kids, to promote economic development.*
>
> *. . . Oh, yeah, they'll meet with us. Oh, listen, they're smart. At the level of public opinion and thinking, black clergy represent the stable elements of the black community. And then the black church is the most organized constituency group. The highest voter turnout comes out of black churches. So, there's the arithmetic of it.*

A specific application: Working with legislators. Suppose we apply the principles of developing and using relationships to working with legislators—since legislators are the frequent targets of coalition advocacy. You may want (or need) formal or informal legislative support. How do you get it?

As an alternative to going to meet them (or any other decision-maker), you can ask them to come and meet you. "Wait a minute—" you say, "no legislator will actually take the time to visit my coalition." But are you certain? Have you ever asked, in a polite and planned-out way? The answer might surprise you.

> *I do recall when we invited the recently elected city manager to one of our coalition meetings. He gratefully accepted, he came, and we let him get to know who we were. We said, "Here we are, and this is all the neat stuff we're doing." And he said, "You all should know that the city needs to hire more Latinos, and how should we go about setting up some connection so that you're aware of what kind of opportunities there are?" The initiative came more from him.*

But if you're not used to contacting your legislators, much less meeting them, how do you start? Some possibilities:

> *I think the way to do it is to start simply. I mean, if you're in a town where there's a mayor or selectman, go meet some of these folks, or meet their staff. Meet the mayor's aide. And with state legislators, go meet the local legislative aide. And just talk with them about what you're doing. That's their job. That surprised me when I first called, that they actually listened. But I realized over time that was what this person was paid to do. And that our need was as legitimate as most everybody else's.*

*   *   *

> *We've invited legislators on a regular basis to hear from the people themselves what their issues are, whether it be medical access or housing or transportation. I'm sure that they're thinking, "Oh, it could be a vote or two." But also, literally, in order to do their job better, they need to feel that they've heard people's concerns. Over the years, people in the legislature have confidence in us, and they see us as sane and reasonable in our concerns, our requests. And they like coming and hearing. It's a forum that they don't often see in towns and communities, so they feel privileged that they can come.*

The key point to remember is that developing a good relationship with you is usually in your legislators' true interest. (As it is for most other decision-makers.) It's not just that legislators want your votes, or that it's part of their job. It's that good legislators need and want to be informed of the issues, of what's going on in the communities they represent. Who better to tell them than a well-connected coalition?

> *The coalition really serves the legislators' purpose. Oh, absolutely. When they come to the coalition, they learn more about the community. They get*

a broad audience with a lot of people. And what they love about the coalitions is that they hear a collective voice on what the issue is, not just a single agency's view. It's incredibly mutual. In my book, it's politics at its best.

And then if there's new state money, maybe they get a single application for it. The state rep can advocate for that. I think legislators like nothing better than to beat up on some bureaucrat in the state system and say, "I want that money for this shelter in my community tomorrow. . . ."

Now, to bring home the point, once you've secured that legislative relationship, you need to use it. The coalition below had no hesitancy about pushing a lot of buttons to get what it wanted. It found the right buttons, and it got results:

A number of the coalitions were involved in the school-linked services initiative out of the Executive Office of Education. And last year, there was money in the House budget for that project, but the Senate just wiped it out. So we did some very active work with our state senator, who was on the Conference Committee that resolves the House and Senate differences. And we got hold of the wife of the fishing buddy of the senator—she was a friend of someone who we were working with. We got to her, and she got to her husband, who was the fishing buddy, and her husband got to the senator. And we were instrumental in having that money restored, and we had this real good program year. So that's pretty typical—it happens frequently.

Did we feel ethically okay about this? Absolutely. Because it's a question of letting the local representatives know what the local needs are so that they can do their job better. I mean the only qualm I feel occasionally is that we're depriving other parts of the state of resources, because we're so well-organized and getting so good at it. But other than that, I need to know what goes on in my community, and then I'm gonna do something to help it. It's not that they're filling our personal pockets. They're helping to provide a service that we know has proven value. So I don't feel bad about those moments at all. I feel triumphant about those moments.

Starting with local action. This past discussion leads to a related principle: You are most likely to be heard by the people in your own community—those people you have relationships with. Yet sometimes your issues may range well beyond community borders. They may be county-wide, state-wide, or even national, on levels where you are less known. So where should you put your main advocacy efforts? What's your choice of scale?

Two points of view:

[#1] A lot of coalitions have focused just on local services, and haven't taken a look at the bigger issues. I think that's a mistake. I think if you're not trying to impact the larger system, you're going to be a victim of the larger

system. Unless we address some of the big issues in this country like the unequal distribution of wealth, we're going to go nowhere.

* * *

[#2] Like Tip O'Neill [the former Speaker of the U.S. House of Representatives] said, "All politics is local." And coalitions are very local. So we really can't leap to the bigger issues unless there's a close connection to what's going on in the community at that moment.

Change comes easier on a local level. The smaller the scale, the bigger your chances of success. After all, you are a *community* coalition. That's where you know the most, where you have the expertise, plus the best ideas, plus the wherewithal to make them happen. So it makes perfect sense that community-level advocacy come first. But viewpoint #1 can't be discounted either. No community exists in a vacuum. Larger-scale issues may be crucial to your coalition's welfare. You may want to do something about them; perhaps you should.

So yes, the larger the issue, and the higher the stakes, the greater the conceivable rewards will be—and also yes, the chances of your advocacy having a measurable impact will diminish in direct proportion to the size of your target population. That's the tradeoff for every community group; and that's the tradeoff you must think about and decide upon.

And yet these viewpoints can be integrated. You can start small, on a local level, gain experience, and work your way up if you're so inclined. Your earlier victories will strengthen both your confidence and your ability to aim higher:

I think there's a hierarchy that goes something like this: Coalitions first dip their feet in by getting to meet the selectmen and the legislators and their aides. Then they invite them to a meeting for a general information exchange. Then, if they get a little bit more brazen, they'll have a candidates' day or night when the people who are running for office come and talk about their stance on service issues to an audience. Then they'll start to do something on a local issue; they want to create a new program. They identify who in state government has the money for that, and then they get their legislators involved in helping them advocate to the state for funding. After that, they might get into some more controversial statewide campaign where they become a player.

So it's a progression. But if you take on the larger issues without having done some of the groundwork, then your impact is much reduced, because the coalition members don't have the advocacy experience. And they don't have the credibility in the eyes of the decision-makers.

Building internal support. It's a clear advantage, too, if your advocacy group is close-knit. Advocates make themselves vulnerable by choice; they stick their necks out, willingly. If it's a controversial issue, they may get banged around and bruised a little. Experienced advocates know this all too well.

To cushion those bruises, it helps to have friends who will pick you up when you fall. It helps in general if you have a cohesive group that supports one another when the going gets tough. Next question: What makes for cohesion?

> *I think we are close partly because this particular coalition really has a history of success. People have put themselves on the line, they've shared the risks, they've shared the responsibilities, and they've reaped the rewards. And it shows. I mean, these are folks who trust one another, who care about one another.*
>
> *And I find when I go someplace else and work with a different group of folks who aren't coalition folks, I'm always surprised; it isn't the same. I go off and I hear the cynicism and I hear the negativism about "Oh, you know, there's nothing we can do about that." I mean, we all know by now how things get done—by positive people who think they have the capacity to do it. That's how things get done.*

So your coalition is more likely to be close-knit in the first place if it has developed a track record of success. And the best way of developing such a track record is to maximize those chances of success—which frequently means to act locally, on a smaller scale. So this point circles back to the one before.

Success leads to cohesion. Cohesion fosters more success. This is how groups work.

Even if you have followed all these principles, developed strong relationships, emphasized local issues, formed a supportive group—at some point you are going to have to speak up. You will have to speak truth to power, and that isn't necessarily easy. Those in power may not want to hear your truth. They may tell you so, devalue your words and your person, threaten you, and act against you.

It may take some boldness, and courage, to speak with conviction and integrity. At the same time, you want to speak with impact, to get results. How can all these qualities mesh together to create effective coalition advocacy? We'll pose some integrating questions around this theme, and offer some possible answers, in our next-to-last section.

Some Key Advocacy Issues

How forcefully should you advocate?

Suppose your more "polite" attempts at advocacy—writing letters, signing petitions—fail to get the job done. This can happen. Do you then confront your opponents head-on, or take to the streets, or engage in other sorts of confrontation?

On this matter, we are pragmatists. Our focus is on what works.

> *It was suggested that we picket. We felt that was not an appropriate thing*
> *to do—that it was better to try to engage people to work with us rather than*
> *alienate them and not get anywhere.*

For *community* coalitions, it's almost always pragmatically better to start politely. The main reason for this is because the people you are opposing, and advocating against, are likely to be members of your community as well. They will stay there. You will quite likely encounter them again, in another setting, at another time, or on another issue.

And in that other setting, they might conceivably be helpful. At that other time, their minds could have changed. On that other issue, they could be your ally. The harder your tactics, especially if they smack of personal attack, the more likely hard feelings are to remain in place. The more likely you will lose out on the good will that could have been yours had you not hammered quite so forcefully.

> *We haven't organized demonstrations in front of town hall, although I think*
> *that kind of stuff is fun. I do have to be careful about that—especially with the*
> *coalition name. I have to be careful, because I have some definite ideas.*

Such confrontational tactics should probably not be your tactics of first choice. As a guideline for local community coalitions, you may want to use the least possible force to accomplish your goal.

And a related question: If confrontation is called for, is that the proper role of the *coalition* as such? Should it be the *coalition* picketing in front of city hall, or should it be somebody else?

> *In the Christina Hernandez case [a local homicide, where some felt the*
> *police had been negligent], although the coalition was not involved, I did*
> *walk around City Hall and picket—but I was not wearing my coalition hat*
> *at that point.*

When direct action is called for, it might better be done by coalition members acting as individuals, rather than by the coalition itself. The same people can be out there, fighting the same battles, but flying other flags. Their success could be as great or greater, because as individuals they don't have to hold anything back. While the coalition may. The coalition, when advocating as such, may be exposed to attack and loss of support. To confront may erode the coalition's position as a community-wide forum and may make the coalition more vulnerable than it already is, in all the ways we discussed at the beginning of this chapter.

> *A perfect example was when our town was a potential site for a haz-*
> *ardous waste plant, and there were a lot of people who felt this was won-*
> *derful because it would give employment and generate tax revenue. I was*

opposed to it. I personally didn't think it would be inappropriate for the coalition to get involved [in opposition]. But wiser heads, perhaps, prevailed and felt that maybe things weren't yet at the point where we needed to take a stand.

So we talked about it quite a bit and decided that the coalition would create a forum on what would be the health and human service implications of this—both the positive things, in terms of better jobs, and the negative, in terms of health risks. But we wouldn't take an advocacy stand on it, because with this kind of strong feeling in the community, it was likely to undo our capacity to be a neutral forum in the future.

These examples illustrate caution. Yet there is definitely a place for harder-hitting action in coalition advocacy. The issue may truly be vital to your coalition and to the community. If gentler tactics have repeatedly failed, you may see yourself with few other options, and you may be right. Sometimes forceful and confrontational advocacy, stemming explicitly from the coalition, is a choice you may need to make.

At one coalition meeting, a representative from our family planning agency announced that they would be closing the clinic in our town. Since this was the only family planning provider for low-income folks around here, we saw this as a crisis. The 30 coalition members mobilized quickly and contacted the board of health. The board agreed to hold a public hearing. Following the hearing, letters of protest were sent, our legislators were contacted, and they in turn protested to the state Department of Public Health, which funded the family planning agency. The state board held two more heated public hearings. Finally, under strong pressure from the legislators, the DPH, and the community, the agency backed off from its decision and kept the clinic open.

In this case, forceful advocacy was necessary. When the situation is stuck, you may need to apply pressure. When positions are frozen, you may need to turn up the heat.

Or consider this story. How would you respond here?

The Amtrak people wanted to build this electromagnetic substation in our neighborhood, and they came in with the perception that this is Roxbury [one of the poorest neighborhoods in Boston], and what do these people care? The Amtrak guy stood up at a meeting and said, "It will be a benefit to the community, because you'll be able to go to Washington, D.C. faster." We said, "We don't want to go to Washington, D.C. We're just trying to live here." Then the guy said, "Well, letting us build this electromagnetic station will give you clean air, even though I know that's something that you folks don't care about." He was almost run out the door. And then a union guy stood up and said, "You people"—which you know is a no-no—"You people don't work, at least this will provide you with jobs, and you won't have to go anywhere."

I mean, how are you going to do anything with those attitudes? They're coming into an area with a perception that it's mostly poor people, mostly black, mostly illiterate, and mostly don't care about the air they breathe. I have challenged the residents to come together and build a coalition to strategize and fight, because Amtrak is coming back. Their message the other day was, "We can write you a hefty check to let us build here." Well, that's not going to help us with our health, and our kids, because our population already has a high cancer rate. How are we going to really fight this, rather than just say no, because we know they're going to keep coming? This is going to be a challenge.

The racism here, more blatant than usual, compounds the problem. These neighborhood residents will need more than good manners to get what they want. Their coalition may need to protest long and loud, to the right people, with all the force it can gather. And even then, it may lose; sometimes David gets crushed by Goliath.

Decisions about how much force to use can be textured and complex. Politeness can be morally and practically superior, or it can be morally and practically weak; so can deciding to go all out. Deliberate thought is called for, a looking with the third eye. Our advice is to pause and reflect before jumping in, and to make sure that the tactics you are using are those which will best help you reach your long-term as well as your short-term objectives.

Where do you find the energy?

But no matter what advocacy strategy you follow, it takes effort. Whether your approach is gentle or forceful, whether you just show the facts or beat people over the head with them, whether you walk softly or carry a big stick or both, you will be spending physical and psychological energy. The source of that energy must be you and your members. This is a given; advocacy does not happen until someone flips the switch.

So there are energy costs. One cost is that for all the time you spend on advocacy, you could be doing something else that might be more productive. If others would only see it your way the first time, then you wouldn't have to keep fighting for what you believe in, fighting the same fight all over and over and over again. Sometimes advocacy feels like pouring your whole being into a bottomless energy pit.

If we didn't have to fight them, there could be energy to go to other things. Because our people are volunteers; they've all got small kids. When you're talking about all the time they have to come out, it's a lot of time. So if we have to fight them to get a safe environment—we should not have to be fighting them for that.

It's not just the physical energy, but the psychic energy too. You get psychological-ly tired of doing the same thing again and again, writing yet another letter, making yet another round of phone calls. Maybe because you are experienced and dedicated, a true professional, you can suck it up and make those calls, despite your fatigue, but eventually your fatigue shows up in your work. Your phone voice doesn't have the same enthusiasm. Your letter seems a little tepid. Your public testimony sounds as if you are going through the motions; maybe you are. It's just harder to get excited about the same thing the 20th time around.

> *That whole advocacy thing has changed, I think. I don't find myself send-ing out alerts to coalition members to call their senator as often as we used to do, to tell you the truth.*
>
> *And we just don't call up our legislators to the same extent, so it must be less effective. We aren't going to make those inroads that we once did. Certainly we do it at times. It's just that I do not see it happening as fre-quently. There's a lack of belief that it's going to make a difference, whereas before, we felt it was going to. Now I think there's a lot of cynicism and a "What's the point?"—that kind of thing.*

And—it's the same for those who are on the receiving end. They've heard it all before: the same techniques, the same real or manufactured passion, certainly from others, and maybe from you. If you are worn down, sometimes they are, too. It comes with the territory.

> *I wonder if there isn't a better way of advocating, but I'm not sure what that is, and maybe we need to identify it. I think we need to address that, and I think we need to address it very quickly, because if we don't, we con-tinue to be eroded in our efforts.*

Which means two things for you as an advocate. First, it means you need to keep looking for fresh approaches to advocacy, not to rely on the same techniques, the same scripts too many times over. If it feels tired for you, it's going to feel tired for your audi-ence. What worked terrifically the first time may by now be long in the tooth. Effective advocacy means something authentic, fresh, and alive right now.

And second, it means you have to keep yourself fresh and alive as well, so that you can deliver your message with genuine spirit, power, and élan. And that comes back to basic homespun lifestyle ingredients like a decent night's sleep, eating well, letting others step forward for a while, taking a break, building in some quiet and reflective time in your life. The best ways to combat fatigue are to get some rest and to vary your activities. Easier to say than to do; but important to say anyway.

How do you deal with attack?

You can be totally rested, though, and thoroughly refreshed, and that will not insulate you from the possibility of being attacked by your opponents. Your opponents may not be polite. They may get nasty. The more successful you appear to be, the nastier they may get. They may block you in ways you didn't anticipate. They may threaten you, and mean it, and act on their threats. They can make your life very unpleasant.

This is especially true if you are young: (The speaker here is the staff person of a coalition of Latino youth).

> *Like this summer was extremely brutal for us, because we were constantly under attack by the city. The image of young people in the city by adults is that they're bad, that they're the reason that the city has sort of like gone in a downward spiral. It's this whole mentality that if you see a group of five young people on a city bench, they're a gang. So we were kicked out of City Hall for doing voter registration. We also had these flower pots in front of our office that the young people painted, and they were literally taken away from us by the city because they were seen as a health hazard. The painted flower pots.*

And especially true if you belong to a vulnerable group in the community:

> *And then—I mean, these are youth that very few people want to work with. They're extremely, quote-unquote, "high risk" for everything. But they also have a huge potential for everything. I mean, we see that. And there's a certain perception among community leaders that we're just a place for the bad kids. That for some reason all 400-and-whatever youth we work with on an active basis throughout the year are all bad. They're all bad youth. You know, there are no good youth in our group.*

And if somebody in power feels endangered by you—feels that they might lose something of value, or might somehow be diminished—they can react emotionally and irrationally.

> *So then there's this park, which is where all the drug dealing and prostitution go on—it's like a very unsafe park. And one of the things that the youth decided to do was to take it over for the entire summer. So, like in the middle of June, they held a community-wide barbecue where 400 people showed up. And then at the end of the summer, they held another huge party with 600 people. I mean, it was packed, and in between they held different events, and they cleaned it up, you know, things like that.*
>
> *And on one side of the park is this wall that's been graffiti'd over. It's a mess. No one's ever taken care of it. I mean, it's really an eyesore. So the youth decided we're going to paint a Central American history mural on it and we got permission to paint it from City Hall. And the week before we were about to start painting it, the permission was taken away from us by*

City Hall, because one of the City Council people basically went on a rampage against us and the young people, saying that we were racist and bigoted [sic], and didn't know what multi-culturalism meant. . . .

Then, with the second party in the park, we didn't get the permit till three days before the event, even though we had already asked for it in May. It kept on getting mysteriously lost. But I mean, we just went forward. We were all expecting to get arrested that day. That was like the mindset amongst the youth and the adult staff, was that we're going to hold the event and we're just going to get arrested. For a party in the park. Right. You know, a positive, community-supported event in a park that nothing positive ever happens in.

And then what happened after the summer, in September, is this City Council person puts in an ordinance basically to the effect that there is to be no public party, no festival of any sort on public property in the city. She also puts in a second ordinance that there was never going to be any public art, ever, painted in the entire city of Chelsea on public property.

You may have to deal with such antagonistic reactions. What's more, your opponents may also go after you personally. They may make ethnic or racial slurs, or more subtle innuendoes. They may drag your name through the mud, and pile dirt on top of it.

Right. And then I got attacked for about 20 minutes by this person personally. Why? The city's always had a very difficult time with me as being director [staff person of the youth coalition] because there's never been a Latino male in a directorship position. Certain department heads and so on won't deal with me. I'd hate to—I'd like to think it's for other reasons, but I know it's not.

As we've suggested before, advocacy involves risk. Risk is embedded in social action. It comes with the job. It can't be avoided. And you, as advocate, have to be tough enough to withstand that risk, to bear up under whatever opposition may come your way. Effective social action can take all you have to give.

The same is true for your coalition, if it advocates. It, too, will have to stand up to attack. Your opposition may try to divide your members, to discredit you in the eyes of the community, to point out every stupid thing you have ever done, and to take away your funding. They may play hardball.

The pressure on the coalition to compromise, back off, ease up, give in, may be intense. To stand up under that pressure, to stick up for what you believe in, involves not only risk, but also courage. You and your members may be personally tested here, in ways you never anticipated and never wanted. Is your coalition strong enough to meet that test? And is this the occasion where you want to make your stand? It will help you to have thought about those questions, and to have positive answers to them, before you enter a difficult advocacy situation. You don't want to find out "no" the hard way.

The Prospects of Advocacy Success

Since we have seen that the advocate takes risks, expends considerable energy, and yet faces harsh attack and possible loss of support, it's reasonable to question the prospects of advocacy success. Coalition advocacy may be morally desirable, or morally imperative. But if we are suggesting that coalitions advocate, as we have done, what are the realistic chances that such advocacy is going to produce desired results, and do any more than make people feel good about themselves? Of course, the answer will depend upon the particular situation. A generic answer is hard to come by. Yet pushed to offer one, we would venture that the prospects for success are reasonably bright. This example is not uncommon:

> *The Medicaid office was closing all the local access points, while we were demanding better access in our area. So we invited the Medicaid people to come to talk—first they said "yes," but then three days before the meeting they said "no"; they're not going to show. But then we informed them that we also had invited three state legislators to the meeting to hear about this issue; at that point they said, "Okay, we'll be there."*
>
> *It was an outrageous meeting. I missed it, and everybody was glad I missed it, because they said I would have gone through the roof and been impolite. But during this meeting they really got pushed for increasing access. And all of a sudden the 800-number that had been promised and hadn't been available for months was delivered very shortly thereafter. So it was an example of taking a position for better services, pushing hard for it, and then getting it.*

It would be misleading and untrue to suggest that coalition advocacy, or any advocacy, will be successful all the time. Even when success occurs, it may be partial, and it may certainly be impermanent. Your victory may be snatched out from under you; the same battles may have to be fought again and again.

> *Well, that was a success. I mean, it was a temporary success, because they gave us the 800-number, but they've continued to dissolve and dismantle the system. So you have to keep at it all the time. It doesn't always lead to long-term change.*

What's more, even seasoned advocates sometimes lose, and lose outright. Part of the explanation may be that they are often competing with equally seasoned advocates who have a different point of view. Precisely because a position is worth advocating for, it is likely to have advocates on the other side of the fence. They may have the same skills and relationships and energy you do; they might have more. And it's barely possible that their position has some merit—not they that are right, because that would mean you are wrong, but that they have an argument or two in their favor.

181

Finally, even if you were exquisitely skilled and there were no direct opposition, you might still not be successful. Here's one place to remind ourselves that even though coalitions are usually more powerful than single individuals, they may still be going up against up social, political, and economic systems that are larger, more entrenched, and much more powerful than they are.

> *There are times when we've been in communities where the superintendent of schools is a tyrant and unhelpful. But you can't make a direct hit on people who are vengeful, because by confronting them they will cut you out of access to any programs with schools. You have to somehow figure out a way to finesse those relationships. So if people are working to come up with a new school committee that will hire a new school superintendent, then if you can support them informally, you do that.*

While it is appealing to think that a skilled coalition can move heaven and earth, it is also a little grandiose; and carried too far, it can be somewhat demoralizing. Moving heaven and earth can be your next project. For now, it may be best to farm a few acres.

So there are limits, as well as uncertainty. But within these limits, there are plenty of possibilities for advocacy success. True, when you win, your wins may be small, or partial. But these are wins that might well not have occurred had you been silent. Those victories belong to you.

And you can improve your prospects. Experience is a veteran teacher, and with experience you can get better at what you do. Simply by repeating your message, keeping up the pressure, and not going away, you are likely to be more effective over time. You may also convert a few more members to your cause, or at least defuse some of your most active opposition. You can certainly advocate without alienating others.

Finally, if you have a cause worth fighting for, it is possible that with continued and thoughtful advocacy, people will gradually come around to your point of view. More than three centuries ago, John Milton wrote, "Let her [truth] and Falsehood grapple: Who ever knew Truth put to the worse in a free and open encounter?" And while Milton did not have coalitions in mind, the sentiment still applies.

> *If you can get politicians to hear and understand what's going on in their community, and if they are reasonable people, then when options are put forth to them and they can understand the implications of those options for real-life situations, the good politicians of any side of the aisle will do the right thing. That's my belief—I've seen that happen a lot.*
>
> *The political process makes a lot of decisions, a lot of policies that impact people. We can't ignore it. We've been talking about how to make it work best for a community. And that we can do.*

We are optimistic enough to believe that in the long run, with repeated advocacy, truth will out, and a just cause will prevail. Not by themselves, for truth and justice themselves have no voice. But with trained and dedicated advocates, fighting by their side, singly and in coalitions, the prospects for success grow brighter with each moment.

Lessons From The Field

Should Coalitions Advocate?

- The pros: The coalition must speak out for what it believes in; the facts don't speak for themselves; the coalition has a leadership role; the coalition has a moral responsibility. And successful advocacy strengthens the coalition.
- The cons: Advocacy can cost the coalition member support, community support, and financial support. The coalition may jeopardize its community standing. Advocacy can alienate people you may need to deal with again. And others might handle the advocacy work.
- On balance: There is a genuine advocacy role for coalitions. Coalitions should certainly advocate on issues their members feel strongly about. But such advocacy should also keep the above cautions clearly in mind.
- Advocacy, even strong advocacy, need not mean antagonizing the people who can make decisions in your favor. It is usually possible to advocate, even forcefully, without alienating decision-makers.
- At the same time, effective advocacy involves some risk; it does take willingness to face and endure potentially powerful opposition. And sometimes, it can take great courage, conviction, and tenacity to stay the course.

Advocacy Tactics

- Any advocate has many tactics to choose from. The list is essentially endless, for creative variations are always possible.
- And to extend your options: a) advocacy tactics can be used in combination, more than one at a time; b) different advocacy tactics can be used for different target groups; and c) different tactics can be used at different stages of the advocacy process. Varying your tactics along these lines is generally a plus.
- What should determine your choice of tactics? Three key factors: a) *your specific goal:* What exactly do you want to achieve? b) *your target group:* What will benefit this particular audience? and c) *your own resources:* Your power; your allies; your

members; your budget; and the time, interest, and passion you and your members have available for your cause. The actual advocacy tactics chosen should be determined by the best fit between these factors.

Some General Advocacy Principles

■ **The right preparation.** Know your facts. Research your issue. Do your homework. Gain as much expertise on your topic as you can. And before you speak, think about what you want to say and how you want to say it.

■ **The right communicator.** Be a reliable as well as a knowledgeable communicator: Mean what you say; deliver on your promises. Show your intended audience that you and your members are similar to them in your interests, values, and ultimate goals. Build a relationship whenever you can.

■ **The right message.** State clear reasons why the decision-makers should adopt your point of view; show why those reasons are in the decision-makers' own interests; back up those reasons with facts; and give successful examples of similar decisions made.

■ **The right request.** Make specific requests, which are feasible for the decision-maker to act upon, and which can be acted upon now. Obtain a public commitment by the decision-maker to act favorably upon your requests, with an agreed-upon timeframe.

■ **Repetition.** Repeat the steps above as necessary.

Some General Advocacy Issues

■ When advocacy is called for, it can be done by individual members of the coalition, as contrasted with the coalition itself.

■ It's almost always better to begin with a gentler and more polite advocacy approach. This may do the job, and it's less likely to backfire among your target audience.

■ But if gentler approaches fail, the coalition may choose to take strong, vigorous, controversial, and adversarial positions, and often properly so. Yet taking such advocacy positions should be done thoughtfully, taking note of prevailing community opinion, and with awareness of the possible negative as well as the positive consequences.

■ Finally, coalition advocacy is based on optimistic assumptions—that the coalition has genuine power, that it can use its power intelligently, and that by choosing the right tactics, and by being as tenacious as necessary, it can really achieve its goals. Advocacy also rests on faith that just causes win. Very often, they do. And very often, that faith helps create the victory.

Legislative Round Table   Issues to be Addressed

Please fill out the form below and either bring it to the next Coalition meeting or send it to Al Bashevkin c/o Coalition NASC. Make copies available to your staff. We'll use this for our Feb 13 Legislative Round Table.

A. What legislative issues are of most concern to you:

       1.

       2.

       3.

       4.

B: Specifically:

       1. Specific bills which you would like to see supported or defeated (list bill # if available)

       2. Specific policy issues you would like to see addressed.

       3. Specific funding issues you would like to see addressed.

       4. Specific new initiatives you would like to see addressed.

C. Do you have a specific response you would like to hear back from the legislators on?

D. Any ideas that you can offer specific information on for our discussions with the legislators?

Your Name:

Agency (address and phone):

Before specific advocacy occurs, a coalition might plan its advocacy agenda and strategies. For legislative advocacy, a simple survey like this one can do the job.

The Fall River
Health and Human Services Coalition

cordially invites you to

"A Legislative Forum"

10:00 a.m., Friday, April 28, 1989

at

White's of Westport, State Road
Westport, Massachusetts

Honored Guests

Representative Robert Correia

Representative John George

Representative Albert Herren

Representative Edward Lambert

Representative Denis Lawrence

Representative Joan M. Menard

Gratuitous Continental Breakfast Served

Guests Welcome!

For more information, please call: 675-6011 Ext. 318

Funded in part through a grant from the Massachusetts Executive Office of Community and Development,
Governor's Office of Human Resources, Youth 2000 Program

With your advocacy agenda, you can invite your legislators (or other target group) to a forum where you can publicly and politely get your points across. Legislators do come to these events, for all the reasons stated in the text.

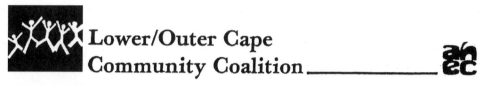

March 21, 1997

Senator Henri Rauschenbach
The State House, Room 315
Boston, MA 02133-1054

Dear Henri:

As members of the Lower/Outer Cape Community Coalition's Advisory Board who are committed to improving the quality of life of Lower/Outer Cape residents, we hereby, endorse and urge your support of the following legislation:

* Newborn Home Visiting Program; H-3064, S-479

* Neighborhood and Family support; H-3059

* The ACE Bill—Affordable Child Care for Everyone; H-1909

* An Act to Utilize Existing Education and Training Programs to Enable Welfare Recipients to Obtain Paid Employment; H-2687

Also, we urge you to oppose the following bill:

* State Controlled Smoking Regulations; H-1313

Please take the needs and interest of the Lower/Outer Cape community into account as you move into the budget debate.

Sincerely yours,

Office: Unit #3, Oracle Square, Orleans, MA   BL Hathaway, *Coalition Coordinator*
Mail: P.O. Box 797, Eastham, MA 02642   508-255-2163, Fax: 508-255-4928, Email: coalition @ c4 • net

Or you can write to decision-makers: here's a hybrid form, combining letter and petition. Perhaps individual letters and calls might have had more impact here. But this coalition represents a tight-knit community. Members know the legislator personally (note the use of his first name), and he knows them, too. They are locally influential people; so the legislator is likely to pay attention.

WE ARE DECLARING NOVEMBER 6 AS "ENOUGH IS ENOUGH" CALL IN DAY!

As human service workers and advocates, we have seen the steady erosion of services to our neediest citizens. (An additional $42.7M was cut from human services on 10/26.) House Leadership is now considering revenue proposals to address the State's ongoing fiscal crisis. **Your phone call is critical** as the House continues their deliberations on taxes and savings proposals. If they don't pass a revenue package now, revenues will likely not be addressed until after the 1990 elections.

THIS IS OUR LAST CHANCE!

We are coordinating a state-wide call in day to carry the message on the flip side of this flyer to the House. We're hoping at least 20 communities will make 50 calls for 1,000 calls on 11/6. Please call House Leadership in addition to your own representatives on "Enough is Enough" day. House Leadership names and numbers are below:

- Rep. George Keverian, Speaker (617) 722-2500
- Rep. Richard Voke, (617) 722-2990
  Chair, House Ways and Means

Please call the following sponsors if you have any questions:

- Deborah Weinstein, Massachusetts Human Services Coalitions, Inc. (617) 482-6119
- Tom Wolf, Area Health Education Coalitions, (413) 253-2646
- Debra McLaughlin, Franklin County/Athol Budget Crisis Coalition, (413) 774-3167

There are times to be more assertive and less polite, such as when your budgets are cut. This phone-in campaign was a statewide effort organized by several coalitions that joined together for the purpose.

**NORTHERN BERKSHIRE
COMMUNITY COALITION**

**NASC B0X 9075
NORTH ADAMS MA 01247
662-5519**

April 12, 1996

Callahan Sign Company
Attn: Maurice Callahan, Owner
4 Westview Road
Pittsfield, MA 01201

Dear Mr. Callahan,

The Northern Berkshire Community Coalition, a conglomerate of Health & Human
Service Agencies from Central and Northern Berkshire County, would like to express our
concern at the placement of tobacco advertising on billboards throughout Northern
Berkshire. We understand that you have met several times with a Billboard Committee
from Berkshire County and that they have expressed the gravity of the situation. Surely, you
have been made aware as to the effectiveness of the Joe Camel advertisements and their
potential impact on impressionable children and teens. As a way of adding our voices to the
ever increasing call for effective restraint in tobacco advertising aimed toward youth;

> *We, the undersigned, as a concerned coalition, respectively ask that
> you do everything within your power, to locate these advertisements
> in discreet areas away from any close proximity to schools, bus
> stops, or other places that youth may frequent.*

_____   North Adams Tobacco Awareness Program
Name   Organization

_____   Dept. of Transitional Assistance
Name   Organization

*Of course, not all advocacy is legislative. This is a letter to a billboard owner
who posted tobacco ads. It got results.*

Athol woman offers advice

By Richard J. Chaisson
Telegram & Gazette Staff

ATHOL — From her cubbyhole office on the second floor of the Athol YMCA Building, Barbara Corey talked by telephone to President Clinton at the White House yesterday afternoon.

"We need your help, Mr. President," she said politely but forcefully. "A (Republican-proposed) cut this immense will cause human misery and suffering.

"The working men and women, the retired who have worked long and hard need you. We need you to stand firm and strong against those Republican bullies. We can't foster this environment that gives to the rich and takes from the poor."

CRITICALLY IMPORTANT

She added: "Our wonderful local community hospital, Athol Memorial Hospital, will surely close. Its affiliate, UMass Medical Center, a critically important teaching hospital, will be severely impacted. This will end up by devastating our local, rural people.

'We need your help," she repeated.

Clinton echoed her concern. "As we lower the costs of Medicare and Medicaid, we need to do it in a decent way. We can do this, but if we do it too far and too fast, we're going to hurt not only the elderly but their children," he told her.

Corey, coordinator of the nine-town North Quabbin Community

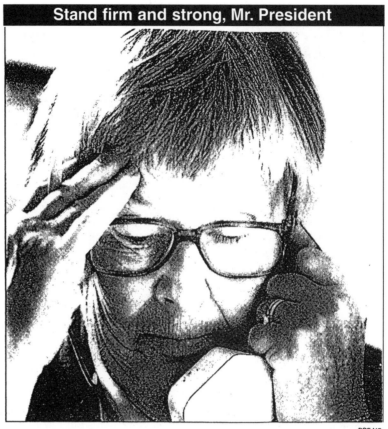

Stand firm and strong, Mr. President

BOB MO

Barbara Corey of Athol talks with President Clinton about conflicts between budget cuts and health care.

Coalition, was one of seven health care activists and providers in New England engaged in a conference call with Clinton, at his invitation.

"In my community, in my work here," Corey said when she took the phone, "I know many people who depend on Medicare. They are great people. They are not lazy. They need you to protect them."

She told the president about a local man whose 76-year-old mother is arthritic, lives alone, has no savings account and survives on a Society Security check of $400 a month.

"She can't swing that without help from her son, George. He is working hard to keep his family of four safe. In both households you have people who worry incessantly about paying their cur-

rent bills, and now they are worrying about increased costs.

"It's a tough time," Corey s

Clinton agreed. "It is a tough time," he said.

For 40 minutes, Clinton told about the potential effect proposed Republican cuts health care on communities

Turn to PRESIDENT:Page

And if you think you can't get through to the President, here's one coalition coordinator who did. We shouldn't overestimate the impact of a single phone call; but neither should we discount the importance of taking advantage of all advocacy channels at your disposal.

Chapter 10

Maintaining The Coalition

Should our coalition keep on growing?

What are some choices other than growth?

How should we choose among the different options available?

What are the coalition's key maintenance needs?

Now that your coalition may be well under way, a question for you: Is it harder to get something started, or to keep it going? In coalition terms, is it harder to begin a new coalition, or to maintain the momentum once it's under way? Think before answering.

If physical laws were our guide, we would say "starting" rather than "maintaining." It takes more force to overcome the inertia of rest than the inertia of motion. It takes more energy to get a train moving out of the station than to keep it going down the track. (Isn't it hardest to get out of bed in the morning?)

But the laws of "social physics" are different; or at least, what applies to trains doesn't apply as neatly to social organisms like coalitions. The coalition is more likely to have a mind of its own. It's more likely to veer off the track. It's more likely to be tempted by spurs and side excursions—scenically pretty, but sometimes dead ends. The conductor may have his or her own ideas. And on the coalition train, passengers can vote on their destination.

What's more, the coalition is more likely to wander because the tracks are poorly laid down in the first place. Few guidelines tell the coalition where to go. The train has it easy; it follows the rails. The coalition—more like a covered wagon—will often have to blaze its own trail.

Metaphors aside, maintaining the coalition is a major issue. You want your coalition to have a long and healthy lifetime, and to do marvelous things in the world. It can, and let's hope it will, but that won't happen automatically. The coalition effort needs to be sustained.

> *Let me tell you, I think probably one of the most difficult things is the sustainability of it. It isn't as difficult getting that first effort under way. What's reared its ugly head on a regular basis is how do you keep it going? Sometimes the picture changes. It's never clear sailing.*

And what if the coalition has an operating budget? Maintenance issues become that much more vital.

> *We're suddenly in this place of saying, "Oh, how are we going to sustain the work of our coalition?" We all know it's not easy to secure funds for indirect services, like ours. Funders want to know how many clients you've served this week, or how many mouths you've fed. So there's a sales piece to it. And we certainly haven't begun to figure it out. I mean, our advisory board just has begun undertaking some of the initial conversations. It's a problem. It's a problem.*

* * *

> *Well, sustainability's a real nightmare. And it's one of the most complicated issues, not just in coalition building, but in all of human service funding. There's a profound American mythology around funding, which is that we will give people seed money, and then someone else is gonna come in and pick it up. It's the concept that there's somehow an ever-expanding amount of pick-up dollars sitting in a community just waiting for a new idea to come along. And I think that's a myth. The hardest money to find is the money to continue a good new idea.*

There are two key issues here. One, and our primary concern in this chapter, is what direction you want to head in. How do you want to develop as a coalition, as you mature? There are many choices available to the coalition, many pathways and destinations. Much of what we want to do in this chapter is to examine some of them. Which direction should you choose, and how should you go about choosing it?

But toward the end, we also want to comment on maintaining the coalition's energy in the first place, so that you can head in some direction at all. Groups need psychological fuel. Without it, group energy can flicker and die—on this point you can probably summon many personal examples. What does it take to keep that energy alive? Not just alive, but luminous and lasting?

Some Possible Coalition Directions

Growing. You can grow. This is a natural tendency of groups and organizations, especially if they are doing well.

And suppose you are doing well: Why not do more of what you've been doing, or branch out or up? You have taken on some tasks successfully; how about some more? How about a new challenge, in a different area? And, you may say, we have operated on a bare-bones budget, or no budget at all—now let's see what we can do if we get a little money. Maybe we're ready for a membership drive, and maybe we ought to start thinking about some flyers, or a media campaign. . . .

Organisms tend to grow as they mature—biological organisms, and social organisms, too. A coalition is a living organism, subject to the same principles. There is a crucial difference, though, between coalitions and simpler living systems: The coalition can choose how it will grow, and whether it will grow at all.

Coalition growth may be good. It may be the right way for you to go. Why not get more done? Why not capitalize and build upon your success? Maybe you can in fact handle more things; maybe the community need is there; maybe your members want to grow; maybe others in the community want that as well: And maybe that's what you should do.

But when you start thinking about growing, look before you leap, or even step. Walk with your eyes wide open. It's helpful for the coalition to know some of the dangers that come with expansion.

1. If you grow bigger, you will need more resources to sustain you. In plainer language, you'll have more mouths to feed. A bigger coalition has higher daily caloric requirements. For coalitions, calories take the form of dollars.

> *We've grown in size, and we've been able to secure some significant grants to keep us going. We've begun some really neat things, and I'd like to see these continue. But now there are money issues. This is the first time we've grown during our 10 years. The question is, are we going to be able to keep these resources coming in from new sources? And I'm worried whether we're going to be able to do that or not.*

2. Growth also puts more pressure on the coalition leader:

> *I think I would take growth very cautiously. Within my job, I'm not sure I can do much more. And if we were to grow more, that would certainly put more pressure on me to do more. So, I would be very careful. . . .*

The leader (and members) can only do so much. And yet, growth can also mean new opportunities for the coalition that are difficult to pass up:

I think we need to look at those growth opportunities, because there's not a whole lot out there, and we need to seize the opportunities we can.

So you make trade-offs:

We're very cautious about taking on new projects, because we are in some ways less available. But over the last two or three years our coalitions have gotten additional money to do special projects in neighborhood development—it absorbs a lot of our focus and time. At this point, we see it as a priority to be developing these grassroots community mobilization kinds of efforts. So it's a trade-off we're willing to make. But it's a risky trade-off.

3. One further concern about growth is more particular to coalitions. As the coalition gets bigger, more visible, and more accepted in the community, there can be pressure to become administrators of community services. Not just to plan, coordinate, and catalyze services, but actually to run them. "It was your idea to start X," your colleagues may claim. "So, gee, you're the natural folks to direct it."

But once you move beyond action planning and program start-up, and into program administration, you may become quite a different type of organization. You lose a certain kind of purity; you can be trapped. For one thing (*see also Chapter 8*), you risk changing your relationship with your own coalition members, who may already be delivering similar services. These are the same members whom you ask for tangible help and support, sometimes money too, and whom you depend on every day.

Coalitions are supposed to be neutral forums. If they are given large amounts of money, they may distribute the money to the members of their coalition. And then they have to monitor those members in terms of how they're doing. I don't know how you remain a neutral forum if you are also monitoring contracts. I think it's impossible to do that. If one of your member agencies doesn't do their job, then all of a sudden you may have to pull the contract. You certainly wield a position of rewarding and punishing members with dollars.

I think that's very hard. "Never" isn't a word that I use easily, because you can always find exceptions. But I think it's very tricky to be a neutral forum and also be essentially a system that is putting out dollars and monitoring the impact of those dollars.

And for another thing: Do you really want to be a direct service provider?

I think every bit of growth has to be very carefully examined as to what it's going to do to the coalition's catalyst role—to how much time gets involved just focusing in on your own program development, and not look-ing at the community at large. These are risks as you grow larger. Again, I hate to lay out specific rules. But in general, I'm very concerned about coali-tions getting large amounts of money and running lots of programs, because they're doing so much internally that they stop looking externally.

They get separated from the community. They are more concerned with their own financial well-being, and also their programmatic responsibilities. They've been given money to run a neighborhood outreach program, or a health education information program, and the coalition is now very involved in all that internal stuff. And they don't have the chance, the time to do the other things; to ask the community, "What are your issues?" To do the newsletter. To gather people together. There's a limited amount of ener-gy, and it gets absorbed in those programmatic things. And if they also get additional staff, then they become the next empire.

4. There's one more growth-related issue that's different from needing new resources, or pressuring the leadership, or running programs. It's that you can get spread too thin. Maybe for very good reasons or intentions, you want to do more. Or people ask you, and it's hard to say no. ("If you want to get something done, ask a busy person.") And then, as for any system, you start feeling the strain of overload. Even if you can manage the strain, the quality of what you do begins to deteriorate. This powerful idea suggests that growth contains the seeds of its own destruction. The danger of success is that it steers you toward failure.

The core of this issue centers once more around time. You simply don't have time to do all you'd like to do, or all that is asked of you, not with your present resources. You get pulled too far, you lose your solidity; your balance weakens, and you can fall.

Someone is asking us to take on a leadership role, or even calling for a support letter. I will prod the coalition to look at all aspects of it. Is this some-thing we want to do? Is this something we want to give our staff time or our volunteer time to? Do we want to contribute to the greater good, or do we want to pull back and focus more on our own internal agenda?

When people call, it is tricky. It's very muddy here. What happens is the more effectively you carry through a particular task, the more work you engender for the coalition, because everyone now perceives your expertise being there. So more is asked of you as new situations come along. We've been talking about perhaps trying not to be so successful.

I think given what I know about our own coalition, it can't expand much more. The expansion would take the coalition too far beyond its own inter-nal agenda and its own internal needs to keep it healthy and dynamic. The coalition needs time for its own community empowerment, and if you're constantly responding to an external agenda then you can't do that. The more it responds, the further it gets pulled away from its internal organiza-

tion, and many, many an agency director has been pulled so far out that they have not given time and attention to the infrastructure within, so that things begin to collapse.

Resolving the issues of growth. While all these issues surrounding growth should make you stop and think, they are resolvable. The resolution begins by realizing that growth is not all or nothing. It's not simply grow or stay stagnant, or grow or die. Your growth can instead be targeted and controlled. You can choose the degree to which you want to grow, when you want to do it, in what respects, and how. You can engage in coalition career planning.

When you do, it always helps if you build from a stable base:

> *We need to be strong with what we already have and be certain that growth is in a healthy and productive direction, before we start tinkering in new areas where we have to relearn again. Each time we grow, we learn. I mean, we're starting all over again. For us to start a whole new area, it's probably going to take some time for us to learn to do it right, and I'd like to make our current work more solid before we start approaching anything else.*

So, in a nutshell: If you choose to grow, you want to be in control of the process, and not let the process be in control of you. If you've come this far in this book, and in your coalition, you can do this. With practice, it can become a matter of course.

Now for a quiz, to test your new knowledge.

Suppose you are a coalition leader and you have the opportunity to acquire some new money, but with only a one-year guarantee. You'd hate to turn the money down. But you don't want to be left holding the bag after one year either.

What's your answer? Make sure you've got it in mind before you read on and see how this leader (in this case, a leader of several different coalitions) did it.

> *State government turned to us and said, "We have a large amount of money as a result of the new tobacco tax. We want to put $70,000 in some communities for one year to start a certain kind of school coalition. Think about it."*
>
> *And so we started to think about it, and one of the things that concerned me enormously was to have five or 10 communities, who had started $70,000 projects with one-year money, no guarantees of a second year. Who, 11 months later, would all be at my doorstep whining,*

> "Where's my next $70,000? How could you have done this to me?"
>
> What we decided was to try to create things that didn't require that kind of sustainability. We went in for training parent leaders, because if we could train parents to be better leaders and better citizens, more involved with their school committees, then that would continue without dollars. And if we could teach the schools, parents, and community-based agencies to build better relationships with each other, then those better relationships could be sustained later on, too.
>
> Another decision we made was to urge people to do lots of small projects. Because it was more likely that a good school superintendent could find $5,000 to continue a small after-school program than to find $20,000 to continue a big after-school program. That was our strategy, and I think it worked relatively well.
>
> We have learned to think ahead about what's going to be needed later on, and to design it that way. But still the sustainability issue is a tricky one. It's very tricky. What you count on is that if you do good enough work, if you are careful about your budget, and if you keep a sharp enough eye open, you'll be identifying another potential funder as you go along. It may or may not happen.

"Spinning off." Growth—planned and controlled—may be a goal for your coalition, and a sensible and wise one, but choosing growth is not the only option. Whatever new initiatives the coalition takes on need not be permanent; they can be temporary. That is, you can take on something new, get it started, and then let it go. You can be the incubator, the mother bird, until the fledgling gets its wings and is mature enough to fly on its own.

The basic concept is simple:

> Every time you create a new program—a shelter, or prevention program, or an information and referral service, or a family place—you have to spin it off and give it to someone else, because by definition you're too part-time and too small to become the agency that runs it.

Yet when you spin something off, there are issues of parental responsibility. How far does your responsibility go? How long do you keep your attachment? You don't want to hang on too long, because that's an energy drain on you, and not healthy for your offspring. Yet you certainly don't want to be accused of child neglect or abandonment.

> So the question then becomes, do we just spin these things off and just let them go off on their own, or do we continue to have a responsibility to make

sure they are functioning? And obviously people feel that we have to maintain the responsibility. But then what happens if you don't have the funds to be able to ensure that?

Also, if you do send the new venture out on its own, you take your chances. The child might turn out to be ungrateful. The project could come back to haunt you.

> *We spun off a shelter in a community, run by a private vendor. Then three or four years later, we worked with a group of parents who wanted a family resource center with books and videos to enrich parenting in the community. I'm thinking, well, let's put it in the living room of the shelter, because it's right downtown, and it's a building that we helped get them. We go to the shelter, and the shelter says, "We don't want that—we don't want those people in our living room." And I think, my God, what have we created here? It's like Frankenstein's monster.*

Spinning off new programs—and seeking to develop new programs precisely so that they can be spun off—is often an excellent choice. True, success is not guaranteed. But when you spin something off, what you can do is to set up conditions, and make the rules of future engagement clear. You can agree to provide technical assistance and consultation and be there for others. You can stipulate as best you can what you will and will not do. Still, the reality is that when you spin a program off, it's largely out of your control—which is part of the reason why you wanted to spin it off in the first place. You can't have it both ways. It's a good life lesson in letting go.

Changing focus. An effective coalition does not have to grow, and it does not have to spin off new programs. It can simply change its focus. The community issues change; so the coalition changes as well. Here's one coalition whose first issue was health care, language translation in particular. That issue was successfully dealt with. Through the coalition's efforts, an effective medical interpreter system was put into place, and the coalition was ready to move on.

> *I think that translation gap has been narrowed. That it's 100 percent closed? No. But that it is 100 percent better than what it used to be? Yes. So we just thought there was no need at this point to continue, and that we could place our energy onto other issues.*
>
> *For example, we've been talking right now about youth . . . and what's interesting is, as we begin to focus on youth, people start to line up and say, "Oh, they're focusing on youth; I'm interested. This is what I'm doing, or I would like to do this." And that's never happened before.*
>
> *With medical interpreting, we went to them. Now people who are already working with youth are coming to us. And I think that's the difference. We were knocking on their door; now they're knocking on our door.*

So this coalition, in a natural sequence of events, looks toward a new issue. Its track record of success both attracts new members and increases the prospects for more success in the future. This is one common evolutionary path of the coalition, and a fully justifiable path, even though we might not choose to call it "growth" as more narrowly defined.

It's also possible to change not only the issue, but also the coalition members who take the lead in dealing with it. Those new leaders could be more appropriate leaders, being closer to and more affected by the new problem. For example, here's another coalition that was concerned with youth from the start. As it evolved, the youth issues broadened. More importantly, the people who took responsibility for running the coalition gradually changed from a group of agency representatives to the youth themselves.

> *We started as a coalition working with young women who were at high risk for pregnancy. But we gradually moved from pregnancy prevention into working more on other issues that affect youth. Also, historically, the coalition was all the youth service organizations meeting to talk about how to work with young people—you know, how they should be responsible sexually, and so on. It was really more of the agency people meeting, not so much the youth meeting.*
>
> *But then youth became much more involved in defining the coalition, because now it had a much broader mission. It was now serving all the young people in the city, particularly high-risk youth. So in that transition phase, from pregnancy prevention to a youth development model, that's where we began to have a much higher involvement of young people— because you can't build a youth organization without young people's input; they have to from day one own it, or else it becomes just another social service agency.*
>
> *Then what really happened in the last year is that the old coalition has basically stopped meeting. I had kept challenging them, you know, "Why are we meeting? Why are we coming together? Is what happened six years ago still functional now?" That was really my big question. And they kept on going back to, "Well, at least we're getting together and talking." To them that was okay. But it was very hard to get any new kind of thinking across.*
>
> *So what's happening now with the old coalition, the agency folks, is that they get monthly mailings as to what's going on. They become more like a mailing list. But I'm also in touch with them on a monthly basis. You know, "Sheila, how are you doing?" Because I don't want to lose any of that contact. . . .*
>
> *Sometimes a group loses its original reason for being there, and I think that definitely happened with this old coalition. It moved from action, to*

advisory, to let's just get together, to let's stay involved. I think they themselves realized that it sort of outgrew its purpose. It was time to grow into something else.

And now we have set up a youth board that fluctuates between 12 and 15 members. The youth facilitate and organize the meetings. And they have created a new force for change.

The original coalition simply lost its reason for existing. A new group took over. Several positive developments probably happened in this process. The new coalition broadened its scope, and the people running the new group, the youth themselves, took more control over their own destiny. Should the old coalition members have stayed together? Maybe. But they weren't discarded. They still stay in touch. They could regroup if the right circumstances arose.

Cutting back. In a different scenario, suppose a coalition hits tough times, external or internal, economic or psychological. Or suppose another group in the community takes shape that seems to be providing the same functions. If either of these situations comes along, and if they are severe or prolonged, you can downsize. You can simply cut back.

There may be good reasons to do so. You may need to consolidate a little after some healthy growth. You may have grown too fast, and need to make some readjustments. A large grant may be coming to an end. Some other group may now be willing to take over an activity that's been an albatross around your neck, praise the Lord. Or that albatross may finally, finally be ready to leave the nest by itself. All these events, like others we have mentioned, are normal events in a coalition's development. (And, as a reminder, neither growth nor downsizing has to be forever. If you cut back now, that doesn't mean you'll never grow again. The evolutionary path of coalitions, and of social systems, is not usually a straight line.)

So cutting back could be a reasonable idea, at least for the moment. It weeds out inefficiencies, and brings you back to basics:

We certainly have seen coalitions close programs when their grants have ended. We have also cut programs for other reasons, but mainly because they hadn't been working anymore.

* * *

If we have to shrink back to the core, that's not a defeat. It's an awareness that we don't want to lose the most important things we do, which are the meetings and the newsletter. . . .

* * *

> *My feeling is that they're probably going to go back to part-time staff, which has its merits. I think it's all right to go back to the basic kind of thing: the monthly meeting, a couple of projects. . . .*

And another possible justification for cutting back is that it prompts you to think more carefully about priorities:

> *Our funding cycle is on the downward trend. We're in the fourth year of a major grant, so the amount of time for the coordinator is going to be cut in half, and so the steering committee needs to think about what they want this coalition to be involved with. Do they want to go back to the more subdued state it was in prior to these last few years, or what? And if they do want it to be staffed at the same level—then what are they going to do about the funding sources?*

Ending. You can also go out of business, simply stop operating. This is often a sad event; but not always.

Some coalitions get started because of external pressures, or external mandates. This is not preferred, compared to when the starting energy comes from the inside; but such coalitions can work if the energy, the impetus, the raison d'être becomes internalized. It can happen.

But if it doesn't, if <u>internal</u> motivation does not develop, then should the external mandate end, the coalition is likely to dissolve.

> *I was part of an inter-agency coalition in my community, which was started by the human service office in the state capital. They wanted the different state-funded agencies in each town to get together to do joint planning. Nobody where I was especially wanted to do this, but we complied. We had to.*
>
> *So we got together once a month, and sat around a table. Refreshments were served. We talked about what was going on in our agencies, chit-chat mostly. Our host, who was the director of an important agency, gave updates about her cats. A legislative aide came to promote his boss's reelection campaign. Nobody wanted to **do** anything. I suggested a couple of proposals for joint action, but they got quashed—no one wanted to get involved in anything new.*
>
> *When the situation changed in Boston, the pressure to have these inter-agency coalitions diminished. So our meetings ground to a halt; no big surprise. Relations stayed cordial, and people would call each other as needed, but there was no desire or perceived need to meet on any kind of regular basis.*

There was no internal purpose for this coalition in the first place, none ever developed, and when the external purpose disappeared, there was nothing left. No one regretted it.

Sometimes the internal motivation to continue is present, but the dollars aren't. If the coalition depends on funding, and the funding ends (and funding can end), the coalition may simply cease to exist.

> *We had a multi-ethnic coalition which focused on substance abuse. We were supposed to teach parents how to teach their kids to avoid drugs—to hold parent trainings and talks, things like that. I'd never been in a group like this before—it was about 25 percent Latino, 25 percent African-American, 25 percent Haitian, and 25 percent Cape Verdean, which was a large local ethnic group. Everybody more or less got along. And actually, we did some pretty good work, some people more than others.*
>
> *The problem was—I don't know, would you call this a problem?—that all of this was funded by a federal grant. The people in the coalition were mostly parents themselves, they got some small stipends. Now I guess you'd have to say that if it weren't for the stipends, the coalition would never have gotten together in the first place. We kept going for two years, and then the time came when the money ran out.*
>
> *We knew this was going to happen. There wasn't anything we could do about it, that was the perception. The local grant holder, which was the school, had other priorities by that time. And I mean, the parents weren't going to apply for grants themselves. We all talked about getting together and keeping the work going on a voluntary basis after the last payday. "Sure, we'll definitely do it." We scheduled meetings, and a few people showed up at the first one. But you could see right off that more meetings weren't going to happen, and they didn't. The coalition needed money to survive, and it ended because it ran out of money, plain and simple.*
>
> *It's too bad—we were doing pretty well—but that's the way it was.*

In this case, there was an legitimate reason to keep going, but this coalition's will to live unfortunately was not strong enough to overcome the ending of dollars. Nobody was sufficiently motivated either to seek out new funding, or to keep going without it. Many groups end their lifetimes accordingly. This is a fact of community work.

Staying the way you are. One more option: You can simply keep going the way you are. If you've been doing something well, why not continue it in just the same way?

This sounds easy; it seems reasonable; but it is among the hardest options to carry out. The outer world, and your inner world, changes. There are ongoing, constant pressures to move in one direction or the other: to grow, or do something different, or fold your tent. To make a conscious choice to stay the same—to maintain that choice regardless of those pressures and stay steady as she goes—that isn't easy to do.

It can be a laudable thing to do. But it's not necessarily the best thing to do, either. The danger is that you can grow stale, or smug, or increasingly less relevant. You can wither on the vine, without exactly falling off.

*Our community coalition was charged with planning the town's future. The town itself started the project, Vision 2020, and many of the best town leaders got pulled into it. There was **big**-time excitement when we got going. There were day-long meetings, upscale refreshments, handouts like you wouldn't believe. This was going to be a great adventure.*

You could see the momentum start to slow down pretty soon. I think an early turning point was the design of the actual community vision. It took God-knows-how-many hours to do. No one wanted to release it until it had been rehashed endlessly, and I mean endlessly. Egos started to surface. We had outside consultants, who'd been hired to facilitate the process, but they were too patient—they just let everything go on and on.

The vision did get released, but a negative tone had been set, at least the way I saw it. The possibility to make some bold recommendations for the town was there, and so was the possibility to spearhead their implementation, but this group became content mostly to talk. One or two good things did happen, such as a human rights commission for the town—though even that is barely hanging on.

That was five years ago. The coalition is still going, but has much less visibility and clout in the town now. People make snide comments like, "Oh, Vision 2020 . . .," and what they mean is, "What did you expect?" The coalition is perceived as mostly liberal do-gooders, which they basically are, except they haven't done much good. At this point, the coalition is like a pensioner living in retirement, living out its life. It continues to meet, and makes a statement once in a while. There's no real reason to consciously end it. But it doesn't really try to do anything anymore. Nobody pays it much attention.

This coalition keeps going in the same way, but in this case it produces few community benefits. It has become marginalized. The speaker above concludes, "When it dies, not too many will come to the funeral."

The Maintenance of Coalitions in Practice

We've treated these different coalition directions as independent options, but that has been partly for purposes of exposition. In practice, the options swirl closer together, and the predominant pattern changes, like weather systems passing overhead.

The reality of coalition maintenance and evolution lies closer to this: You keep going, because you're doing some good. You have some core functions. Perhaps you take on something new from time to time, wisely or not. Maybe that something dies on its own. Maybe somebody else kills it; but maybe it works, and you keep it. Or maybe you spin it off, so it can stand on its own. New opportunities like that keep coming along every so often. You can choose among them.

If you need money, you've usually got enough to sustain the core operation, at least enough for today. Sometimes a gift comes your way, and you go with that flow. You accept it even if you didn't originally plan to, or even want to. You have to grab the opportunity. It's too good to turn down.

But sometimes you get hit, and bad things happen, when you lose something you'd rather keep. Your control is not total. There can be injuries ranging from slight to very serious to mortal. (Even slight injuries are worrisome, for often they go untreated, not being visible to the coalition's eye.) You try to recover, to get full functioning back. Sometimes you have to keep going in an impaired state, at least for a while, and you may never be quite the same again. You might actually emerge in better shape, but you could also wind up worse than before, or just different in some other ways.

In the broadest sense, it doesn't matter. For either way, new circumstances will keep appearing in the distance, and then keep coming into fuller view, circumstances that hold the promise of changing you further, in ways no one can now comprehend.

That's the way coalitions evolve in practice, as do social systems more generally, and as do our own lives. Except that coalitions are more vulnerable than humans. Their care-and-feeding requirements, though very real, are less easy to discern than those for people. Most coalitions are young; they need constant supervision. And when they get hurt, they have neither health insurance, nor primary care physicians, and sometimes no person who can be reached in case of emergency. Sustaining the energy, maintaining healthy coalition life, is more of a challenge.

How can that challenge best be met? To answer that question, it will help to reflect on and review the key elements that ultimately sustain any social organization.

Key Maintenance Needs

First among these elements, of course, is accomplishment. If the coalition, if any organization, is doing good work and that work is recognized, the community is much more likely to support it. New members and new funding are easier to come by. Success is reinforcing. So if the coalition (and its leadership) can find a way to keep generating positive events, other things will tend to fall into place. And this applies *regardless* of whether the coalition chooses to grow or contract or move in a different direction.

A second key element is an institutional consciousness. This means that the coalition and its members believe and act as if they are an integral part of local life, a prominent and constant feature on the local landscape. The larger community feels the same way. The coalition has a sense of permanence. It's here to stay; everyone knows it. It's become institutionalized.

To develop an institutional consciousness takes strong, committed coalition leadership. (Accomplishment helps, too.) But it also takes effective coalition *structures* (*see Chapter 4*). Members need to know that attendance at each monthly meeting is expected, that they are expected to serve on at least one task force, that elections will be held on the last Wednesday in September, and that the first post-election business will be a coalition action plan. These or equivalent structures, reliably and repeatedly utilized, strengthen allegiance. Over time, they deepen the coalition's roots. Institutionalization means rootedness—even though the coalition's roots, like the roots of a tree, lie below the surface.

One coalition describes how it became institutionalized, after a couple of false starts:

> *. . . So if anything made a difference that last time around, it was probably that we had more sustained interest, on the part of enough people, over a long enough period of time, so that the structures didn't disappear, and had some inertia. And we were able to get some history under our belts after a while. People began to see some things happening, were willing to look at the coalition as more of a permanent part of their schedule, rather than, "Oh, yeah, here we go again."*
>
> *There certainly is a sense of institutionalization about it all. Most of our lives are constructed with things that we've done for a long time. At the start, you might go to a coalition meeting, and then you think, "Well, should I go to the next one?" or should I say, "The hell with it, it's not important enough to me." Then, it doesn't move.*
>
> *But I think we've gotten over that hump, to the point where I think now it's hard for people to consider how we would operate without the coalition. I mean, it really has built itself into people's consciousness. There's an expectation that it's going to be around. . . .*

Good works, and good institutional structure. But finally, what you also want to sustain is good *feelings*—the positive spirit of the coalition that brought people together and kept them coming together in the first place:

> *We all know one another. We are genuinely glad to see one another. The coalition is probably one of the most nurturing places that we have.*
>
> *We all come together, we're all scratching our heads and thinking, "Wow, what's going to come down the pike next?" But this is one of the places where we take care of one another. It's one of the places where after we get through our complaining, which of course there's always a little of, then we can go on to the positive things and feel good. So, you know, people smile when we walk in the door, because that's who we are. We're coming together. And the more we can bring people into that warmth and that feeling of being a part of it, the stronger we are.*

The personal closeness, the cohesion, the camaraderie are hard to overestimate. We spend our personal time where we feel comfortable, accepted, and valued for who we are. Why should we think that our own coalition members would feel, or act, any differently?

205

After the coalition is established, it may choose among many different maintenance options. And there are genuine choices; it's best to choose consciously. Which choices are made depend upon your particular coalition's history, personality, assets, community needs, environmental factors, and available time. Many choices are justifiable, and many different choices may be made over a coalition's life span.

If your coalition is doing good work, you will probably choose to sustain it, in one form or another. Continued accomplishment, institutionalized structures, and vibrant spirit will help you maintain your efforts, and your successes. These coalition needs are interrelated, and they are continuous; they never go away. A wise coalition leader will come into alignment with these principles of coalition life, and will steer one's craft carefully, flexibly, and with lightness of being on its extended voyage through waters yet unknown.

> *Coalition building is a very lengthy process, and it's one that doesn't always go smoothly or according to anybody's pre-established timeline. People in coalitions need to remember that, and to accept that, and not be disappointed that things don't go as quickly as they want to. As each new member comes in, it changes the whole dynamic and the whole focus, and that's part of it. It's constantly evolving. The coalition never has an end in sight, not unless you want to disband it. It just doesn't have an end. It just continually changes. You just have to keep going and plugging away. That's just the nature of it. . . .*

Lessons From The Field

Coalitions Change

■ A coalition is a social system. As such, it is subject to the same principles as all other social systems.

■ Change is an inevitable part of system life—for social systems, for biological systems, for systems on every scale.

■ A coalition will change and evolve over time. It won't always stay exactly the same. And in most cases, it shouldn't.

■ However, a coalition can control change. It can determine its own direction, at least partially.

■ That prospect itself can energize and guide the coalition's work.

Some Possible Types of Coalition Change

- In short form, these are:
  - ~ Growing (in many different possible ways)
  - ~ Staying the same (or attempting to)
  - ~ Combining (including sharing, merging)
  - ~ Shrinking
  - ~ Ending.
- Each of these major directions has several variations. And more than one directional change can take place over a coalition's life.

Making the Choice Among Change Options

- How do you do it? You can start by considering and assessing these variables:
  - ~ The *people* who belong to your coalition—their backgrounds, preferences, styles, and desires;
  - ~ The *time* that your coalition members have available—or are willing to make available;
  - ~ The *resources* available to your coalition, both current and projected—in this case, material resources mostly, but also in-kind support;
  - ~ The community *needs* at the present time—what are they? How strong are they? Are they long-time needs, or are they relatively new? Who else might be available to meet them?
  - ~ The external *environment*—a catch-all category, which might include community attitudes toward your coalition, local politics, larger social forces, and special circumstances unique to your own situation.
- Of course, simply considering these factors is not enough; they should be combined and weighed for each option. But consciously stopping to weigh them—placing them carefully on the scale—will more often than not lead to a better decision about change for your coalition.

Looking Toward the Long-Term Future

- A coalition should be able to live and flourish for quite a long time. How long? It's hard to say exactly. But it will certainly live a longer and more productive life if regular and careful attention is paid to its maintenance.
- In other words, coalition operations should never be taken for granted.
- At the same time, coalitions are not forever. No group is. At some point, you may choose to stop, or be obliged to stop.
- If a coalition does end, that can be sad. But it may have fulfilled its useful life expectancy. And new forms rise out of old. A different coalition, based on the original one, but keyed to present needs, may arise to take its place.

FALL RIVER HEALTH AND HUMAN SERVICES COALITION

SELF ASSESSMENT

Name _____Agency/Affiliation_____

Title_____

1. Overall Impact:

   A. Do you feel that the Coalition has made contributions to the Fall River community?

1	2	3	4	5	6	7	8

   little or no   some   major
   contribution   contribution   contribution

   B. Do you feel that the Coalition has been helpful to you personally?

1	2	3	4	5	6	7	8

   not at all   somewhat   extremely
   helpful   helpful   helpful

2. Accomplishment of Coalition Goals:

   A. Has the Coalition been helpful in providing information to you, your agency, and to your clients? Any examples?

1	2	3	4	5	6	7	8

   not at all   somewhat   extremely
   helpful   helpful   helpful

   B. Has the Coalition been effective in mounting advocacy efforts for Fall River? Any examples?

1	2	3	4	5	6	7	8

   not at all   somewhat   extremely
   helpful   helpful   helpful

3. Suggestions:

   A. How might the Coalition act in the future to best meet your own needs?

   B. What changes would you suggest of the topics the Coalition addresses?

Should your coalition grow, change, or stay just as it is? One way of deciding is to learn what coalition members think. This coalition is not afraid to ask them formally. (The assessment form here is abridged.)

Lower/Outer Cape Coalition
Community Advisory Board

Name: Phone:

___Yes, I will continue to serve on the Coalition Advisory Board for the 1997-98 year.

___No, I am unable to continue to serve on the Coalition Advisory Board for next year.

Please consider _____
(name, organization, phone) as a potential member of the Board.

Coalition Priorities 1996-97   Priorities 1997-98
1) Poverty Prevention
2) Health Care Access
3) Transportation
4) School-Linked Services
5) Onshore Needs of Fishing Families
6) Tobacco Reduction

Please complete the following to assist in the preparation of the 10th Anniversary
Final Report and the new Coalition brochure:

1) For the past ten years the Coalition has...

2) Significant Coalition successes include...

3) The most rewarding or meaningful thing for me about being a member of the
Coalition is...

My hidden talent:

*This survey has the same self-assessment goal despite its different format—it relies
less on numerical rankings, and more on prose.*

TASK FORCE EVALUATION AND RESOURCE ALLOCATION LOWER/OUTER CAPE COMMUNITY COALITION

1. Does this Task Force address the mission of the Coalition to improve the quality of life for those living on the Lower/Outer Cape?

2. Which goal(s) does it support?

_____To mobilize and maintain broad-based community development and collaborative problem-solving initiatives around health and human services.

_____ To insure the availability of and access to basic opportunities and services.

_____ To provide leadership in developing policies, practices and programs that are effective, responsive and accountable to those they serve.

3. Will allocating resources to this Task Force detract from the core services?

4. Is there a cross-section of the community represented on the Task Force?
    If no, who else should be represented?

5. Is the goal achievable?

6. What is the likely disposition of this Task Force in the future?

7. Are members providing resources to support the Task Force?

8. If additional funds will be needed, what potential sources exist?

9. Other

Coalition support to be provided:

_____ None at this time.

_____ Chair meetings (schedule, set agenda, facilitate meetings)

_____ Participate in meeting

_____ Type and mail minutes and other correspondence

_____ Send meeting notices and make follow-up calls

_____ Promote work and activities of Task Force

_____ Evaluate progress and outcomes

_____ Carry out activities of the task force (specify):_____

_____ Other (specify):_____

…And this document is designed to get similar feedback on task forces of the coalition.

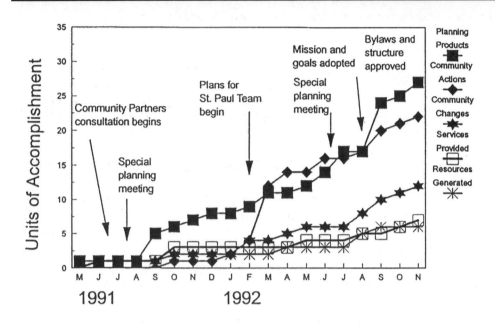

Gloucester Human Services Council

Recent Accomplishments

- Adoption of Mission, Goals, Bylaws
- Standing committees established
- Election of officers
- Candidates Forum
- AIDS Prevention Forum
- "My View" series

Some coalitions, such as this one, collect systematic data on their accomplishments to help them both evaluate and plan their futures. The graph above is actually simpler than it may look. Could something similar work for your coalition?

Chapter 11

Pitfalls And Challenges

Did anyone ever say that coalition building was a simple task? It sure wasn't us. Very often, coalitions somehow get launched with the idea that they are efficient, sure-fire, 100-percent successful methods for accomplishing almost anything in the community, and that their creation follows a straight and narrow path. But nothing could be farther from the truth.

Coalition building in real life is a complex, slowly winding journey with many pitfalls and challenges along the way. Events will unfold in ways you never anticipated, even if you are skilled. Your problem-solving abilities will be fully tested, yet there's no way to study for the exam. If you as a coalition builder can understand and accept that, then each of the potential pitfalls can be seen as a challenge, even an exciting challenge, as opposed to a frustrating roadblock in what was supposed to be an open highway. As one of our mentors once said to us, "Make change your friend."

So in this next-to-last chapter, let's describe some of those pitfalls and challenges that coalition builders will typically encounter, together with ways the pitfalls can be avoided and the challenges met.

1. Failing to Engage Citizens

One key assumption of coalitions is that they engage the community in a collaborative process. Yes, ideally, but most community coalitions are dominated by the community's major institutions: human service agencies, hospitals, schools, businesses, churches, police, or local government, depending on the coalition's goals. This is understandable: Members of institutions usually start coalitions; they have the time; they have the status; and coalition work can be seen as part of their jobs.

Yet the coalition is there to serve the whole community. Citizens are at the core of that community. If citizens are not part of the coalition process, what is ultimately being accomplished? So more and more coalition leaders are focusing their energy on engaging ordinary citizens, hard-working and overcommitted citizens, with day and/or night jobs, and this becomes one of the great coalition challenges.

It isn't easy. Sometimes it takes a while even for the pitfall to be realized, as one coalition found out:

> *We were sitting around the United Way office with the leaders of all the agencies, talking about prevention services for families, and what was available. We were writing them on a flip chart, and we must have had 60, 70, maybe 80 different services in the community listed out around the walls. So we were saying what good work we were doing, and people felt good about that.*
>
> *Then all of a sudden we stopped. There was silence. We spent some time with that silence. We wondered what was that about. We thought about why, in spite of all the services we had, things were still so bad. Why weren't things getting better? What were we doing wrong?*
>
> *And actually I think this was a very critical point in the coalition's history— where we shifted the focus from what organizations were doing to what people were doing, and how we could better engage and involve the citizenry of the community.*

But deciding that a coalition is going to engage more people from the community and actually making it happen are two different matters. For one thing, as a community professional, coalition building can be paid work time; as a resident, that isn't so.

> *When we are working with coalitions that involve residents, we just have to be real sensitive about time, because these people are already working a separate job. They can't take time off from their job to do this. So I'm thinking of one coalition, when I went to this meeting, they said, "Well, we do everything, but the residents won't come out." Well, why? They could only hold meetings at 9:00 in the morning. Well, people work. Why won't they come out? Because they can't take time off work.*

For a second thing, many residents (and many people in general) will feel uncomfortable and inhibited when meeting in a strange room full of strangers.

> *Residents have a real hard time coming to a meeting with a lot of social service people, with the kind of jargon people throw around, and stuff like that. I know this from experience. People leave. We have had people leave. We were able to get some people to come, but they wouldn't be consistent.*

For a third thing, your issues are not necessarily theirs.

> *If you want the residents involved, the issues you want them to react to may not be the issues that they want to work on. Even though you think*

crime may be the issue, they might feel that high school dropouts is the issue that they want to work on first, or street lighting . . . .

So let's say you talk to the citizens; you find out what their issues are. You find a good location in the neighborhood that people feel is safe and neutral. You set the time of the meeting in the evening, when people aren't working. These are all the right moves. But then only a few people show up. Even under the best conditions, this can happen. It's not a matter of finding someone to blame. It's rather, what do you do next?

Do you remember one coalition leader's story about meetings? We'll excerpt it again:

> *Even if there are five people at a meeting, you still hold the meeting. You do it because those are the people that came out, that want to do something. If that group of five wants to do something, like a cleanup of a park, or whatever, then that's what you do.*

An axiom in community work is that you start from where you are. You make something happen with what you've got. You build gradually, one small step at a time, and you keep on building.

2. Distrusting Citizen Participation

Suppose you have a coalition that started out with members from service agencies and other institutions in the community. Now you begin to add citizens, more and more of them. And suppose, on the surface, you are successful.

We hope you are not surprised to learn that new problems may arise. One frequent and major problem is that the basic attitudes and training of the professionals may get in the way of welcoming citizens to the coalition.

> *I think there's a distrust by people in the helping professions, including most of the coalition coordinators. Most of them come from a health and human service background. They have a basic distrust of regular people, of the people they are trying to work with.*

Hard words, but too often true, as in this example:

> *There was a real big lack of respect between the professionals and the parents. Parents would go to the meetings, and they wouldn't say anything. They would wait until after the meeting, and call me at home and say, "I agree with what you said." I'd say, "Well, why didn't you say something at the meeting?" They'd say, "Well, I didn't want to be called this, or I didn't want to deal with that."*

And maybe there was good reason to keep quiet. Because if you are an uppity parent (or citizen) who speaks up too much and doesn't know one's place, some people's noses can get bent out of joint. Your ideas and your presence may not be too enthusiastically received.

> *I was one of the few that would call a nickel a nickel when things were wrong, and I was beginning to be targeted by some of these folks, to the point that there were letters being written about me. I thought it was time for me to leave, because it was just more than I could take. . . .*

Distrust in general stems largely from lack of prior contact, which in turn often arises from social, ethnic, or cultural barriers, as well as from a lack of proximity and perceived similarity. Applied here, there's an all-too-frequent gap between community members and service agencies, with the perception that agency personnel are not nearby, not similar, not a true part of the community. Too often, they aren't: In many communities, health and human services workers sleep somewhere else at night. That shores up the barriers.

> *I remember a minister from a community asking me for my phone number. So I reached into my wallet and I gave him my business card with my number on it. And he looked at me and said, "No, not that phone number." He wanted my home phone number, because that was going to be a sign of my commitment to him that he could call me at any time, not just 9:00 to 5:00 at the office.*

* * *

> *I think one obstacle is if you're not seen as part of the community. I mean, if you're seen as an outsider. That's a very difficult obstacle to overcome; one way of overcoming it is that you demonstrate through action that you have a commitment to the community or neighborhood that you're working in. Because a lot of times people think, "Well, you're not from here, so what do you care? You're just going to go home at night and, you know, I still have to hear the fire engines at 1:00 in the morning while you're sleeping." And you can get a lot of that kind of anger.*

Regardless of where they sleep, in daily community life human service professionals and citizens are not quite equal. The service professionals make the rules; the citizens follow. But within a community coalition, the two groups have equal voice, or should have. This can take some getting used to, and some role readjustments on both sides. Agencies and citizens are like oil and vinegar. They can mix successfully, but it takes some encouragement.

I think you need to build in a process where people can express them-selves and feel safe when there is something that they don't like or something that offends them. We don't know what's going to offend somebody. Words mean different things to different people. But if you set up a process, you can address it right then. Then you have a way of dealing with it all along.

Like with one group, one of the things that used to offend the parents was when they were called "clients," even though they were asking us to sit at the same table with them. But when you call them clients, the assumption is they have nothing to offer. Then you set up a barrier. Things like that hit nerves in people.

. . . For human beings are sensitive. Their feelings can get hurt. If they feel deval-ued, they won't come back. But if they are valued—better, treasured—they are likely to return.

Someone at a training said, "Everyone at the table has a responsibility to make sure the expertise of every individual there is brought to the table and laid out." I think that is so key, to make people open up and share what they can do, and let them know that it's of value—to make them feel that it's a worthy donation, contribution, or asset to the group, whatever it is. And that takes a lot of work.

3. Keeping Too Much Control

The problem is, once people start expressing their abilities, they may find themselves with ideas of their own. Those ideas may not be yours. Success brings its own pitfalls, and one of the most bittersweet is when the people you have so diligently recruited now begin to oppose you.

The goal is to get people mobilized, to get people active. But sometimes we do that and then we look at what we've created and we're like, "Oh, my God," because these people we've mobilized start rising up against us. But I think we need to see that as basically a good thing. I still think that essen-tially health and human service providers should be trying to put themselves out of business.

Well, maybe those lines are a bit overstated. But were we to tone them down, what else would you expect, or want? You probably don't want nonstop unanimity. The gentle irony is that one criterion of coalition success is free expression of diverse opin-ions. If you really do the job of empowering your members, be they citizens or pro-fessionals, they are going to start demonstrating their empowerment, in what might once have been "your" coalition. But no longer; now it's "theirs."

Residents have a lot of ideas. But when there is a resident out there who has an idea of what they want to do, they are just like human service providers. They have a hard time letting go of their idea. They want to do it their way.

*We do have some residents that come to partnership meetings. We invite them, and they participate, but their focus is still much more into their own ideas. This is my idea—it's not **that** idea, it's not **this** idea, it's **my** idea that's going to work. Partly it's because these people have not really been affirmed a whole lot in their ideas before. But to try to get people to work with other groups has proven to be a little difficult.*

The pitfall lies in resisting citizen expression, and possible opposition. Resistance can lead to high-stakes emotional dramas, with all the expected fallout. You want instead to understand that opposition, to respect it, and to give up some of your control. You want to guide any good ideas, wherever they come from, into pathways that will benefit the initiators, the coalition, and the community. You want to move from "yours" and "theirs" to "ours." It takes a mature leader to do that, as we'll note again shortly.

4. Protecting Too Much Territory

If the coalition leadership must yield some control, coalition members must do so, too. One specific area where control issues frequently occur involves territory. And one of the most common barriers to successful coalition building is the ongoing tug of war for territory or turf that goes on between organizations, even when these organizations proclaim themselves committed members of a collaborative.

Why is this? Some would argue it's because human beings, like their evolutionary forebears, are territorial by nature, acquisitive as well. Children have to be taught to share; so do adults. We get ego-involved in what we own, and feel threatened if someone tries to take it away. From even before the dawn of civilization, we have defended ourselves against such threats. The same ancient dynamic gets played out in coalitions, and it's difficult to overcome.

Everybody wants to do information and referral. There's always been a very strong need for it, but it's been a very politically charged issue in the community. You wouldn't believe it. Oh, you wouldn't believe it.

The Department of Human Services in the city claims that it does information and referral. At the same time, the United Way supported an information and referral line called the Info Line, which was very successful. Citizens for Citizens, the anti-poverty agency, does information and referral, too. But instead of everybody getting together and saying, "This is ridiculous. Why are we all doing this? Let's just have one place that we refer people to," everybody wants to hold onto their territory.

> *If we had one number, and somebody called and had a question, we could say, "Look, call 1-800-xxx-xxxx." And that's where you'd get your information, instead of everybody else trying to do it. Because a lot of people are falling through the cracks. They get irate: "You're the fourth person I've talked to. . . ." You know, that kind of stuff.*

Logic says this issue should be easy to sort out; but logic does not always rule in coalition work, no more than it does in interpersonal relations. Emotions come into play.

If the turf is physical instead of conceptual, so much the harder to deal with. And if there's a history attached, if the turf-holders have been invested in their territory for years, they may very actively resist any change attempt. They will fight you hard. In their eyes, you are intruding on their home.

One coalition organizer found out how powerful these territorial forces were when given an outside mandate to join four neighborhoods into one coalition. He learned that those neighborhoods were quite happy as they were, thank you very much, and see you much later.

> *In this community, the definitions were already established, and very well established. This is Hyde Square. This is Bromley Heath. This is Egleston Square. This is South Street. You know, this is this, that is that. And we're also talking about individuals who are leaders in their communities, who have been doing the work sometimes literally for decades.*
>
> *So there were pretty heated discussions with neighborhood folks about like why Hyde Square, which had been doing its own organizing work for many years and had its own council, is not its own neighborhood, and why do they have to work with Bromley and with South Street and with all the others?*
>
> *All this stuff had already happened before I was hired as the coalition coordinator. And I have to say that at the end of my tenure there, I was so happy to be just a resident of the community again. It's like I would rather be ignorant than to know all this historical stuff.*

The lesson is that there has to be some sort of buy-in on what the definition of the community is. That definition has to come from the community itself. Should you impose it from the outside, get ready for resistance. If people don't resist you actively, they will resist you passively, as in the story below. Both active and passive resistance have the same bottom line: Nothing gets done.

> *I was part of a multi-town coalition which was supposed to come up with common health goals and actions. The state organized it, and dangled money in front of it. And these towns were geographically right next to each other, but they were psychologically distinct. Revere, to name one, was right*

next to Winthrop, but they were really two different communities which saw themselves as having little in common, and acted that way.

Yeah, people did show up at the meetings. But it was clear that a lot of them were there because their bosses told them. A few of them would sit in the back of the room and close their eyes. A couple would say straight out, "You know, I really don't want to be here."

As you can imagine, this was not a very effective coalition. When the state leadership changed, the coalition just dissolved.

Once again, "forced coalitions" rarely work. But turf pitfalls, even in voluntary coalitions, are tough ones to escape. Advance planning will definitely help, so that you take territorial and historical factors well into account before venturing forth. But if you get ensnared, the best way to get out will involve patience, gentleness, persistence, finding ways for each coalition member to leave with something positive, and keeping the greater good of the community both visible to all and at the top of your list.

5. Avoiding Meaningful Action

At the core of coalition building is the implicit assumption that coalitions, once mobilized and functioning, are going to take concrete actions in the community that lead to concrete changes.

But sometimes they don't. Sometimes the coalition doesn't act at all, even when control issues are resolved and diverse members meet in harmony. One of the great coalition pitfalls, which often leads to losing membership and power, is doing an enormous amount of planning, but then not moving on to community action and change.

*Lots of human service councils get together and are really set up for information exchange, not collaborative problem solving. But over time, they can really burn you out because they don't do anything **but** exchange information. There can be fires going on all around them, yet they don't bother putting them out. They just tell you what's new with their agency. So the inability of these groups to do any kind of collaborative problem solving is often a downside.*

It's more than a downside; it's often a stake in the heart. If you don't act, if your group doesn't act, then neither you nor your group will get rewarded. There are no long-term benefits for anyone. Without such eventual rewards or benefits, what's the reason for staying?

For most coalition members, there is a cost-benefit scale in the back of their head that asks, "Is the time that I'm putting into all these coalition meetings worth it?" And the benefits are the outcomes and actions that the coalition can create, beyond what any individual organization could create on its own. So all the folks in the room are always weighing the amount of effort it's taking against the kind of outcomes that are being produced. And we need to attend to that.

Community action is the coalition's currency. If the coalition fails to act, it will soon be out of funds. And, by and large, people *want* to act, given half a chance, rather than hang around. The coalition and its leadership have an obligation to foster such actions.

We also find that residents want to be more involved in doing things, not just sitting around and talking about doing things, but actually doing things. The residents that we found in our door-knocking were people who had ideas and wanted to do stuff. They just needed someone to help them.

6. Accepting Weak Leadership

The stimulus for action ultimately has to come from the coalition leader. And while we've spoken of leadership several times before, we can't emphasize enough how important finding the right kind of leadership is. For on the one hand, the leader can't push too hard:

Part of the leadership problem is always gauging how much people are able to do, and not running your expectations too far down the line. That certainly was the case with one of our coalition leaders. He was probably the one person I remember who expressed a desire for the coalition to become a lot more than it ever did become. And then he felt let down that we weren't becoming that.

On the other hand, you want to push hard enough. Suppose you don't, and instead take on all the work yourself. This is also not recommended.

So when the follow-up doesn't take place, you know, people get discouraged because they don't feel like they're getting anywhere. But they also have to take responsibility for following up, and that's part of the problem that I see with our coalition right now. People have become very dependent on me to do a lot of the follow-up; but at this point I'm saying "no" on a lot of things unless they're critical to the health of the community.

That belongs to the easier-said-than-done department:

. . . Of course, you can say that anything is critical to the health of the community.

So here's the leadership challenge: You want to delegate (and you should). But your vision of the work may run broader and deeper than that of your members (which might have gotten you chosen as leader in the first place). Therefore, when you delegate, you may be giving your members more than they can handle, or want to handle. They may not come through for you. Then you may get upset at them; if you show it, they may get upset at you. This serves no one's purpose. The coalition leader must find a middle ground.

The question of how much to push is only one leadership issue. The leadership also has to strive extra hard to represent the whole coalition, regardless of personal points of view. This is because coalitions are at risk for excessive concentrations of power, even for power grabs. And that is because the coalition really doesn't have the built-in checks and balances that might be part of a tighter, more formal organization. It is looser by definition, and if some hotshot wants to walk in and use it for his or her own purposes, the coalition is vulnerable.

> *This coalition as it's set up is subject to takeover. Two or three or four people could really come in and pretty much commandeer our $10,000 budget or whatever. It's not a huge amount of money. But certainly in terms of getting recognition and a platform, you could at least look like you were the whole health and human services community for a good while here until it became clear you weren't. You'd probably do a pretty good snow job on the media and a number of other folks; you might even get some funding. . . .*
>
> *I've known organizations that have folded because of that. I mean, you get some kind of hostile takeover, people abandon the coalition, and the people who remain can't sustain it.*

That is the pitfall; and here is an effective preventive response:

> *The people who have been selected for leadership are people who tend to be pretty fair and balanced and not out for one particular point of view about things. I think our current coalition leader is very good at that. Once it's clear that a least a few people in the group have got something in mind, he's not about to just kind of let it sit there. He wants to move it forward and get something going, take some action, leave something behind after a period of time, as opposed to talking it to death.*

In other words, the coalition has to seek and choose balanced leadership, and create a culture where action is proportionate to commitment, where responsibility is proportionately shared, and where power plays are less likely to happen.

7. Losing One's Balance

All this balancing could tire you out, even if the coalition's demands on your time were not already intense. Although, more often than not, they are quite intense indeed:

The work is extremely intense. To get the stuff done takes, I mean, it just takes an extraordinary amount of work. It's managing a series of crises. It's eight days a week. In the '60s we used to have this saying that, you know, "If you get too involved in the movement, you become the movement." You lose yourself. It depends on your level of commitment and passion, I suppose, but it can become one's identity. You have to be careful of that.

The coalition gives you an opportunity to refine and deepen your own identity, and specifically, to sort out this intensity-of-work issue, if you are up to the task. The music is playing. How much do you want to dance?

So one of the challenges is how do you maintain your own identity, your uniqueness. To do whatever it is that your energy is about, and whatever you've chosen to do, and still participate in the dynamic of community. And for some of us, this is our music. This is what we dance to. But other people would rather be on the balcony, watching the people on the floor. It's interesting. . . .

As authors, this work is what we dance to ourselves. And if you are like us, you want your coalition to consume your attention and interest. Yet you probably don't want it to consume all of you, nor to take over your life entirely. Granted, if that happened, you would probably survive. But point #1: You are entitled to a personal life outside of coalition work. Point #2: A consumed coalition leader has a hard time lasting over the long haul. And point #3: The long-term achievements of the totally consumed leader are not guaranteed to be any greater.

Yet we would never argue that coalition leaders keep regular business hours. They shouldn't and don't. There's a pitfall of extending yourself too much, and there's a pitfall of extending yourself too little. Sometimes you do have to push your limits, to the point where you can feel the stretch.

If you have to set up a meeting at 9:00 at night, you do it if that's what the neighborhood or the community wants. You don't say, "Well, it has to be at 6:00 because I have to get home." That's where it really becomes looking personally at what you can commit, because there's a huge time and energy commitment that goes along with it. I mean, it's exhausting work. Obviously, community coalition work isn't for everybody.

Each of us will feel the stretch at different points, depending upon our level of conditioning. What do you think of how this coalition leader resolved the issue?

It's kind of hard to keep things separate. Sometimes, for example, after work I go to community activities. I don't see that as part of work. I see that as part of overall organizing, overall getting to know people. You can't be that rigid.

It's a real balance to come up with. Sometimes you take your work home; or on Saturday I may do something like go to a neighborhood activity on my free time. That's what I've learned, is that people really want to see you as someone who's not just there 9:00 to 5:00, Monday through Friday, but as someone who will come out on a Saturday for an event and who will do this kind of stuff at night or whatever. That, I think, is important.

On the other hand, you can't be that enmeshed that you don't have your own private life. I have seen people come here and they get blown out, because they are so enthusiastic and like 100 percent focused on what they are doing, they don't have a private life, they don't have anything outside, and all of a sudden they just get blown away by the whole thing.

Do you still believe in balancing? Part of the challenge, then, is not to become overwhelmed with the responsibilities of coalition leadership, while at the same time not being so removed that the community sees you as distant or uncommitted. We agree: It's a narrow tightrope to walk, even if you were the one who climbed onto it.

8. Letting the Flame Die

Originally coalitions were thought of as short-term problem-solving alliances. Many of them were generated through time-limited funding mechanisms—state, federal, or foundation grants lasting a couple of years. You can do great things in a couple of years. But needs don't end if the grant must stop.

Now we think of coalitions as lasting for much longer periods of time. Even if money is not an issue, sustaining the work, keeping the flame alive, is still hard. As we talk to coalition coordinators who've been at it for close to a decade or even more, over and over they come back to what a demanding process this really is.

Among many other tasks, you've got to find the right pace for change:

Even when people say they want change, the change sometimes comes too quickly for a lot of people, and then they get nervous. In one example, we had a chief of police who got very involved in community policing with us, but we just moved too fast for him. You're going to move too fast for some people. You're also going to get attacked from places that you don't expect to get attacked from.

Anytime you become successful in organizing people, there are others who will feel threatened by that. So success breeds problems in that sense.

You've got to deal with people who straight-out don't care for each other:

There are always relationship problems. You're always going to end up with people that just don't like each other. Speaking as an organizer, you've

> *got to recognize that. You've got to make sure you don't put them in the same room too often, or you have to have plenty of other people around to dilute it. There are also people that you yourself don't like, and you've got to recognize that, too. And you're always going to run into people who feel like they're out of the loop; if you don't take care of that kind of business, that's a real danger.*

And, strange as it may sound, you've got to keep reinventing the wheel. For the old wheels wear out, and fall off the vehicle. Sometimes you've got no replacements; you must then fashion new ones:

> *It's very fluid. People may be doing well, but all of a sudden things fall apart, and then you've got to work to get them back together again. You've got to find new people, but sometimes there is no time to do that. Sometimes somebody new comes along with the energy and the vision, and then things pick up again and it goes on. But it's not structured. A lot of it is very, very liquid.*

Though keeping the wheels attached, aligned, and moving forward can be too much for one person over a long period of time:

> *One of the things that happens to adults, and happens to me, and I think happens to everyone, is that you make a commitment to something, and you do it for a while. And then you get tired, your life changes, things happen, and you move on.*
> *So we always have to be looking at who's going to be taking my place when I'm tired, where's the new fire in the belly going to come from, where's the passion, how do we stay current? All that stuff takes a lot of energy. Coalitions always have to get fresh legs.*

But what if no one is there to take your place? What if there aren't fresh legs? What do you do then?

9. Lacking Sufficient Faith

While most of this book has dwelt upon actions the coalition leader should take in the outside world, here is a place to remind ourselves that the work of the coalition does not always face outward. Much of what makes the coalition soar or stumble takes place within each coalition member. We can't see it; it lives within. Successful community action, for coalitions or any other group, derives from qualities inside the person, joined with thoughtful application of tested techniques.

High, maybe highest, on the list of these qualities is faith—a charged word, one not often found in the community literature. (*See also Chapter 2.*) It can be religious faith, as in this dialogue:

What sustains you?

Faith. My belief that this is what I'm called to do. That makes a world of difference for me. Faith. The stuff that I preach is what sustains me.

It's got to be pretty deep.

Oh, yeah, I know it is. I know it's pretty deep.

It keeps you going through fatigue and doubt?

Oh, yeah. Like I say, you do what you got to do. There's just no getting around that.

Is it possible to do this kind of coalition work without faith?

Not and make it last. You can do it without faith, but you eventually burn out or you're ineffective.

You're talking about religious faith?

Broadly defined.

That would suggest the coalition leader needs to find some kind of spiritual source within?

Yeah, that would make sense. Yeah, I think that's right.

And were we to do a study on the relationship between religious faith and desired community outcomes (a wonderful topic, for another book), we suspect we'd find a significant positive correlation.

The type of faith we have in mind, however, need not be conventionally religious. It need not involve reference to a higher power. But it must involve a strong conviction—and we would call it a spiritual conviction—that the proper frame of mind, combined with proper action, will bring you to your destination.

That frame of mind can be quiet acceptance:

> *Once again, it's the metaphor of the river. Five years ago, we were at the river and it speeded up. And we just kind of went with the current, and that's when we grew. And right now, this pace feels comfortable. We don't know what's ahead. I don't know what lies in store, but I would like to stay with the river as it is right now.*

Or it can be more active and dynamic:

> *You have to understand that working in the community requires a great deal of patience. You have to hang in there, you have to learn that. And you aren't going to get quick answers. But because you bring a passion to what you're doing, you're willing to hang in there with the issue. So I always tell people to bring a certain passion to the job, to keep the goal in mind, and to keep the passion alive.*

It may seem surprising that these two different mind-states, receptive and active, can lead to the same goal. But on second thought, it's not surprising at all. Underlying them both are the common beliefs that our work on earth has meaning and value, and that holding to such value strengthens the work itself. More than that, there's a common belief among many coalition leaders in the possibility of achieving a higher form of unity:

> *I get out of bed in the morning, and think of the work that lies ahead. Most days, all I can deal with is the work right in front of me, the things I've got to do, even though I know I'll never do all of them, which gnaws at me.*
>
> *But on some days, the best days, I think not just of tasks, but of visions of unifying the community, of creating all kinds of linkages and interconnections, where the whole community is cohesive and tight and networked together, and where it feels that way, too. It's finding a way of expressing the true unity of human beings through community work. And when I feel like that, there's a beauty to it which sustains me and keeps me going. I know it's right, and I know I'm in the right line of work. That's what I'm aiming for. . . .*

That's what we are aiming for, too—the creation of higher-order structures that bring about unity where no such unity existed before. To us, belief in such structures is an act of faith, and the search for them is spiritual. How one seeks and finds that faith is difficult for us to prescribe. We believe it's well-nourished by quiet inner states, be they prayer, meditation, or other forms of reflection. Beyond that, it's an individual matter; we won't advise further here. But we will say that sustaining this faith also sustains the work, keeping it fresh and alive. From the beginning and until any end, it provides the spirit of the coalition.

If we look back at the formidable list of pitfalls and challenges surveyed in this chapter, we might ask ourselves why we are attempting something so hard to do. Our answer is that the longer we work at building community coalitions, the more we understand that we are not trying to build coalitions just to improve interagency communication or planning, nor to deliver specific community programs. Coalition building at its roots is about transforming our communities so that they meet our dreams.

As you can hear in the voices in this volume, successful coalition leaders take on this task almost as a spiritual mission. Therefore, pitfalls and challenges can be seen as natural events on the road to transformation. A passionate spiritual commitment to bettering the communities we live in is fundamental to successful coalition building, and resonates both in the words and deeds of the leaders who carry out this transformative work.

No one ever said coalition building was going to be an easy process. No one ever said it was going to be totally efficient. Quite the contrary, let us tell you that coalition building is sometimes obstacle-strewn, often emotionally demanding, and almost always a challenge. But if it weren't those things, and if the compensating rewards were not there, the work would hardly be worth doing. All of the pitfalls we have discussed have been overcome in one community after another. They can be overcome in your community, too.

Lessons From The Field

This time, to change the format a little, we'll offer a table that lists each challenge (phrased here in positive terms) and some tested strategies you can use for meeting it. (*See also Chapters 8 and 10 for more challenges relating to money and growth.*)

1. Engaging Citizens

- Learn about citizens' groups and associations.
- Develop contacts and relationships with these groups.
- Keep on the lookout for potential new recruits.
- Make personal contacts with prospective citizen members.
- Suggest giving the coalition a try (a small commitment).
- Provide an incentive (e.g., status, a small stipend, a name on a letterhead).
- Offer a range of ways people can help.

2. Building Citizen Participation

- Hold meetings at convenient times and locations.
- Provide time for informal interaction.
- Let people share their goals, expectations, and feelings.
- Make sure citizens have an equal voice.

- Hire agency staff from within the community.
- Allow time for trust to develop.

3. Giving Up Control

- Solicit and encourage ideas and issues from everyone.
- Listen to and validate those ideas and issues.
- Provide specific procedures and clear ground rules.
- Believe in your own members' abilities.
- Accept that mistakes may occur.
- Consider that disagreements may be healthy.
- Don't feel you have to do everything.

4. Giving Up Territory

- Be aware of past history and past territorial issues.
- Openly acknowledge that territorial concerns may exist.
- Understand current territorial definitions.
- Respect members' self-interests and their need to hold on to some "territory" of their own.
- Find ways to cooperate that don't involve territory.
- Be gentle, persistent, and patient around these issues.
- Keep coalition members focused on the greater good.

5. Taking Meaningful Action

- Discuss and clarify the overall goals of the coalition.
- Create a coalition plan based on those goals.
- In the plan, include clear objectives with actions and timelines.
- Agree upon small, feasible, easily realized actions.
- Give members advance notice of decisions that need to be made (e.g., on coalition agendas).
- Follow up on decisions made and actions needing to be taken.
- If needed, discuss in a meeting why decision making and action seem to be difficult.

6. Exerting Your Leadership

- Make sure your leadership represents the full coalition.
- Clarify work expectations together with coalition members.
- Make sure that taking some responsibility is part of the membership expectation.
- Find those members most willing to accept responsibility.
- Delegate responsibility, within agreed-upon limits.

- Follow up on responsibility delegated.
- Offer leadership training for prospective new leaders.

7. Balancing Your Life

- Find a balance that works for you personally.
- Review that balance from time to time.
- Set aside personal time and personal days for yourself.
- Lead a healthy lifestyle, making time for rest and vacations.
- Find some interests beyond the coalition.
- Find supportive people you can talk to when needed.

8. Keeping the Flame Alive

- Plan future directions together with coalition members.
- Move at a pace consistent with member needs.
- Groom new leadership.
- Take on winnable activities, and develop a track record of success.
- Reward members for accomplishments.
- Build in some celebration and fun times for the coalition.

9. Keeping the Faith

Faith is found in many places.

We can't tell you how or where to find it. It is a personal matter.

But we do know that faith in the coalition and in its success is essential—and we hope that you can find a way of maintaining and sustaining it for yourself.

Chapter 12

Conclusion:
Coalitions In The Future

Reasons for Optimism

In concluding, and projecting ahead, we find good reasons for optimism about coalitions. Coalitions are relatively recent arrivals on the human services scene. A generation ago—or half a generation—they were rarely mentioned in the human services literature. Only within the last decade or so have they hit their full stride.

In that short period, coalitions have already proved themselves as valuable mechanisms for getting things done on a community level. They have been productive, in terms of their accomplishments. They have been feasible, in terms of resource demands. And what it takes to run them successfully can be taught. No deep secrets are involved. In fact, a summarizing lesson is that community coalitions can work without great amounts of money or specialized skill, and that time demands, while genuine, can be reasonably managed.

Much added optimism comes from our conviction that existing coalitions will get better at what they do. They are still at the start of their learning curves. They will learn from experience, as should any thoughtful organization. As they do, their skill levels will increase. They will evolve to better meet the needs of their own communities. More resources will come their way, and they will gain more community support.

More than that: Success breeds success. Existing coalitions will be models for new ones. Coalitions about to form, or that are now just vague intentions, will naturally want to adopt what has worked well elsewhere. If good cross-coalition communication mechanisms are in place, successful coalitions will be able to show others how it can be done. They will learn what works and what doesn't, how to do it and how not to; they will avoid unnecessary mistakes.

There's one more advantage of coalitions, another source of optimism, even though this one is indirect. The coalition provides an arena for diverse community members to meet face to face. Those opportunities are sometimes in short supply. And when people do meet, and trade smiles and hellos, who knows what will happen? Sometimes what happens can be wonderful.

For when people encounter each other, they build relationships. From these relationships, events occur years later and miles away. The complexity of community life may not permit direct attribution to their meeting in the coalition, but perhaps, as an article of faith, we can believe in those causal traces.

So, for example, two people introduce themselves at a coalition meeting, and strike up a pleasant conversation:

Some weeks later, **A** makes a referral to **B**.

Or **B** writes a letter of support for **A**.

Or **A** knows someone who can help **B**'s teenager get a summer job.

Or **B** is remodeling, and **A** has a friend in building supply.

Or **A** and **B**, together with **C** and **D**, decide to collaborate on a new project.

Or several years later, in another group entirely, **A** and **B** run into each other again, and that new group is stronger—the community is stronger—because of their previous relationship.

This is the nature of community life. One thing leads to another, though we rarely know what "another" will be. We might call this the Law of Unanticipated Consequences. Coalitions are breeding grounds for such consequences. There might be other forums, but maybe not all that many, where people from all across the community—especially *diverse* people, who normally would not interact—can get together, build relationships, and allow these unpredictable, unanticipated, yet community-strengthening consequences to unfold.

So community coalitions have moved from something virtually unknown to a valuable local resource in a short period of time. That movement will continue, and probably change, but there's no reason to think it's going to end. Many evolving species and variations of coalitions are not described here at all. And despite the fact that there are already thousands of coalitions on the local community development scene, there's room for many more. There are over 19,000 incorporated places, and more than 85,000 local governmental units, in the United States. . . .

Limitations

But how far should coalition thinking extend? From a recent dialogue:

> **Bill:** *If coalitions have generated so much progress in so many different communities, how far do we extend this? We could say that every community should do the same . . . a coalition in every community.*

> **Tom:** *That is a concept that immediately terrifies me. . . .*

We'll agree that the mere existence of a coalition is insufficient. And while "terror" may not quite be the right word, there are limits to what a coalition can do. These limits are both internal and external.

231

Coalitions are imperfect because they are composed of imperfect human beings, who may make poor decisions or fail to carry out good ones. Internally, all kinds of things can go wrong: The goals of the coalition may not be clear. The coalition may take on too much, or too little. What it does take on may not be related to community needs. The coalition members may not be representative of the community, nor of the target group the coalition wishes to serve. The coalition structure may not mesh with its setting. The leadership of the coalition may be poor, or erratic; or it may clash in style with the coalition members or the rest of the community. A dedicated and trusted leader may get a new job offer elsewhere. The coalition may not have enough money or, alternatively, more than it can responsibly handle. There may be personal conflicts within the coalition, with no knowledge of how to resolve them.

This is the short list. To it we can add the pitfalls and challenges recently described in Chapter 11. Even with those, we've got just a sampling. And in addition, even an internally strong coalition may still be faced with external obstacles that are hard to transcend:

■ The coalition may run up against community forces that want to protect the status quo, or that have a different view of what needs to be done. Those forces may simply be more powerful. The allies and supporters of the coalition may be no match for the political and/or economic clout its opponents can generate. The coalition may be outspent, outflanked, or outmuscled.

■ Even without direct opposition, many community problems are tough to solve. Not very surprising, actually. If they were easy to solve, the chances are they would have been solved already; there would have been less need for a coalition to form in the first place. Are you really going to take on racial conflict, or street crime, or low-income housing in your community? Many good men and women have given their souls to these issues, and have left the battle with little but scars. So the coalition may simply not succeed. Or it may win a battle, but lose the war. And even if it does succeed, success is rarely forever.

■ Or, a different obstacle: The original need in the community for which the coalition was formed may have diminished or disappeared. The starting rationale for the coalition may no longer exist. To add some irony, the coalition itself may have helped meet that original need. In those cases, the coalition can become a victim of its own success.

So coalitions have limits, and they're not alone in having them. In the private sector, a majority of new businesses fail in the first few years. Coalitions have an easier time, for they need not make a profit. They may not stand or fall on their financial bottom lines. But the long-term survival of any organization, coalitions included, is hardly assured.

And in a sense, the utilization of coalitions *should* be limited, meaning that there are other mechanisms for getting community work done. We are partisans of coalitions, but not to the exclusion of other community structures. Look up "social service organizations" in your local yellow pages; start with "Alcoholics Anonymous" and end with "YWCA." Each of these groups has (and needs) a piece of the action. To them, add those more informal groups which will never make it into a telephone directory—the church sodality, the high school reunion committee, the Friends of the Drama. Each of these has a role to play.

Then, there is the responsibility of an individual to act, on his or her own if need be, independently of a coalition. An immediate problem calls for immediate action, without waiting for other people or groups to join in.

Finally, there is also the responsibility of the larger social and political system to act, which means major social institutions—businesses, churches, schools, the media—as well as government itself. Institutions in general, the public sector in particular, and local government especially have major shares of responsibility for working to solve public problems. That responsibility will not go away, whether its bearers choose to meet it or not.

To summarize the broader point: The coalition has an important place in local problem solving, but its impact has limits; and it is by no means the only player on the scene.

Future Directions

Despite these limitations (what doesn't have limitations?), the number of community coalitions and their variants will most probably continue to grow. Nor is their evolution likely to stop. That evolution is already taking place rapidly, almost before our eyes. And already, it's not too hard to see where the coalitions of the future are heading, as they adopt new forms to adapt to new challenges of local community life.

1. As their numbers rise, local coalitions will begin to form larger organizations of their own. Within the past few years, we have already seen an increasing number of coalitions themselves made up of existing coalitions—or, as one of our respondents put it, "coalitions squared." An illustration follows Chapter 4; the portrayal is of a wheel with member coalitions as the spokes. As another example, our own home organization has formed a network called "Healthy Communities Massachusetts," composed of coalitions from across the state. In both cases, a main purpose is to exchange ideas and information; for without an overarching and linking structure, locally and statewide, how is Coalition **X** going to know what Coalition **Y** is doing?

The advantages of higher-order structures go beyond simple exchange. The overall amount of coordination and responsive planning in the community should then increase. The larger coalition, the coalition of coalitions, will also have more members, resources, advocacy power, and (we would expect) community backing. These advantages aren't without cost, though. Somebody has to convene that higher-order coalition meeting; who will accept the responsibility? People have to attend; where will they find more time in the day? Someone has to keep the fires burning between meetings—any volunteers?

Will the rewards of higher-order coalitions justify the extra cost? Many times, perhaps, but not every single time. Higher-order efficiency, in the long run, might gradually increase. In any event, it's not surprising that new forms like this have begun to evolve. Organizational forms *do* evolve, in ways not unlike the evolution of species.

2. A greater percentage of coalition work—and community service work—will take place electronically. The private, for-profit business sector will continue to set the pace for computerized sophistication, but the electronic literacy of the community service sector and the general public will continue to grow.

Most readers of this book probably use e-mail at work, or the Internet, or both. But most of our use tends to be more for specific job-related communication than for broader coalition development. We send e-mail to friends and co-workers, or colleagues at a distance; we download off a Web site, or do a Web search. But most of us don't yet use such technology to foster the development of a coalition or to bring community members together.

We could, and a good guess is we will. It's conceptually easy enough to keep members of a coalition informed by a weekly group e-mail; to create a local list-serv; or to post committee meeting notices, agendas, minutes, and other documents electronically. (Postage costs would decline; so would mail preparation time, and the time between transmission and receipt.) Maybe it's also feasible and useful to have real-time conferences, discussions, even some meetings on line. (Travel costs would diminish; so would time on the road.)

This doesn't yet happen frequently, since most of us are not yet completely comfortable with the technology. Some of us may not yet have the technology to begin with. Electronic communication is not as meaningful, many would insist, as sending a letter, and certainly not as natural as talking. It's not yet second nature.

But it will become more so. Part of this is just a matter of exposure and of practice; many of us can tell powerful tales of change in our own work lives. Five or ten years ago, how many of us were electronic babes in the woods? But look at us now. Some further change will be generational. The next generation of community workers, let's say the ones now in high school, will feel a lot more at home in cyberspace than we do, and may well carry around their keyboards as routinely as we carry notebooks.

Electronic communication will not replace live, face-to-face coalition meetings, nor should it. But it can supplement in-person contact, and make those contacts more focused, more informative, and more productive.

3. Coalition members are likely to come from more diverse ethnic and cultural backgrounds—if only because American communities are themselves becoming more diverse. It follows that if the coalition is to be representative of the community, these newer members must be actively recruited. This implies the need to understand and respect different cultural styles, and to find ways to do coalition business that takes them into account.

Cultural differences are subtle. A familiar error is to be insensitive to, or simply unaware of, cultural differences that may exist. But it's almost as common to assume that differences *must* exist, merely because members of different cultures are in the same room. It's not necessarily so. Members of all cultural groups share the same core values of strong and cohesive communities, where they and their households can be happy, healthy, productive, secure, and safe. These values are constant.

More specifically, we asked in some depth about cultural issues when interviewing our coalition leaders. Our sample of 16 included three Latinos, two African Americans, and one Asian American. We found many more similarities than differences; the organizational issues that coalitions face, and the skills needed to deal with them, are largely culture-independent.

This is not to say that differences don't exist. We sense and feel differences just by looking at others who have walked through the door. Our personal histories come with us to each coalition meeting, invited or not. And there may also be some true cultural differences in style—in starting time, in meeting tone, in expression of feeling—perhaps relatively small, yet which when ignored are seen not so much as offensive or disrespectful, but rather put one out of sync with the rest of the group.

Coalition workers of all cultures will gain from learning more about such differences, about when they do and don't exist, and about absorbing the lessons into their coalition work. How can that be done? Part of it involves exposure, as in the telecommunications example above. It also involves developing a more open and thoughtful communication style—asking questions, checking for feedback, and being especially cautious in making assumptions about the behavior or motives of others whose backgrounds might be different from your own.

4. Coalitions will also be influenced by social policy. The current period of reduced reliance on federal spending has already been putting pressure on states and communities to increase local self-sufficiency. This trend shows no sign of reversing in the near future. And what that implies is a continuing search for effective low-cost mechanisms to ensure that local communities can respond adequately to community problems.

Community coalitions are one of those mechanisms. Social policy is thus likely to spur their growth and development, directly or indirectly, and to do so independently of general economic conditions. As we write, such conditions have been good across much of the country; but we don't have to be economists to know this can change fast. If it does—if national and then local economies slow down, and local governments become more hard-pressed—that will be an additional factor encouraging coalition development, as a means of identifying and maximizing the utilization of all community resources. In a purely economic sense, coalitions are a good hedge against bad economic times.

The Coalition and Social Change

Coalitions are important community-building mechanisms at this stage in our evolution. That evolution edges us toward larger and more complex levels of social organization. In education, we see movement toward cooperative learning and small study groups. On the job, we find a profusion of workplace teams. Neighborhood associations are on the rise; so are computer networks. Collaborations and partnerships are becoming more embedded in daily life and consciousness. Community coalitions are one more example.

While the trends we have cited are based on experience, we don't know for certain how coalitions will look 10 years from now. The safe bet is they will continue to evolve. They might be much the same as they are now, only better—more effective, more productive, more deeply rooted. Or another structure might begin to emerge, based on the coalition. It might go by another name. It might be different in ways hard to foretell. Even at that, we can predict that the newer structure will be a direct descendant of the coalition, a blood relation, but better suited to the needs of that particular time.

Such is the nature of evolution, for social organisms as well as for biological ones. One difference is that the pace of organizational evolution is fast, probably faster than the evolution of biological species. New social forms can emerge in a generation, or less. We might see such new structures in our lifetimes. In many ways, we hope we will, for community problems will continue to exist, and take new forms themselves. We will need new structures and new approaches to deal with them, simply to keep pace with change. That, we believe, is part of human existence.

Yet structure and form, while vitally and centrally important, will never be the whole story. Flesh-and-blood human beings, with their passions and drives and mixed motives and flaws, are still going to be the actors, the ones who will fill whatever structures and forms that exist, old or new, and who will be responsible for making them work. Our basic human nature will not change that quickly.

In other words, community problem solving will continue to call upon a full complement of our personal strengths, including but certainly not limited to enthusiasm, conviction, desire, optimism, resilience, dogged tenacity, and strength of character. The community worker needs to be willing to hang in there and persevere when the work is on the verge of falling apart, to stretch out one's arms and hold it all together, with all one's might, with hope and faith that everything can, will, and must come out all right. These qualities, too, are job requirements for successful coalition building. We might go as far as to call them spiritual. But even without that designation, it is certain that community work draws out our best natures; it asks for the best we have to offer.

At the very least, community problem solving in the future will require highly developed communication skills, surely going beyond the everyday, walking-around communication skills we have acquired through experience, and which serve passably well, most of the time, in easing us through our lives. We will want to build upon and improve upon such skills, especially in relating to others in groups, in understanding where the other person is coming from, and in responding sensitively and effectively. It's ironic: Here we are in an era of exploding communications technology; yet at the same time the traditional, homely, but fundamental face-to-face communication skills will be the most prized.

This leads us to restate perhaps the central theme that emerged from our interviews, and from our own practice: the importance of building relationships. Social problems are created by social beings; we must then solve them as social beings, in our full complexity. Solution means more than pushing buttons or turning switches. It involves establishing good human relationships, both with your own coalition members, with your allies on the outside, with the community at large, and even, when you can, with those you regard (for now) as your opponents.

> *Our job as an organization is to convene people and help them build relationships, and celebrate them in the community. . . .*

* * *

> *. . . It all happens person to person. All of this coalition-building work really is based upon relationships and building relationships. It's really the key in healthy communities. Healthy communities are made up of healthy people with healthy relationships with one another.*

Good relationships build reciprocity and trust. They generate shared goals, which lead in turn to shared action. Shared action, with everyone's shoulder to the wheel, lifts spirit and predicts success. Spirit, and success, are what keep people coming back to any group. Buoyant spirits and successful outcomes meet most everyone's needs.

The better human relationships we need begin with the inner desire to make them better, and continue with more careful listening and thoughtful speech. There's more, of course, though the details of relationship building, the how-to's, are harder to teach on the printed page. They are subjects for another book (and there's no shortage of books that discuss them). In these chapters, we have focused more on coalition-building strategies and skills. But in doing so, we don't at all mean to downplay the enormous role, the essential role, of relationships and relationship building in coalition development.

It's time now to bring this manuscript to a close. If you are in a coalition now, we hope you will work to make and keep it stronger, and that the stories and lessons here will guide you along the way. If you've been in a coalition before, we hope you will have the chance to join another, and to make it an even more positive experience than the previous one. If you have never been in a community coalition, we hope you will find an opportunity to join one—and to learn what community problem solving is like from the inside, to gain experience that no book can teach you, and to be motivated to carry on.

May success come to all of you. But in any case, we hope that you will stay involved in community work and in community problem solving. There is plenty to do for everyone; everyone is needed. In community work, a group's voice is often heard more clearly than that of a single individual; a coalition is an excellent place for such voice to find expression. For the community, there can be measurable improvement. For the individual, there can be meaning, satisfaction, and joy. For both, there can be a lifting of the spirit that will keep people working together, and that will strengthen us as individuals, as citizens, and as a society.

Selected Accomplishments

We've been fortunate to be associated with coalitions that have made unusual and distinctive contributions. While many of them are noted throughout the text (*see especially Chapter 1*), others don't fit neatly within the individual chapter discussions; so it's worth a moment to showcase a few of them here. In our view, the exhibits on the following pages are just samples of what coalitions can do for the communities they serve.

A Resolution on Opportunities :

Family Bill of Rights

1. **Whereas** : <u>Children</u> are society's greatest resource. In their own right and as future leaders and producers, they deserve and need the opportunities that will maximize their individual potential and healthy development.

Whereas : <u>The family</u> is the primary institution shaping the development of children. Children do not live in isolation. Their lives and healthy development are dependent upon and affected by the quality of their family life.

2. In this document, the following basic ideas are recognized as essential.
   A. Children are valued and vulnerable citizens.
   B. Parenting is a challenging job for everyone.
   C. Alternatives to interpersonal violence exists.

3. **Whereas, as a <u>community</u>**, we have an obligation to create a nurturing environment for our families **and children**. The proposed Bill of Rights for "Families" serves as a necessary guideline for us to strive for in how to treat our fellow human beings.

Thereby : We agree that The Community, Family, and Children of Northern Berkshire Need

- The freedom found in a sense of love and belonging.
- Freedom in establishing relationships based on trust and care.
- Freedom found in adequate food, shelter, clothing, and medical care.
- Freedom of a healthy and safe environment.
- Freedom of a quality education and a sense of competence.
- Freedom found in an open space and time for play.
- Freedom from physical **discipline and abuse**, verbal abuse, and humiliating treatment.
- Freedom from pressure induced by alcohol and/or drugs.
- Freedom from violence where it may be seen or experienced. (home, TV, neighborhoods, etc.)
- Freedom of choices in their future.
- Freedom found in a "voice" in the community and opportunity to develop a sense of responsibility and control over one's life.

We thus resolve to work to ensure we have healthy families in Northern Berkshire, thus creating a healthy environment for ourselves.

The Northern Berkshire Health and Human Services Coalition's Family and Children's Task Force hopes that passage of the "Bill of Rights for Families" will foster community conversation about what is indeed important for "Our Families".

...A Family Bill of Rights, which received extensive publicity and generated considerable discussion throughout this coalition's service area.

Learn How to Organize your Neighborhood!

Are you interested in making your neighborhood

❖ a healthier community?
❖ a safer place for children?
❖ a kinder place for elders?
❖ a place where people stand up against injustice?

An African Proverb says, "It Takes a Village to Raise a Child."

We'd like to introduce you to a process which builds individual dignity, mutual trust and respect, and affirms the importance of spiritual values.

Can you pull together at least three people in your neighborhood?

If you enroll together, your neighborhood group will be eligible for $300 start up costs to put your new skills to work in your community!

Come Find out How to Get Started!

The classes will take place on Tuesdays from 6:00 p.m. - 7:30 p.m. at Northern Berkshire Neighbors (North Adams State College Townhouse #16, Montana Street)

Oct. 18th   What is a Neighborhood?

Oct. 25th   Running a Meeting

Nov. 1st   Finding our Leaders

Nov. 8th   How does a neighborhood grow?

Nov. 15th   What is Power? What isn't Power?

Nov. 22nd   Graduation! Let's Go!

...A neighborhood leadership training program; the intriguing feature here was that groups completing the course received a small stipend to use for their own neighborhood's improvement.

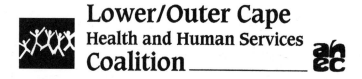

❖ AN OUNCE OF PREVENTION... ❖
A Directory of Preventive Services on the Lower Cape

"An ounce of prevention is worth a pound of cure." This is not only an old folk saying, but a fact of social science and medical research. We may often recognize early signs of problems, but are uncertain what to do. This Directory lists the many resources in our community for helping us prevent problems or for recognizing problems early and preventing small ones from becoming bigger ones. Prevention approaches do work, and usually at considerably less cost than intervention strategies. An investment in prevention is a wise investment in the health and well-being of all citizens of our community.

The information in the Directory is arranged in major groupings by types of problems or needs. They are BASIC NEEDS, ELDERS, HEALTH AND HEALTH CARE, EMOTIONAL HEALTH, CHILDREN AND FAMILIES, SCHOOLS, and RECREATION. Under each major category are listed the non-profit agencies and the types of services available to you on the Lower Cape. A brief description of each is included along with telephone numbers for the services. Additional information may be obtained by making a call to the agency or to the United Way's INFO LINE at 1-800-462-8002. All of these services were designed for you. Use them in good health!

The Prevention Directory was developed by the members of the Prevention Task Force of the Lower/Outer Cape Health and Human Services Coalition. For future changes or additions contact the Coalition at 255-2163. Funding for the Prevention Directory was provided by The Cape and Islands Partnership to Reduce Substance Abuse and Massachusetts Executive Office of Communities and Development through a Small Cities Grant.

❖ BASIC NEEDS ❖
HOUSING

INTERFAITH COUNCIL FOR THE HOMELESS: 255-9667. Homelessness prevention. Counseling and guidance for the homeless or those at risk of homelessness. Advocacy/Access to housing programs and funding. Budgeting. Negotiating for rent/mortgage back payments. Information and referral. Project Homeshare matches homeowners with homeseekers.

HARWICH ECUMENICAL COUNCIL: 432-6393. Housing for homeless families. Mentor counseling. Preventive program for those at risk of homelessness.

HOUSING ASSISTANCE CORPORATION: 432-6983. Emergency Prevention funds for mortgages/rents/utilities. Section 8, Rental Voucher Assistance programs. Family/Individual homeless shelters.

LOCAL TOWN HOUSING AUTHORITIES: Subsidized housing for elderly/disabled and families. Programs may vary.

FAMILY CARE PROGRAM: 771-1800 Ext. 2405. Adult Foster Care to prevent institutionalization for persons with chronic illness.

ELDER HOME REPAIR: Housing Assistance Corporation, 432-6983. Assists elders with home weatherization repairs.

HABITAT FOR HUMANITY: 255-2167. Housing rehab program. Minor repairs, painting, ramps.

INCOME SUPPORT/EMERGENCY FUNDS

DEPARTMENT OF PUBLIC WELFARE: Orleans, 255-4403. Emergency Assistance to Elderly and Disabled. Aid to Families with Dependent Children. Must meet eligibility and income guidelines.

LOWER CAPE OUTREACH: 240-0694. Emergency funds for food, shelter, clothing.

CAPE COD COUNCIL OF CHURCHES: 394-6361. Emergency funds.

ST. VINCENT DE PAUL: 385-3253, 255-8080. Vouchers for rent/mortgages/food.

CONTINUED on next page

...A directory of preventive services. Guides such as this are tried-and-true; but when you can distribute 10,000 of them, as this coalition did, it increases community awareness of services as few single activities can.

You make a difference for the Northern Berkshire community !

Saturday, Oct 22 is "Northern Berkshire Make a Difference Day." All around the nation, civic groups, schools, individuals, and community leaders are participating in activities that make a difference for their communities. Each day in Northern Berkshire, residents make a difference in the quality of life for this community. Participating in booster clubs, helping out a neighbor or relative, selling tickets for a local event, volunteering for a local service organization, raising money for charity, raking your neighbor's leaves, or just being friendly are ways that we make a difference in the quality of life for this region.

We are encouraging all Northern Berkshire residents to mark October 22nd by spending at least a few minutes, an hour, or the day performing an activity that will make a difference in the quality of life of the citizens or towns of the Northern Berkshire community.This could be a new activity, or one that you do every day. Then, during the week of October 24-28, tell us what you did on the reverse side of this flyer. No effort is too small or too big. We will then publicize what we did, and submit our findings to the National Make a Difference Day panel for their review and possible award.

Saturday, October 22nd   Make a Difference Day

Tell us what you did by sending in a description of your activity (see back) to :

**Northern Berkshire Health and Human Services Coalition
NASC Box 9075
North Adams, MA 01247**

NBHHSC • North Adams State College Box 9075 • North Adams, MA 01247 • 664-4511 x 519

This coalition took on local sponsorship of a national Make a Difference Day. Through wide-scale publicity, the coalition stimulated citizens from all over the community to take on small but meaningful community service projects of their own.

THE CHINATOWN COALITION

Accomplishments

COALITION BUILDING

- Successful expansion of the coalition to include agencies which serve the elderly and individuals specializing in gerontology.

- Participation by major service providers serving youth.

- 500 families represented by the membership of the Castle Square Tenants Organization.

- Sponsored the November, 1994 Asian Pacific American Agenda Coalition Leadership Conference with over 200 participants and several discussions and workshops based on topics in the agenda document.

- Completed the Chinatown Needs and Resource Assessment Report.

- Establishment of a quarterly newsletter.

- New business members: Asian American Bank; Lawrence K. Cheng and Associates.

ECONOMIC DEVELOPMENT

- Sponsored an Economic Town Meeting and Job and Job Training Fair attended by 150 community members.

- Conducted a recent Job and Job Training Fair with 21 employers and job trainers present and 140 community members/ residents attending.

- Sponsored a Second Economic Town Meeting and Third Job and Job Training Fair attended by 250 community members.

- Assisted consortia of University of Massachusetts/ Boston Institutes' HUD successful application for economic development funding.

EDUCATION

- Hosting presentations by Boston Public School principals and program coordinators on issues affecting Asian students.

- Addition of the Franklin Institute of Boston to the coalition.

PUBLIC SAFETY

- Participation on the Chinatown/ South Cove Neighborhood Council's Public Safety Committee as a result of the survey of residents' concerns.
- Co-sponsored a community meeting on public safety and traffic issues attended by 130 community members.

HEALTH

- Supported Asian health data roll-out attended by 70 service providers.

6/29/95

This coalition is one of many that puts together a list of its accomplishments as part of a report back to the community. The list here covers only about a year's time—otherwise it would fill many more pages.

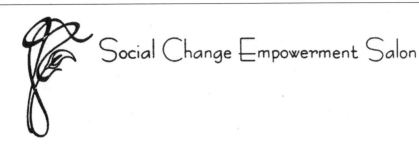

Social Change Empowerment Salon

The next meeting of the Social Change Empowerment Salon will be held:

Date: **Friday, December 5, 1997**

Place: Lord Jeffrey Inn, Amherst, MA
            Living Room

Time: 2:00 PM – 4:00 PM

Light refreshments will be served.

We will read parts of an exciting new book by Lisbeth Schorr entitled *Common Purpose*. This should be a great discussion.

AHEC/Community Partners
24 South Prospect Street
Amherst, MA 01002
413•253•4283

Coalitions can also work to support their own members in nontraditional ways. Our own organization has sponsored a reading group, a "salon" where coalition members read articles and books and then took time from work to discuss them.

Community Catalyst

A newsletter of community innovations

December 1997   *Volume 6, No.5*

Innovations

The Southeast Asian Festival: A Civics Lessons for All
By Linda Silka

Buddhist monks, Laotian and Cambodian boat racers, Khmer dancers, Hmong artists and many others shared their talents to recreate a Southeast Asian Water Festival, a centuries-old custom in Cambodia and Laos. This meaningful festival emphasizing the importance of water in diverse cultures took place on August 23, 1997 before an estimated crowd of 10,000 along the banks of the Merrimack River. With great effort and the involvement of many, the traditions of the Merrimack and the Mekong came together. The story behind this celebration of water is a tale of community partnership, environmental justice and political participation.

Twenty thousand Southeast Asians now make Lowell their home. However, "home" is not the way many newcomers describe Lowell and the Merrimack Valley. Instead, they point to the barriers to full participation in city life. Job openings are still filled through informal networks closed to newcomers. Neighborhood associations are not yet places where Southeast Asians share their concerns about creating safe places for their children. Even after a decade, few of the elected leaders in the community are Southeast Asian. How can opportunities begin to open up?

This question about opportunity confronted the members of an environmental justice partnership in Lowell. Funded by the National Institute of Environmental Health Sciences, this partnership's aim was to bring together the Southeast Asian community, primary health care providers and environmental scientists to address environmental justice issues in the city. For two years we held community conversations to learn about people's urban environmental concerns. We discovered how prominently water featured in many of the concerns. Lowell is one of the most industrialized areas of the United States, with a long history of environmental contamination, yet newcomers hope to continue traditions such as fishing. The community felt a water festival would be a culturally appropriate way to establish a sense of ownership for Southeast Asians, bring together generations and reshape environmental issues.

Throughout our third year, the partnership brought together many groups and organizations—groups that had sometimes been at odds with one another—to learn about environmental issues in ways that unite cultures.

Participants preparing boats for the
race on the Merrimack River

We learned from each other by listening to traditions. We learned about our lack of power and experience. Staging an event of this magnitude required permits and permission from a large number of organizations, many of whom had no written rules, but shifting requirements that must be met. We also had to counter unexpected prejudices; for example that any Southeast Asian event will include gang violence. We learned the power of working together and understanding systems.

In the final planning stages, we attended a neighborhood association meeting where the Water Festival would take place. The long-term residents of the neighborhood expressed many concerns about the festival and its unfamiliar hosts. Although representatives from the Laoti and Cambodian communities tried to allay these concerns, neighborhood residents remained uneasy. Then an elder from the French Canadian community stood up and described his many years of fishing the Merrimack. He spoke with fondness of his own secret fishing hole. Taking possession of the river, he argued, had always been the

continued on page 2

For five years, we also published a newsletter on coalition activities and community innovations across our state. Here's one sample cover story.

Once a year, we organized a conference for all coalitions in our state, each time with a different theme. Above are a few samples of conference brochures.

Healthy Communities Massachusetts Network

Are you involved with an effort to make a Massachusetts community a healthy place to live?

Join the new Healthy Communities Massachusetts Network. It's free, and now is the time to become one of its original endorsers.

Convening this Network is a way to join forces, reach out to each other and support the existing efforts of organizations and individuals who are working to make the Commonwealth's cities and towns healthier places.

HCMN sponsors are: AHEC/Community Partners, Healthy Boston, the Office of Community Programs of the University of Massachusetts Medical Center, the Massachusetts Municipal Association, the Local Officials Human Services Council, and the Massachusetts Executive Office of Education.

Attached you will find documents, created by a self-chosen working group from the November, 1994 Healthy Communities Massachusetts Summit, which delineate the Network's mission, goals and plan.

If you agree that now is the time, and Massachusetts is the place, fill out the attached Response Form. In the fall, we plan to announce our presence — and we want you to be a part of it.

A next step was to create a network of coalitions across the state, for information-sharing, for advocacy, and most recently for training. Our Healthy Communities Training Institute now runs ongoing three-day training program.

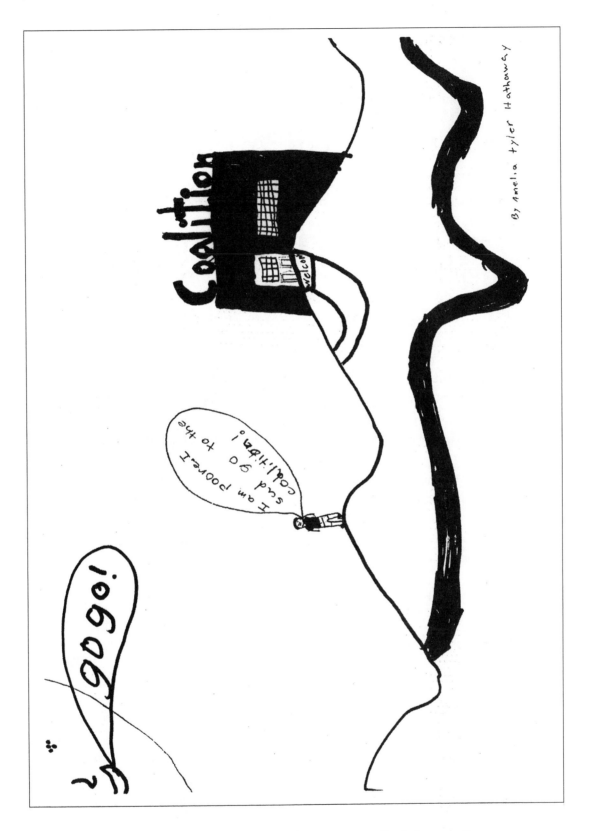

A coalition coordinator's daughter drew this. But you don't have to be poor to go to the coalition. Coalitions are for everybody!

About The Authors
And Contributors

The Authors

Bill Berkowitz, Ph.D., has been involved in creating, directing, and writing about community programs for the past 25 years. His previous books, *Community Impact*, *Community Dreams*, and *Local Heroes* deal with the skills, ideas, and personal qualities involved in successful community development. He has also been a staff consultant to coalitions in more than five different communities, and has collaborated  with Tom Wolff in coalition development at AHEC/Community Partners since the late 1980s. Presently, Bill teaches in the Psychology Department at the University of Massachusetts Lowell, where his work includes administrating its graduate program in community social psychology.

 **Tom Wolff, Ph.D.,** is a nationally recognized expert in coalition building and community development, who consults to and trains coalition practitioners in diverse settings across the country. As Director of AHEC/Community Partners for the Massachusetts Statewide Area Health Education Program and as a faculty member in the Department of Family Medicine and Community Health at the University of Massachusetts Medical School, he has been responsible for the development and maintenance of more than 10 coalitions in Massachusetts, as well as the statewide Healthy Communities Massachusetts network. Tom is the author of many professional articles and book chapters on coalitions, including, as coauthor with Gillian Kaye, *From the Ground Up! A Workbook on Coalition Building and Community Development*. Both Tom and Bill are elected Fellows of the American Psychological Association, and both have won, in separate years, national APA career awards for Distinguished Contributions to Practice in Community Psychology.

The Contributors

Brian Angus has been Coordinator of the Fitchburg Safe and Healthy Neighborhood Coalition since 1992. A community organizer of 25 years, and former director of nationally recognized energy conservation programs, Brian has received a gubernatorial citation as well as national citations from two U.S. presidents. His coalition leadership was instrumental in Fitchburg's designation as an All-America City.

 **Al Bashevkin** has been for the past 13 years Coordinator of the Northern Berkshire Community Coalition, serving small communities in Northwestern Massachusetts. The Coalition has helped build five active neighborhood organizations, disseminated over $30,000 in incentive grants, conducted innovative leadership development training, and hosted a local-access cable TV show, "Northern Berkshire Tonight!" Al is also an adjunct faculty member at the Massachusetts College of Liberal Arts and the University of Massachusetts Medical School.

Barbara Corey recently retired as Coordinator for the North Quabbin Community Coalition. During her 13-year tenure, the coalition gained local and regional recognition for its work on the prevention of sexual abuse of children and domestic violence, as well as for the creation of Valuing Our Children, a program to help strengthen families. Barbara is also active around needs to preserve and protect open space and clean water.

 Heather Danton has served as Coordinator, Chairperson, and consultant to the Greater Taunton Health and Human Service Coalition. Her recent primary work has been providing economic development assistance and loans to emerging small businesses. She has also made frequent trips to Africa as a community development consultant for the Save the Children Federation.

Geraldine David has been a member of the We Have A Dream and Roxbury Unites coalitions in Boston, as well as Project Director of the Whittier Street Tenants Association. In her professional community work, she has most recently served as Community Outreach Coordinator for the Boston Persistent Poverty Project, a major initiative of the Boston Foundation; Geraldine is also an instructor and Coordinator of the Partnerships Program at Wheelock College.

BL Hathaway, Coordinator of the Lower/Outer Cape Community Coalition since 1995, supplies this Jeopardy!-style biography, and asks the reader to supply the questions: "Glens Falls, New York. Syracuse University. University of Minnesota. Educational Psychology. 1972. Pennsylvania Department of Education. Massachusetts Department of Mental Health. Community Development. CSAP. Cape Cod. Three years. Yes. Two. Class of 2003. Class of 2006. I love it!"

Ramon Hernandez was staff person to the Chelsea Coalition for Youth, a project of Reaching Out to Chelsea Adolescents, a multiservice organization serving a low-income, multiethnic community. Previously, Ramon was a community development leader in Lawrence and then coordinated the Healthy Jamaica Plain Coalition, working primarily with adults in diverse multicultural neighborhoods.

Wendy Krom, now in private consulting practice, was the Coordinator for the Berkshire Prevention Alliance, a federally funded regional community prevention coalition serving many rural and isolated communities. Wendy also worked as a Neighborhood Planning and Development Specialist for the City of St. Louis, Missouri, assisting residents in two inner-city neighborhoods to develop strategic community plans.

Monica Escobar Lowell is founder and original Coordinator of the Worcester Latino Coalition, a resource and advocacy organization whose mission is to improve the quality of life for Latinos; she has also done lasting advocacy work around health care access and medical interpreter services issues. Monica serves in addition as Director of Cross-Cultural Health Initiatives at the Office of Community Programs at the University of Massachusetts Medical School.

Mary Lou Pettit was Coordinator for the Lower/Outer Cape Community Coalition from 1987 through 1995, where she helped organize an interfaith council, a community development corporation, and a children's center; she continues to consult to the coalition on poverty prevention. Her previous background also includes 25 years service as Housing Director for the New Jersey League of Women Voters and authorship of *Housing the Single Parent Family*.

The Reverend **Eugene F. Rivers III** is a product of the streets of inner-city Philadelphia. He returned to his Boston birthplace to address the desolation and poverty confronting the African-American and Latino populations there. Among many other projects, Rev. Rivers has developed the local Azusa Christian Community and the Ten Point Coalition.  The primary mission of that coalition is to help provide African American Christian churches, locally and now also nationally, with the resources necessary to improve the conditions of inner-city youth.

 **Phil Salzman's** leadership of the Gloucester Prevention Network, with over a dozen integrated coalitions, has resulted in both book publication and national recognition for directing an Exemplary Community Prevention Program. His methods for collecting process and outcome data have been adapted to community coalitions across the country. An educator by background, Phil presently directs national consultation work emphasizing prevention's role in improving the lives of ordinary citizens.

Christine Sicinski worked as Program Assistant for AHEC/Community Partners from 1990-1995. During that time, she was the primary day-to-day contact person, administrative support link, publications coordinator, computer consultant, and graphic design professional for a growing network of community coalitions across the state. She is currently the  Program Coordinator for Safe Roads, a regional community-based traffic safety program.

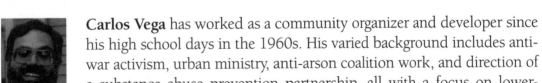

Carlos Vega has worked as a community organizer and developer since his high school days in the 1960s. His varied background includes anti-war activism, urban ministry, anti-arson coalition work, and direction of a substance abuse prevention partnership, all with a focus on lower-income neighborhoods. Carlos is currently Director of Nueva Esperanza, a community development corporation, where he continues to focus on meeting the needs of those on the bottom rung of the economic ladder.

Dave Weed, Psy.D. has worked in community mental health settings for the past 25 years. He was a key organizer in forming the Fall River Health and Human Services Coalition; he has been a member and leader of an extraordinary number of local coalitions, as well as a catalyst for similar coalition building in several nearby communities. Dave's recent work

includes formation of Partners for a Healthier Community, a broad-based partnership of citizens committed to health promotion in the Greater Fall River area.

 Beverly Wing is staff person to The Chinatown Coalition, which has focused extensively on local economic development and immigration issues in Boston. Her background also includes work in job skills training and organizational development. Beverly notes that "as a third-generation Bostonian, I recall the diversity, vitality, and cohesiveness of old Boston neighborhoods. My work with coalitions reflects people's basic needs not only to feel connected to, but also to be knowledgeable and valued members of, their communities."

For Further Reference

1. Coalition Building: Books and Manuals

Blank MJ, Danzberger JP. *Creating and Nurturing Collaboration in Communities: Stories From the Collaborative Leadership Development Program.* Washington, DC: Institute for Educational Leadership; 1996. [Available from the Institute at 1001 Connecticut Avenue, NW, Washington, DC 20036.]

Brown CR. *The Art of Coalition Building: A Guide for Community Leaders.* New York, NY: The American Jewish Committee; 1984.

Chrislip DD, Larson CE. *Collaborative Leadership: How Citizens and Civic Leaders Can Make a Difference.* San Francisco, Calif: Jossey-Bass; 1994.

Dluhy M. *Building Coalitions in the Human Services: Guidelines for Practice.* Newbury Park, Calif: Sage Publications; 1990.

Fawcett SB, and associates. *Evaluation Handbook for the Project Freedom Replication Initiative.* Lawrence, Kan: University of Kansas, Work Group on Health Promotion and Community Development; 1993.

Gray B. *Collaborating: Finding Common Ground for Multiparty Problems.* San Francisco, Calif: Jossey-Bass; 1989.

Habana-Hafner S, Reed HB. *Partnerships for Community Development.* Amherst, Mass: University of Massachusetts, Center for Organizational and Community Development; 1989.

John Snow, Inc. *Creating Partnerships That Work: A Developmental Manual for Ryan White Title II HIV Care Consortia.* Washington, DC: U.S. Department of Health and Human Services, Public Health Service, Health Resources and Services Administration; 1995.

Johnson K. *Collaborating to Improve Community Health: Trainer's Guide to the Seven Leadership Strategies.* San Francisco, Calif: Jossey-Bass; 1997.

Kaye G, Wolff T, eds. *From the Ground Up!: A Workbook on Coalition Building and Community Development.* Amherst, Mass: AHEC/Community Partners; 1995.

Mattesich P, Monsey B. *Collaboration: What Makes It Work: A Review of Research Literature on Factors Influencing Successful Collaboration.* St. Paul, Minn: Amherst H. Wilder Foundation; 1992.

The Medical Foundation. *Community Organizing for Prevention: The First Steps.* Boston, Mass: Department of Public Health, Bureau of Substance Abuse Services; 1994. [Available from the Foundation at 95 Berkeley Street, Boston, MA 02116.]

Mondros JB, Wilson SM. *Organizing for Power and Empowerment.* New York, NY: Columbia University Press; 1994.

Mulford CL, Klonglan GE. *Creating Coordination Among Organizations: An Orientation and Planning Guide.* Ames, Iowa: Cooperative Extension Service, North Central Regional Extension Publication 80; 1982.

The National Assembly of National Voluntary Health and Social Welfare Organizations. *The Community Collaboration Manual.* Washington, DC: Author; 1991.

The Ohio Center for Action on Coalition Development. *Building Coalitions: Reference Manual.* Columbus, Ohio: Author; 1993.

Rosenthal BB, Mizrahi T. *Strategic Partnerships: How to Create and Maintain Inter-Organizational Collaborations and Coalitions.* New York, NY: The Education Center for Community Organizing, Hunter College School of Social Work; 1994. [Available from the Center at 129 East 79th Street, New York, NY 10021.]

Winer M, Ray K. *Collaboration Workbook: Creating, Sustaining, and Enjoying the Journey.* St. Paul, Minn: Amherst H. Wilder Foundation; 1994.

2. Coalition Building: Articles and Shorter Reports

Butterfoss FD, Goodman RM, Wandersman A. Community coalitions for health promotion and disease prevention. *Health Education Research.* 1993; 8: 315-330.

Butterfoss FD, Goodman RM, Wandersman A. Community coalitions for prevention and health promotion: Factors predicting satisfaction, participation and planning. *Health Education Quarterly.* 1996; 23: 65-79.

Cohen L, Baer N, Satterwhite P. Building Effective Coalitions: An Eight Step Guide. Contra Costa Health Services Department Prevention Program; no date. [Available from the Department at 75 Santa Barbara Road, Pleasant Hill, CA 94523.]

Collaborative problem solving. *National Civic Review.* 1991; 80 (special issue): 101-236.

Community Anti-Drug Coalitions of America. CADCA Strategizers. [A series of technical assistance booklets for community coalitions, available from CADCA at 701 North Fairfax Street, Alexandria, VA 22314; see also CADCA's newsletter, *Coalitions.*]

Feighery E, Rogers T. Building and Maintaining Effective Coalitions. Stanford University School of Medicine, Stanford Center for Research in Disease Prevention, Health Promotion Resource Center; 1990. [Available from the Center at 1000 Welch Road, Palo Alto, CA 94304.]

Florin P, Mitchell R, Stevenson J. Identifying training and technical assistance needs in community coalitions: A developmental approach. *Health Education Research.* 1993; 8: 417-432.

The Harwood Group. Making Community Coalitions Work. Pew Partnership for Civic Change; 1993. [Available from the Partnership at 145-C Ednam Drive, Charlottesville, VA 22903.]

Himmelman AT. Communities Working Collaboratively for a Change; 1992. [Available from the Himmelman Consulting Group, 1406 West Lake Street, Suite 209, Minneapolis, MN 55408.]

London S. Building Collaborative Communities. Pew Partnership for Civic Change; 1995. [Available from the Partnership at 145-C Ednam Drive, Charlottesville, VA 22903.]

Marzke C, Both D. Getting Started: Planning a Comprehensive Services Initiative. [Resource Brief 5.] New York, NY: National Center for Service Integration; 1994. [Available from Child and Family Policy Center, 218 Sixth Avenue, Suite 1021, Des Moines, IA 50309; see also other Resource Briefs in this series.]

Morse SW. Building Collaborative Communities. Pew Partnership for Civic Change; 1996. [Available from the Partnership at 145-C Ednam Drive, Charlottesville, VA 22903.]

Potapchuk WR, Polk C. Building the Collaborative Community. National Center for Dispute Resolution, National Civic League, and Program for Community Problem

Solving; 1994. [Available from the Program for Community Problem Solving, 915 15th Street, NW, 6th Floor, Washington, DC 20005.]

White JA, Wehlage G. Community collaboration: if it is such a good idea, why is it so hard to do? *Educational Evaluation and Policy Analysis.* 1995; 17 (1): 23-38.

Wolff T. Coalition Building: One Path to Empowered Communities. Worcester, Mass: University of Massachusetts Medical Center; 1991. [Available from AHEC/Community Partners, 24 South Prospect Street, Amherst, MA 01002.]

Wood DJ, Gray B. Toward a comprehensive theory of collaboration. *Journal of Applied Behavioral Science.* 1991; 27: 143-149.

* * *

AHEC/Community Partners also publishes other materials related to coalition building, including a multi-part series of two-page "Tip Sheets" on various aspects of coalition development. Topics include Coalition Start-Up, Stages of Development, Planning, Membership, Leadership, Engaging Residents, Evaluation, Principles of Success, and Sources of Innovative Community-Building Ideas. For further information, contact AHEC/Community Partners at 24 South Prospect Street, Amherst, MA 01002; (413) 253-4283; info@ahecpartners.org.

Index

APHA's Mission

The American Public Health Association is an Association of individuals and organizations working to improve the public's health. It promotes the scientific and professional foundation of public health practice and policy, advocates the conditions for a healthy global society, emphasizes prevention, and enhances the ability of members to promote and protect environmental and community health.